THE WORLD OF JOHN McNULTY

by John McNulty

with an Appreciation by James Thurber

THE WORLD OF JOHN McNULTY

Doubleday & Company, Inc., Garden City, New York 1957

Library of Congress Catalog Card Number 57-9506

Printed in the United States of America

Designed by Diana Klemin

CONTENTS

III

IV

V

MY FRIEND McNULTY

The angel that writes names in a book of gold must long ago have put McNulty down as one who delighted in his fellow man. His delight in human beings was warm and deep and, though he deserved to be called a social critic, he was concerned mainly with men, not Man, with persons, not People. McNulty's love of humanity was not expressed at a distance, from a platform, but in pieces that have the lasting pulse of life in every sentence. He moved among men, shoulder to shoulder, from morning till night until the end of his too brief sixty years on earth.

American writing in our time has developed few men with so keen an eye and so sharp an ear. Nothing, however commonplace, that he touched with words remained commonplace, but was magnified and enlivened by his intense and endless fascination with the stranger in the street, the drinker at the bar and the bartender behind it, the horseplayer, the cabdriver, the guy at the ball game, the fellow across the room, the patient in the next hospital bed. John McNulty, city man and newspaperman, self-assigned in his mature years to human-interest stories of the world about him, left not only a body of work that throbs with his love of life, but a vast and equally durable legacy of spoken words that remain vivid in the memory of his friends. The only person who could get McNulty down in words was McNulty himself, but those of us who knew and loved him like to sit around at night in Tim and Joe Costello's Bar and Restaurant on Third Avenue and talk about him. This is the only real way to bring McNulty to life. Cold type could never do justice to such a man.

After John McNulty died last summer I wrote a short piece about him for the crowded pages of *The New Yorker*, and I reproduce it here in part: "Nobody who knew McNulty as man or writer could ever have confused him for a moment with anybody else. His presence in a room—or in a town, for that matter—was as special as the way he put words down on paper. His death darkened the skies for literally countless friends and acquaintances, for he seemed to know everybody. He came back to New York in the early thirties from a long sojourn in the Middle West, and in 1937 he began writing pieces for *The New Yorker*. They were the reports of a true and eager eye and ear that found high excitement in both the unusual and the common phrases and postures of men, and turned them into the sparkle of his unique idiom.

"The days didn't go by for John McNulty; they happened to him. He was up and out at six every morning, wandering the beloved streets and 'avenyas' of his city, stopping to talk and listen to everybody. His week was a seven-day circus that never lost its savor. He was not merely an amusing companion; he was one of the funniest of men. When he told a tale of people or places, it had a color and vitality that faded in the retelling by anyone else. The name McNulty, for us, meant 'Inimitable,' and at the same time something in lower case, familiar and cherished—a kind of synonym for laughter. We grieve that such a man cannot be replaced, in our hearts or on our pages."

The pages of *The New Yorker* sparkled with his pieces from the first one, which appeared on Christmas Day, 1937, until the last one, which was printed on New Year's Eve, 1955.

McNulty and I were reporters together on Columbus, Ohio, newspapers in the early nineteen-twenties. He did general assignments for a morning paper while I covered City Hall for an afternoon paper, but our offices were just a few blocks apart, in the center of town, and I bunked into him almost every day, often at the corner of Broad and High Streets, the city's main intersection. He was invariably excited about something, the cabin lights of the Shenandoah which he had seen twinkling in the sky the night before, a girl at the James Theatre who sang "Roses Are Shining in Picardy," Donn Byrne's novel *The Changelings*, which he demanded that I begin reading right away, there on that crowded corner, or a song called "Last Night on the Back Porch," which he insisted on playing for me, then and almost there. Actually, he took me around the corner to a music store and began beating out the song on the first piano he came to, to the astonishment of the store's staff. "It's McNulty," I explained to them in a whisper and they all nodded and breathed his name in unison, obviously believing that he was a great pianist, come to play at Memorial Hall, who had suddenly been seized by a rare moment of relaxation and frivolity. He had once played the piano in a movie theatre in the days of silent films and, within his range, there wasn't anything he couldn't make the keys do. While playing "My Gal Sal" he used to recite the succession to the presidency, and it was upon the conclusion of that bravura performance that we left the music shop and its startled and transfigured staff. Once he got me up before breakfast to play on my victrola two records that had entranced him—"Singin' Sam from Alabam'" and a bright arrangement of "Everybody Calls Me Honey," in which piano, trumpet, and banjo alternately took over the solo.

McNulty was a widely experienced newspaperman at twenty-five, when he arrived in Columbus from the East, to work for the *Ohio State Journal* at sixty dollars a week, higher pay than any reporter in town had been getting. I have forgotten, if I ever knew, what whim or compulsion had sent him into the Middle West. It was probably an impulse peculiar to his volatile spirit, such as that which sent him one day, years later, to New Iberia, Louisiana, to visit the tabasco factory there. In Columbus he lingered for a dozen years. Before the first of these had passed he knew more people in the city than I did, although I had been born and brought up there. They included everybody from taxi drivers, cops, prizefighters, and bellboys to the mayor of the city and the governor of the state. He wrote speeches for one successful candidate for governor, and in that as in everything else, he had the time of his life.

John once explained to me, "Two-thirds of the Irish blood is grease paint," and he was a fine offhand actor and a raconteur rampant, who would jump from his chair in a living room and theatrically bring to life one of the characters he had so fondly collected during his wanderings. I think he did as much as anyone, with his acting, to ridicule the Ku Klux Klan out of existence in Columbus some thirty-five years ago. He had arranged for me to accost him whenever I saw him at Broad and High in the company of a group of men—he was always surrounded by men—and loudly try to enroll him in the Klan. "We are looking for likely one hundred per cent Americans," I would say, "so we can build up in this city the biggest Kleagle in the country."

"Klavern," he would correct me, and while his companions stared at me in disbelief, he would take off his hat, present to me the shining map of Ireland that was his face, and say proudly, "The name is John Aloysius McNulty." At this I would slink away, muttering, while his friends stared after me. "Them guys must be crazy!" I heard a boxer named Sully exclaim after one of these rituals, and the word got around town that the local Klan was made up of imbeciles. It didn't last long.

Trying to describe McNulty is a little like trying to describe Ed Wynn or George M. Cohan. "A small, jaunty man, best described as Irish of face and manner" is the way the New York *Times* went about it in that paper's appreciative obituary. He was small, I guess, measured by physical height and weight, but I have a tendency to look up when I think of him, for to me he was nine feet tall. This was the stature, at any rate, of his unflagging comic spirit. The dictionary has no exact words for the face and voice of the man, or for the shape and color of the moods he put on every morning with his clothes. There was nothing of the literary elf about McNulty, who once said to me, "Only people with Vincent for a middle name write about leprechauns." It is true that the world of John McNulty bordered on Oz and Wonderland, but it consisted mainly of Ireland, New York's Third Avenue, the city rooms of American newspapers, and the race tracks of the world, with many an odd and unexpected nook and corner. From the border states came curious and wondrous figures, attracted to McNulty, not magically, but naturally. This gave his world, and his comments on it, a strange truth, undreamed of in ordinary philosophies. When he said, of 1885, "That was the year the owls were so bad," or when he told a lady trying to think of her hairdresser's name, "Girls named Dolores become hairdressers," or when he tracked down a bookie in a jewelry shop by suddenly remembering "All watch repairers are named Schneider," the listener felt that this was not mere whimsy, but McNulty fact. There was always, faint or sharp, in what he said or did a critical comment on our tangled civilization, a sound parody of the ways of men. Walking about the streets of any city with McNulty was to be taken on a guided tour of what William James called, in another context, unexplored experience. Two men would pass by you, one of them saying, "It's the biggest gorilla in the world. They call it Garganetta," or a waiter in a café would tell him, "We get stranglers come in here at all hours." Through the ears of many of us such things pass unregistered, but McNulty's sensitized mind recorded everything. "The lady was a Bostonian, they call them" rang like a bell in his consciousness. To a man whose awareness was always on the lookout for the unusual, as well as the typical, the world was a book he was reading with intense concentration. He loved sentiment, being Irish, and he came right out with it. Of a pretty young bride he once wrote about in the *Daily News* he said, "She was as cute as a little red wagon." He once called me long distance to tell me he had just read something lovely which I had to hear. It was the four words of a lover: "My eyes desire you." My phone brought me often, but not often enough, phrases, sentences, or paragraphs from an enthusiastic McNulty who had just stumbled upon them. Sometimes he read me a whole piece.

There were a dozen shops of all kinds on New York's East Side with whose proprietors McNulty, making his daily rounds, kept up some kind of running gag. Once when I lived in East Fifty-seventh Street, a region he knew well, he took me into a small corner store after explaining, "There's a wonderful guy runs this place." He was a wonderful guy, too, in the McNulty tradition, perfectly suited to their particular running gag, which was managed deadpan, as if the two had never met before. "What can I do for you, sir?" the man said. McNulty consulted the back of an envelope. "Elephant goad," he said finally. An amateur actor of McNulty's stripe, the man began snapping his fingers, humming, and searching his shelves and opening doors underneath the shelves, at length turning around to report, "Sorry, seem to be fresh out of elephant goads. Anything else?" Mc-

Nulty shook his head sorrowfully and out we went. I found out later, dropping into the shop, some of the other things McNulty had asked for in vain—fetlock cleaners, beagle harness, and noiseless dice. "He says he supplies dice to a couple of fugitives holed up in this house with marble floors," the proprietor said. This is the thinnest ice of comedy and it takes experts to skate on it without falling in, and you had to behold such performances yourself to understand the skill of McNulty and his stooges. I have never read a critic who captured the subtle essence of Beatrice Lillie's comic art, and none of them could do justice to McNulty's, either, on flat paper. His timing was perfect, and so were the tricks of his tones of voice. One day a few years ago I phoned him to ask if he remembered the year he had interviewed Donald Ogden Stewart (a great McNulty admirer) for the *Ohio State Journal.* McNulty's answer was prompt, and in the tone of a professional quiz panelist. "It was the year Black Gold win the Derby," he said, and having given me all the help a true horseplayer should need, he hung up. I had to look up in the World Almanac the year Black Gold win the Derby. Checking later with the *Journal* files, I found out, of course, that the answer was correct.

John Augustine McNulty (Aloysius had been invented for effect) was capable of a fine anger that could rise to fury. Like my own temper, his was sometimes as unreasonable as it was quick, but our occasional disagreements, as sudden as summer storms, passed just as quickly. After one loud hour of argument over the play *Shadow and Substance,* about which I think we were both right, we parted like men who would never see each other again. But we had a running gag manner of making up, during which the cause of the trouble was never mentioned or even hinted at. Spotting him in a bar, I would present myself, politely, as a man just in from Columbus, Ohio, with a letter to him from Sully. "Let me see the letter," he would say, and there ensued a search through all my pockets, in which he helped. "Let me have another go at your coat," he would say grimly, but the letter was never there. "Well, when you find it," he would say, "bring it around. If I'm not here, I'll probably be somewhere else. Meanwhile, let's have a drink to old Sully. I like Sully." His gallery of persons he disliked was not large, but it included the right figures, the phony, or "wax banana," the snob, the show-off, the blowhard, the bigot, the unfriendly, the humorless, and all their cold ilk.

I happened to be in Columbus in 1933 when McNulty decided to return to the New York he hadn't seen for more than a decade, and I came back on the train with him. We hadn't ridden in a taxi more than three blocks from Pennsylvania Station before he began waving at guys he knew. "You're obvious New York born and bred, Mac," the taxi driver told him, adding that he was studying "human psychology." He picked me as a stranger "from the outlands" and said to my companion, "Better look after your friend. You don't know your way around, it's a tough town." In the next few years McNulty worked on the *Mirror*, the *Daily News*, and the *Herald Tribune* under its great city editor, Stanley Walker, who once told me, "There is a kind of story that only McNulty could write, and it was a pleasure to have him around." He meant the kind of feature story that calls for the use of the heart as well as the mind.

McNulty was a fast writer, but before he reached his typewriter his alert photographic mind, backed up by an amazing memory, had worked the story out in all but a few details. He was temperamental if the thing didn't come out right, but he discarded his temperament like an overcoat when he set out to explore his fascinating world. His first assignment on *The New Yorker* was a "Reporter at Large" piece, and he went out, got the facts, came back, and batted out the story within a couple of hours. "He can't get over writing for a newspaper deadline," said the late Harold Ross, but McNulty learned to slow down. When he left for a stint in Hollywood, Ross was genuinely reluctant to see him go. "Well, God bless you, McNulty, goddam it," said Ross. As John told me later, "Ross has two gods, Upper Case and lower case." Through Ross and the rest of us McNulty met a few people he hadn't known before. I remember his delight, one night in "21," when Marc Connelly told him some of Lloyd Lewis's anecdotes about the Southwest, one of which involved a rancher whose cat had been missing for three weeks. "Then one day I turned over my mattress," said the rancher, "and there, between the mattress and the springs, was Boss, pressed as pretty as a flower." The next day McNulty said to me, "The cat's name wasn't Boss. The cat's name was Pete. All ranchers' cats are named Pete." I'm sure Connelly would have lost money betting against this intuitive bit of McNulty truth.

McNulty was not New York born, for he first saw the enchanting light of his world in Lawrence, Massachusetts, where his mother ran her little store after the death of his father. Her son has done some justice to these early scenes, but not as much as I wish he had, for his mother is one of the vivid memories of my life. I first met her in Columbus when she visited him there, and he and I went to the train together to see her off, both of us, by coincidence, carrying identical boxes of candy. He knew what to do about that. "If you cry," he told her affectionately, "you get the box of candy that's poisoned. If you're good, you get the other one." The leave-taking was as jolly as it could be when two McNultys parted. Years later in New York, Mrs. McNulty was knocked down by a taxi on Park Avenue, and my wife and I went with John to call on her. Before we could tiptoe into the bedroom, where she was supposed to be lying wrapped in bandages from head to foot, we heard a small clatter in the kitchen and her son went out to investigate. It was Mama, of course. "And did you think I'd let the Thurbers call on me," she said indignantly, "and not fix them a cup o' tea?" It took more than a New York taxi to finish off a McNulty. John himself, although he never talked about it, and wrote about it only sparingly and obliquely, had gone through some of the toughest battles of the First World War, in the Infantry. He got a leg full of shrapnel at Fère-en-Tardenois and he was made a sergeant when the company's sergeants were killed in battle. After the war, he spent a year in hospital, and his wounds gave him trouble from then on. He was once a pet patient for three weeks in a hospital in Columbus, but none of us knew for a long time that Fère-en-Tardenois had sent him there. He made lasting friendships, of course, with doctors, nurses, and orderlies.

A few years before he died he gave me his precious copy of Mencken's *The American Language*, saying, "This is the book I love the most." Mencken once spoke to me, in the Algonquin lobby, in praise of McNulty and his handling of the people and the parlance of Third Avenue, and I remember how McNulty's face lighted up when I told him about it. He had a lot of favorite books, including the Oxford English Dictionary, which he read as if it were a novel, filled with wonders and suspense. There must be many of us who have books that McNulty once owned. "He couldn't keep a book he loved," Faith McNulty told me the other day. "He wasn't happy until he had given it to some friend."

In the last ten years or so, alas, we ran into each other only occasionally, but we talked a lot on the phone and exchanged letters. His letters were invariably carefully thought out single sentences, each relating some highlight of his city adventures. The last one I ever got was different, though, and puzzled me. It began, as always, "Dear Jimmy," and went on to say, "I think that maybe threescore years and ten is subject to change without notice." I searched it for the laugh, and realized there weren't going to be any more laughs. One night shortly afterward my phone rang in the country and I was told that he was dead. I had been planning to write him suggesting that he read certain poems and pieces by Dylan Thomas, particularly the poem that ends: "They shall have stars at their elbows, and at their feet, and death shall have no dominion. And death shall have no dominion." But I was too late. If Thomas was right about these bright eternal ornaments, John Augustine McNulty has his stars, and never you mind about that.

James Thurber

West Cornwall, Connecticut, 1957

THE
WORLD
OF
JOHN
McNULTY

I

SOME NIGHTS WHEN NOTHING HAPPENS ARE THE BEST NIGHTS IN THIS PLACE

The boss of this saloon on Third Avenue often says he wishes there was such a thing as a speakeasy license because when all is said and done he'd rather have a speakeasy than an open saloon that everybody can come into the way they all are now. Not that he is exactly opposed to people coming in. They spend money, no denying that. But a speakeasy, you could control who comes in and it was more homelike and more often not crowded the way this saloon is now. Johnny, one of the hackmen outside, put the whole thing in a nutshell one night when they were talking about a certain hangout and Johnny said, "Nobody goes there any more. It's too crowded."

The point is that some nights when there's hardly anybody in a gin mill and nothing happens, why, those are the best nights in one way of thinking. They're more interesting and not such a hullabaloo of juke-box music and everybody talking at once and all of it not amounting to any interest for the boss or any of the regulars, unless you'd count a lot of money coming in.

Like the other morning about half past two it was more like a speak-easy, only a few there and odd ones coming in that the boss knew well and didn't mind any of them, each one different than the other.

Jack Yee come in first. The boss was having a cup of tea. He's a regular old woman about having a cup of hot tea down at the far end of the bar every now and then. Jack Yee is a favorite of the boss. Jack is a Chinaman that weighs pradickly nothing at all but he'll live to be a hundred easy. He starts out from Pell Street or Doyers every night around midnight and comes up Third Avenue on a regular route selling little wooden statues they send over by the millions from China. He sells them to drunks in saloons and about three, four o'clock winds up his route selling them in a couple night clubs.

The boss asked Jack to have a cup of tea, because he's always glad to see Jack. He can't understand how anybody could be as thin as this Chinaman and still keep going up and down the avenue night after night. Coldest night, Jack got no overcoat, just a skinny raincoat tied around him and always smoking a cigarette that's stuck on his lower lip and bouncing when he talks. So Jack put down his bag of statues and had a cup of tea with the boss, and first thing you know what are they talking about but how tough it is talking Chinese for a language.

You must know the boss come from Dublin and naturally has no hint of talking Chinese, but like everything else he has ideas about it just the same. It's no sense trying to tell how Jack talks but what he says to the boss is that there's the same word means two things in Chinese. Depends on how you say it, this word, high and squeaky or low and groaning.

Jack says "*loo*" if you say it down low it means "mouth." Then he tells the boss if you say "*loo*" up high it means "trolley car."

"Oh my God!" says the boss to Jack while they have their cup of tea opposite each other on the bar. "Oh my God, Jack, the same word mean 'trolley car' and 'mouth'?"

Jack says yes, and then he makes it worse by saying another instance, you might say. He tells the boss when a Chinaman says "*pee-lo*," something like that, and says it low and moaning it means "a bird," and if he says the same thing high it means "come in!"

"Oh my God!" says the boss after another sip of tea. "The same word, Jack, mean 'come in' and 'bird'? And the same word mean 'mouth' and 'trolley car'? Then by God, Jack, if they're ever gonna make a start at getting anywhere they'll have to get that ironed out!"

With that, Jack is laughing because, like the boss says often, Chinamen are great people for laughing. They'd laugh if you shoot them. Fact is, he says that's what probally discourages the Japs, because the boss figures that Japs only grin but it has no meaning to it and Chinamen laugh from inside. They're great people, he says.

While the boss and Jack Yee were finishing their tea, they gave up the Chinese language as a bad job entirely, and at that minute who came in finally but the sour-beer artist to get his Christmas money and this the middle of February. The sour-beer artist is quite a guy in his own way. In this neighborhood they got a tradition that at the couple of weeks before Christmas there has to be written on the mirror back of the bar "Merry Christmas and a Happy New Year." The sour-beer artist goes around and puts that on the mirror. He does it with sour beer saved in the place for the purpose. You write with sour beer on the glass and it makes shiny crystals in the writing. Anybody could do it, of course, if he has sour beer, but this artist writes it with curlicues and that's the tradition that it has to be written that way. They give him two bucks and a half for it, but he's a foresighted guy and he can see ahead he'll be drunk and wandering by Christmas and likely in trouble, so he leaves the two bucks and a half unpaid some places to collect it after Christmas, when he's broke and hungry. That's why he just come in the other night, to get the two and a half, and of course he was welcome. Turned out he got a little stretch on the island for fighting around New Year's and here he was, sober and hungry. So the boss gave him the dough and threw in some soup and a roast-beef sandwich, and out went the sour-beer artist, saying to the boss, "Thanks, Tim. I'll see you around Christmas time." And it is true for him that's about when he'll show up, no questions asked, in time to write the curlicues on the mirror. In some ways the sour-beer artist is a little unusual, but that's the kind comes in on the quiet nights nothing happens.

Giving out the Christmas money to the sour-beer artist moved things back to Christmas for a few minutes in the place, and the boss got started into giving quite a speech on Christmas.

"I'm glad it's over, with office parties for Christmas starting unpleasantness," the boss says. "I mean I worry every Christmas about those office parties they have around here. Somebody always goes too far at them being chummy with the boss of their office, maybe one of the girls kissing him and then wondering for months afterward did she go too far. But Christmas is over and done with. The thing I remember about this one was something that I had a chance to sit back and have nothing to do with it. I was on a train going up to see a nephew of mine is in a seminary a little ways up in the state and it was Christmas Eve. Well, first of all, it's the bane of my life around here that if a drunk gets to be a nuisance, by God it is always another drunk only not so far gone that thinks he can handle him.

"A thousand times in here I've seen a man beginning to drive out other customers by noisiness, or butting in, or something like that—well, I'd just have my mind made up I'd do something about him, even throw him out cautious if necessary. And that minute, without fail, up would come another less drunk drunk and say, 'Lemme handle him! I can handle this cluck!' That's the horror of 'em all, because then you got two drunks instead of one.

"On the train, in come this guy with bundles and his overcoat half on half off, and the minute he got on I shrunk back in my seat. I ran into them like that so many times, I was thanking God I was not in it at all and it was in a train and not here in my place. He begun singing 'Silent Night' and so forth and next nudging the guy in the seat with him to sing it, and then got sore because the man wouldn't sing 'Silent Night' with him.

"Then the drunk started changing seats like they change places at the bar here when they get like that. And he was by then opening up bundles and trying to show presents to a decent, quiet girl in the train. And hollering 'Silent Night' all the while. It was bad. And do you know anything about trains? The conductor won't throw you off if he can help it. They got rules the conductor has to get a railroad cop. That's because guys sues that get thrown off trains.

"Now up came the second drunk, the kind there always is. 'Lemme handle him,' says the second drunk to the conductor, exactly word for word what the second drunk always says in the place here. 'No,' says the conductor, but that wouldn't do. The second one grabs the first one, and by then we're pulling into 125th Street. And of course there's no cop on hand when they wanted him, the cop probally having a Christmas Eve for himself somewhere away from the station. Off goes the first drunk, the second drunk on top of him, the bundles half in the car, and the first one's overcoat left behind and the train pulls out. I gave thanks to God for once there was two drunks and me no part of it, because I've had it so often, even with the 'Silent Night' part thrown in for Christmas."

It was quite a speech about Christmas, nothing exciting but the boss was launched off on talking about it and it was one of those quiet nights nothing happens.

Still and all, Eddie Clancarty at the other end of the bar, drinking alone the way he mostly does, was trying to start an argument. He was hollering for a drink while the boss was talking about Christmas. People keep away from Eddie. He's quarrelsome. Came over here from the old country as a gossoon, and hardly made any friends because he'd take issue with everybody about everything. You can't say a word but what Eddie Clancarty would take you up on it.

"You bums, why don't you go into the Army?" Eddie hollered back at the other few in the place. "Whyn't you go into the Army?"

Without Clancarty hearing, one customer said to the boss, "Why don't you throw him out, he's always starting a fight?"

"Oh, leave him alone," says the boss. "He's going into the Army tomorrow." He went up and served Eddie a drink, then got away from him quick.

Well, it got to be near four o'clock, time to put the chairs on top of the tables and close up.

"We'll go over to Bickford's and have some scrambled eggs when I get the joint closed," said the boss to a couple of the customers with him, saying it low so Clancarty couldn't hear. The boss likes to wind up the night in Bickford's having some eggs and some more tea before he goes home, and reading who's dead in the *Tribune* and having a look at the entries in the *Mirror*.

"What're you heels talking about?" said nosy Clancarty. But nobody answered.

"Drink up, Eddie, we're closing!" said the boss. Eddie hollered some more but drank his drink.

In a minute or two they all had gone out on the sidewalk, some waiting in a little bunch while the boss locked the door. Clancarty was cursing at nothing at all, just in general, and started away by himself.

"Let him go," said the boss, though there was no need of it, with nobody stopping such a quarrelsome guy from going. The boss and the others started for Bickford's, and Clancarty was off the other way. The boss looked back at him going and said, "Now, isn't that a terrible thing? Sure I just bethought of it now! There he is, going into the Army tomorrow, and I can see plain as day what's the matter with him. The poor man has nobody at all to say goodbye to."

TWO BUMS HERE WOULD SPEND FREELY EXCEPT FOR POVERTY

Nobody knows how the boss of this saloon on Third Avenue reaches such quick decisions about people who come in, but he does. Like in the case of the two bums who came in Sunday afternoon off the avenue.

It was that time on Sunday afternoon that the inhabitants of this place call the Angelus. That's about four o'clock when late hangovers from Saturday night come in one by one. They stay that way, too, one by one. Each man makes himself into an island, standing in front of the bar, and everyone keeps a space on each side of him the way water is on the sides of islands. These hangovers feel too terrible to talk to each other for a couple of hours yet, anyway. Each of them keeps staring into the mirror in back of the bar and saying to himself, "Look at you, you'll never amount to anything. You went to school and grew up and everything and now look at you, you'll never amount to anything." Old veteran Third Avenue bartenders call this fighting the mirror, and they all think it is very bad for a man. The place is sad and quiet when a batch of hangovers are doing this and so someone nicknamed this time of Sunday afternoon the Angelus.

The boss was tending bar himself. He was on the pledge again this Sunday afternoon, so he was standing behind the bar and not saying hardly anything. He is a sour man when not drinking, because he is a man who doesn't take very well to not drinking.

The two bums came in walking as if they had the bottoms of rocking chairs for feet. They had that heel-and-toe walk that punch-drunk fighters have that roll from heels to toes like a rocking chair rocks from back to front. They were never fighters, though, these two bums, too frail-built and no cauliflower ears on them.

They were scratch bums. In this neighborhood they call them scratch bums when they've got as far low as they could get, and don't even try any more to keep themselves without bugs on them. Therefore, scratch bums.

One bum had a version of a straw hat on him he rescued, most likely out of a ash can in a fashionable neighborhood. It had onetime been one of those peanut straws they call them that look like a panama that's got sunburned, only cheaper price. The hat had a hell of a swaggering big brim on it, and looked funny over the scratch bum's crummy clothes. The other bum carried a closed cigar box under one arm, for God knows what and nobody ever did find out. The two bums were arm in arm and they came in without making hardly a sound.

The boss took a drag on his cigarette and laid it down, the way he does when he's ready to tell bums to turn right around and get out of there, but the bums reached the bar before he did that. They come rolling up to the bar on the rocking-chair feet and one bum, the most sad-faced one, dredged up two nickels out of his pocket and slithered them onto the bar.

"How much is a glass of wine?" the bum asked, and even the hangovers heard him and looked surprised. Nobody ever asks for a glass of wine hardly in that neighborhood. Except maybe on Christmas Eve some nondrinker might unloosen himself up that much on account of Christmas. They keep wine only for show-off, so when the bum asked for wine a couple of the hangovers looked at him and so did the boss. He didn't seem to believe his ears, but he answered the bum. "Aw, wine is twenty-five cents," the boss said. He shoved back the puny pair of nickels at the bum.

"Oh!" the bum said. Just plain "Oh." He picked up his two nickels and him and his pal turned to go out. They took a couple steps toward the door when all of a sudden the boss yelled, "Hey, just a minute!" and wiggled a finger on one hand for them to come back to the bar.

Well, the two bums stood there, wondering what was going to happen. The boss walked down to the other end of the bar and he reached back and got two of the best wineglasses and wiped the dust off of them. He walked back with a hell of a flourish and set the glasses on the bar in front of the two bums. In this place they keep the imported stuff that's hard to get on account of there's a war in a little locker under the back end of the bar. The boss stalked back to this locker and out he hauls a bottle of imported Spanish sherry. Not the junk, a bottle of the McCoy, the real stuff, best in the house. He went to the bums and poured out two glasses full. Then he said, "Drink up, fellers, and welcome!"

You'd think the bums might be surprised, but they didn't look it. They seemed to take it in their stride like everything else. They lifted the glasses and drank the wine slow.

"Thank you, sir," the one with the big-brim hat said. "We won't be botherin' you any longer." And the two of them give their mouths a slow swipe with the backs of their hands and swivelled around from the bar and walked out. The bums looked dignified.

"Now, why in the hell did you do that?" one of the hangovers asked the boss.

"Never mind why I done it," the boss said, grumpy. "Those fellers would spend thousands of dollars if it wasn't for they haven't got even a quarter. Only two nickels. Never mind why I done it."

The boss kept smoking his cigarette a while and paying no attention to the hangover customers. After a couple minutes, damn if he didn't go down again to the far end of the bar and get his hat. He kept trying it on this way and that in front of the mirror.

"I wish to God," he said, "I could get my hat to set on my head the way that hat set on the bum. Now, didn't it have a hell of a jaunty look to it?"

BARKEEP WON'T LET ANYBODY AT ALL SHOVE THIS HANDYMAN AROUND

The boss of this saloon on Third Avenue was kicking out loud to himself one day about how things were going in the place and he said, "Nobody works for anybody around here." Well, they don't.

The help there aren't so many. There's Paddy Ferrarty the bartender, and Dinny the regular waiter, and Garabedian the chef, they call him Mike, and The Slugger. All of them seem to have hired themselves, and if there's firing to be done, they'll fire themselves when they get around to it and not before. The boss has nothing to do with it, practically. The gin mill gets along that way, after a fashion, and the boss hasn't got any feeling that he's authorized to give orders. He makes an occasional pass at giving orders but everybody goes on doing whatever they're doing in their own way, which generally is the opposite or at least a lot different to whatever way the boss told them.

The Slugger is the handyman. He tries hard enough, but the poor guy doesn't seem to be able to do one single thing exactly right, not one thing, although he tries hard enough, God knows. So the way things work out, not being able to do one thing right makes him the handyman, entitled to take a whack at doing everything. Being a handyman lets him do all kinds of things, only all of them in a catch-as-catch-can style with nobody allowed to bawl him out much at any of the jobs because he's always only temporary at whatever the hell it is he's doing. He's a very temporary man.

Sometimes he's the waiter if Dinny don't show up. Now and then he's the chef for a few hours if Garabedian gets drunk and nobody can find him. When The Slugger is the waiter, he forgets to bring people butter. Then he mutters when they mention it. He gets mad because the butter didn't get there by itself and he feels that it is not his fault it didn't. When The Slugger is the chef, he does the best he can at it and he feels fine wearing the tall white hat that goes with the job. Only he is daffy on the subject Lima beans and will serve Lima beans with everything you could mention, might even work them into the jello if he could, regardless of what the customer ordered.

The Slugger weighs only about a hundred sixteen pounds, but they call him The Slugger because he talks very ferocious whilst drunk and he has big ideas about who he can lick then. He could lick hardly anybody at all. A customer one time said The Slugger looked like a guy that was maybe a small altar boy and fell into bad company for thirty-forty years. He is frail and got practically no health at all left from ramshackle living. Most of his teeth are gone and he must be nearly fifty years of age. Everybody likes this little guy, never mind his faults, they don't do any harm at all.

The Slugger believes everything he reads in the newspapers, especially about wrassling. Oftentimes, as a result of this, he stands in the middle of the saloon floor and tries to show single-handed, with no opponent at all, how Danno O'Mahoney worked the Irish whip. It's quite a strain on him. O'Mahoney was a big lummox of a wrassler and the Irish whip was a holt of his there was a lot of blather about in the papers a couple of years back.

Nobody pays any attention to The Slugger when he's talking big or showing wrassling holts, except Paddy Ferrarty, the bartender. Now it's a funny thing about a lot of Third Avenue bartenders like Paddy. They each got a kind of helpless little man to help them with odds and ends, and they treat him like a godson. With Paddy, The Slugger is such a little guy. He seems to Paddy Ferrarty to be like a fifty-year-old kid that has to be taken care of and people have to be blocked from picking on him or shoving him around.

Exavvy Mullane was saying the other day that this protecting The Slugger the way Paddy Ferrarty does can sometimes go too far, and sometimes it would surprise you. Exavvy is a bartender that works in a bucket of blood up the Avenue a ways and sometimes comes into this saloon to stand on the other side of the stick, that's what they call the bar around here. That's how Exavvy relaxes. Another thing that maybe better be explained about Mullane is his first name. His father was a rebellious, stubborn man, a thorn in everybody's side in the old country, and he noticed that hundreds of guys were named Francis Xavier this and Francis Xavier that. Mullane's father said the Xavier was the big punch in a name like that, so why not leave the Francis out of it entirely? There was quite a family fight about it, on account of some said it was sacrilegious toying around with a sacred name, but in the end Mullane got named Xavier Mullane, no Francis to it. So they call him Exavvy and sometimes just Zavvy Mullane.

Anyway, Exavvy was saying Paddy sometimes got the boss's hands tied in running the place with this watching out for The Slugger. "A couple of times I saw the boss tell The Slugger for God's sake wash the windows you could hardly see the 'L' through them," Exavvy said. "And The Slugger would walk toward the back of the place, his head hanging down, until he come to where Paddy was standing. 'What's the matter with you, did he say something to you?' Paddy asked The Slugger both these times. And The Slugger said, 'He told me to wash the windows again.' 'He did, did he?' said Paddy, sore as he could be, and marched up to where the boss was trying to look out through the front window to see if he could.

"'Did you tell The Slugger to wash them windows again?' Paddy says to the boss as bold as hell. 'They're dirty,' the boss said. 'They're not too dirty at all,' said Paddy back to him. 'You're trying to kill that little guy, that's what you're doing. You know he's sickly and you'd be too. Sure the man has only et offhand for twenty years and the way he lives it's a wonder he's alive at all, and he can't sleep unless he'd be drunk in them cheap furnished-room beds, you got to put a lot of booze in you first or else the bumps in the bed would keep you awake all night. The Slugger's too tired and hard-worked to do the windows and for God's sake leave him alone.'

"'Oh, all right, all right, let the windows go,' the boss says. 'Only don't be talking back to me like that.' Then Paddy says to him, 'I'm not talking back to you, it was me that began the talking.'

"Almost the same thing, word for word, happen twice, and of course it's all right with me, but you can see how it ties up the boss's hands. There's no sense in saying why don't the boss fire Paddy, because nobody gets fired here, and in the second place who knows the customers and their likes and dislikes like Paddy, how could you break in a fresh bartender to understand a place that's peculiar like this?

"Still and all," says Exavvy, "that was a great miracle, pradickly, that Paddy work out the time The Slugger collapse. It stands to reason he'd sooner or later collapse, with him so skinny anyway and no care taken of himself. It's come-day, go-day, God send Sunday with The Slugger. If he can chip in a half a buck with some other little guy and win a one-dollar bet on a horse, that's as happy as he can get. It's all the fun he has besides being cockeyed now and then, you might say. It's a hell of a life he leads, The Slugger.

"When he collapse that day it was a kind of parlay of a half a dozen things the matter with him that hit him all at once. The chef found him all slumped up in a booth one morning when he came in early. The poor Slugger's mind was a porridge of the war and submarines and race horses. He was mumbling, with his eyes looking funny, and you could see he was sick from a dozen things at once. Some of the things the matter was not eating right all those years, and drinking, and bum sleeping, and God knows what. He kept saying it was five to one they'd torpedo Johannesburg, South Africa, which was the name of a town he picked up somewhere and the name sounded so fine to him he was always saying it. He was delirious, that's what he was. The chef took a look at him and called Joe, the cop that was out on the corner steering the kids across the street safe on their way to school through the trucks and the taxicabs.

"When Joe come in, The Slugger started swinging at him and muttering still about the torpedoes and something about it was six to one that Johannesburg would win the whole race. He was gone entirely, with the sickness hitting his mind. Joe the cop says he'll have to go to Bellevue. With cops, Bellevue is the answer to anything strange that happen, only of course in this instance he's right. The Slugger's delirious, no doubt about it. Off they took The Slugger to Bellevue.

"Paddy didn't come in to work till late that day and by the time he did, The Slugger was far gone at Bellevue. When Paddy heard what happened, he says, 'Oh my God, the poor little guy!' Well, they got hold of Father Carmichael somewhere and sent him to Bellevue to see The Slugger. In a couple of hours, Father Carmichael come back and he shook his head at Paddy. 'The Slugger's a dead pigeon,' says Father Carmichael. 'I don't mean he's dead yet, but there's no hope for him. It's no use going to see him at all, he can't recognize anybody, me or anybody else.'

"Paddy didn't do anything about The Slugger that day, and those who knew The Slugger or gave a damn kept waiting to hear was he dead yet. But it was the next day, with no word come, that Paddy went to the hospital. Before he went, Paddy says to me, 'I got an idea if I could get through to the little guy's brain or whatever the hell it is he uses for a brain, I might get him to pull out of it.' Well, I didn't say anything to that, and Dinny, not the waiter, the other Dinny, the cabman, took Paddy to Bellevue in the cab. He didn't throw the flag on the clock at all. Taking a personal friend to see a dying man, naturally he wouldn't.

"Dinny told me afterward about in the hospital. They had The Slugger tied down, but anyway he was so weak there wasn't any need of it. Paddy walk in, and even when he got up to the bed, The Slugger had no idea who Paddy was that took care of him for years, you might say.

"Then, the way Dinny told me, Paddy pull a chair up close to the bed and he lean right over The Slugger, who somehow kept still a minute or two anyway. 'Don't die, you little son of a bitch! Don't die, you little son of a bitch!' That's all Paddy say to him. Dinny say to me later he never hear anything like it in his life, how earnest Paddy said it, paying no attention at all to who else heard him, only making sure The Slugger could hear him.

"And with that, Paddy get up, shove the chair back, and says, 'Come on, Dinny, come on back to the place.' On the way back in the cab Paddy holler up to Dinny in the front, 'I think I got through to him.' That's all he say.

"Well, they come back and Paddy went to work, up and down behind the bar and saying nothing to anybody. Well, everybody knows

The Slugger didn't die, because he's still around here. Fact the matter, five days after Dinny and Paddy was at the bed, in walks The Slugger into the saloon, teetering on his legs as if they were made out of ropes, but walking. Paddy grinned like an ape when The Slugger come in. He says to him, 'Hello, you wobbly little cluck,' and he told Garabedian, the chef, 'Hurry up get The Slugger something to eat.' "

THIS LADY WAS A BOSTONIAN THEY CALL THEM

Little Marty is one of the hackies who play the corner of Forty-second Street and Second near the Shanty there. He has a way of talking that he can pronounce capital letters. If he says a fare was a Society Playboy, why, it sounds as if there was a capital "S" and a capital "P" on the words. One time he was telling about a celebrity that was in his cab and Little Marty said, "They call his folks The Salmon King." You'd know there were capital letters on "The Salmon King."

Another thing. Little Marty has the idea the slightest thing happens to him, it's important. They're not important's a matter of fact, but Marty tells them anyway. Take, for example, here's what he was telling last night having a couple cups coffee in the Shanty, with the cab outside.

"This Lady is twenty-nine years of age—I didn't ask her but she told me her Life History, you might say. She's a Bostonian they call them. She isn't out of in Boston, she lives in a place right outside of Boston, she told me the name, a small place anyway.

"She got clothes looks thicker than the clothes they wear here. Women, I mean. They cost dough, you could see that. They're tailor-mades—thick, though. More like men's clothes than women's clothes in this city.

"Anyway, no sooner she got in the cab, it's about two o'clock this morning, she Explained the Situation. She don't want to go home, at the same time she don't want to go in and have a drink alone anywhere. That's how it was she put it up to me cold turkey would I go in someplace and have a drink with her, she'd pay for it. I'm not the type guy drinks much anyway, especially whiskey, which you'd have to do, I figure, on a time like this. And another thing, I got no shave and I don't look good—how can I look good wearing the cap? But we're by this time passing a Third Avenyuh place I know one the bartenders and he would know with me there's Nothing Wrong no matter how it looks, so in we go. I know him for years since kids. We went to St. Gabriel's. They tore it down, you know, and put in the tunnel to Queens. St. Gabriel's gone and now they got a tunnel hardly anybody goes through it, they tell me.

"Well, to make a long story short, this is a pretty decent place where we went into, me and the Bostonian. It don't get real Third Avenyuh trade, instead customers comes over from on Park and around there. So when we went in there, the best I could do was braze it out, so first off I excuse myself and slip in the men's room and put water on my hair and plaster it down with my hands before I go back and sit on a stool with this Lady at the bar.

"The bartender was surprise seeing me and a Lady like this popping up but he never blink an eye, too use to see all kinds of things happening all the time.

"Well, the upshot of it was we sat there. The way she told it she came here for the dog show. They had it in the Garden. People come from Boston and Chicago even. It's an International Affair. By the time the dog show's over, there's a week of it, this Lady win a couple prizes. No question about it, she has Dough. An' after a whole week of dog show, why, she stayed here a couple weeks, didn't have to go back to Boston, either her or her husband. The two of them's the kind they don't haff to go any place only where they feel like it, they got that kind of dough. I got to say I was surprise she had a husband—somehow I got the idea from the thick clothes she wouldn't have a husband.

"The husband was over in their hotel, a kind of family place off of Fifth, and here it is getting near three o'clock, quarter a three, and the upshot of it was I kept thinking isn't this a hell of a thing now? Nothing wrong, but it was what they call Quite an Adventure for me, even if it got embarrassing.

"In front of the bartender knew me for years, this Lady Bostonian kept saying, 'This is quite a picturesque scene, isn't it? This is quite a picturesque scene.' How could it be a picturesque scene me with no shave, three o'clock in the morning, sitting up at a bar with a Lady I never see before?

"The upshot of it was I maneuver it to get out of there after a while. I made out to do it no hurt feelings all around, but out we got. Then what happens but the Bostonian wants Sen-Sens. I think this Lady got self-conscience-stricken herself at about Forty-ninth Street. She maybe got to thinking about this Husband at the hotel, and so I had to stop the cab and go get Sen-Sens. I don't understand them at all. What's the sense of Sen-Sens and cloves and coffee beans on a wife that's coming in three o'clock in the morning? Anyway, that's all there was to this Bostonian, the end of the matter. At that, she gave me a dollar-ten tip at the hotel, there was only ninety cents on the clock so she gave me the dime and another whole buck. And then with the doorman there listening and all, damn if she didn't say it again, 'It was quite a picturesque evening.' I scrammed out of there."

ATHEIST HIT BY TRUCK

This drunk came down the street, walking in the gutter instead of on the sidewalk, and a truck hit him and knocked him down.

It is a busy corner there at Forty-second Street and Second Avenue, in front of the Shanty, and there's a hack line there. Naturally, a little crowd and a cop gathered around the drunk and some hackies were in the crowd.

The cop was fairly young. After he hauled the guy up and sat him down, he saw there wasn't much wrong with him. His pants were torn and maybe his knee was twisted slightly—maybe cut.

The cop got out his notebook and began asking questions and writing the answers down. Between questions he had to prop the man up. Fellow gave his name—Wilson, Martin, some noncommittal name—and his address. Everybody around was interested in these facts.

The blind man in the newspaper hut felt a little put out because nobody was telling him what was going on, and he could hear beguiling fragments of it. "What happen? What happen?" the blind man kept asking, but the event wasn't deemed sensational enough for anybody to run and tell him, at least until afterward.

"What religion are yuh?" the policeman asked the man, who propped himself up this time and blurted out, "Atheist! I'm an atheist!"

For some reason, a lot of people laughed.

"Jeez, he's an atheist!" one of the hackies said. He shouted to a comrade who was still sitting behind the wheel of a parked cab at the corner, "Feller says he's an atheist!"

"Wuddaya laughing at?" the cop asked, addressing himself to the crowd generally. "Says he's an atheist, so he's an atheist. Wuddaya laughing at?" He wrote something in the book.

Another policeman, from over by Whelan's drugstore, where there was a picket line, strolled up. He was an older cop, more lines in his face, bigger belly, less humps around his hips, because the equipment —twisters, mace, and all that stuff—fitted on him better after all these years. "Wuzzamadder with 'im?" he asked his colleague.

"This here truck hit him. He isn't hurt bad. Says he's an atheist."

"I *am* an atheist!" the man yelled.

The crowd laughed again.

"Did you put that down—atheist?" the older cop asked.

"Yuh, I put it in where it says 'religion.'"

"Rubbid out. Rubbid out. Put in Cat'lic. He looks like a Cat'lic to me. He got an Irish name? Anyway, rubbid out. When he sobers up, he'll be sorry he said that atheist business. Put in Cat'lic. We gotta send him to Bellevue just for safety's sake." The young cop started for the drugstore to put in a call.

"Never mind safety's sake. I'm an atheist, I'm telling you," the drunk said, loud as he could.

"Cuddid out, cuddid out," the older cop said. Then he leaned over like a lecturer or somebody. "An' another thing—if you wouldn't go round sayin' you're an atheist, maybe you wouldn't be gettin' hit by trucks."

The crowd sensed a great moral lesson and didn't laugh.

"Jeez! The guy says he's an atheist," the hackie said again.

A little later the Bellevue ambulance came.

"I yam a natheist," the man kept muttering as they put him into the ambulance.

PEOPLE DON'T SEEM TO THINK THINGS OUT STRAIGHT IN THIS GIN MILL

The way they got things twisted around now, the whiskey firms begrudge you every bottle of whiskey they sell you if you're a saloon. But at the same time they keep giving out advertising and one of the whiskey people gives out a kind of barometer, just a cardboard one, to put behind the bar. This is what started a set-to in this gin mill on Third Avenue the other day. It wound up with a cynic throwing an Old-Fashioned glass into the mirror. An Old-Fashioned glass is one of the worst things you can throw into a mirror, with the heavy bottoms they got. Any bartender will tell you that.

The bartender in this place is named Peter Mugivan and he didn't have much to do this particular time when the barometer argument came up. It was the lull between the noontime hangovers and the late afternoon, when there's the overcured hangovers and the early beginners on the night drinking.

So this quiet time, Peter was standing behind the bar with nothing much to do and only a couple guys in the place. One was a regular, got a bad temper. They call him Red Barron because he has red hair. He is a cynic, and when he is drunk he don't believe in anything. You can't tell if he believes in anything when he is sober because then he don't say.

Red Barron was standing in front of Peter and this barometer was in back of Peter on the back bar. Red was hung over and he had an Old-Fashioned in front of him all the time.

The barometer is cut out of cardboard like a little house. There's two doors cut out of it and there's a wooden stick on a pivot, so that there's either a woman, cut out of cardboard, can come out one door, or a man, a little tough guy, also cardboard, can come out of the other door. If the woman is out, it means fair weather coming. If the man is out, it means bad weather coming. There must be some kind of chemical worked into it to make it run, but anyway—the woman out, fair; the man out, lousy.

Peter was poking at the barometer and Red was watching him.

"What are you doing?" Red said to him.

"Nothing," Peter said, but just the same kept on fiddling with the barometer.

"I mean what are you doing to that thing?" Red kept on. He had got out of the hangover enough to want to talk to somebody about something, almost sure to start an argument.

Peter answered him anyway. "I'm shoving the little guy back in the house," he said. That's what he was doing, and he was kind of picking at the cardboard under the little guy's door with his fingernail.

"Why?" says Red.

"If he comes out it gets lousy outside," says Peter. "Look out the winder, see how nice it is with the woman out the way she was almost three days now. *He* started to come out about an hour ago. I always keep an eye on the two of them."

"Who started to come out?" Red asked then, because he must have lost track of what they were talking about.

"The little guy here, starts the storms," said Peter.

Red grunted and took another whack at the Old-Fashioned.

Nobody said anything for a couple of minutes. Then Red spoke up again. "Why don't you leave the thing alone. What do you want to mess with the thing for?"

"Oh, I just thought I'd keep him in and let the woman stay out, that's all," said Peter. "Nothing serious, just fixing the thing so he can't get out."

Peter was using his fingernail to poke up some of the cardboard so it blocked the man's end of the pivot from getting out the door.

"Well, stop it then, stop it anyway," says Red. "Go on and do something else around here. You're driving me crazy."

"Why should I do something else?" Peter says right back to him. Bartenders get independent now. They know they're hard to get and they talk back more than they used to.

"Aw, for God's sake!" Red mumbled, and he told Peter to make him another Old-Fashioned. Peter did, but he squashed the sugar cube in the bottom of the glass by pounding it, not just pushing down and twisting the muddler on it. He knew pounding it would get Red sore, just like making any small kind of racket would burn him up. Peter must have been a little cross, too, somehow.

"That's enough pounding!" Red barked at him. "Put the whiskey in it and be done with it."

Peter poured in the whiskey and gave the drink to Red, then back he went to poking at the barometer. Red picked the chunk of orange out of the glass and threw it on the floor.

"If I keep the little guy in, it will stay nice out, like it is now, and I'm off tomorrow," says Peter.

"Listen, you goddam idiot!" Red hollered at him. "That thing, that barometer there, that follows what's going on in the sky, in the air outside, you cluck! That thing *follows* the weather! The sky and the air out there don't follow that thing. It don't get stormy because that piece of cardboard comes out! Do you hear me, you superstitious son of a bitch?"

Peter was getting sore too. "What are you hollerin' for?" he said. "I can hear you, and don't call me that. How do I know if you're kiddin'? And I can keep the little guy in if I want to. You don't give a damn is it lousy weather or good weather or what. You don't care about anything. I watched you for years."

"Don't tell me what I care about and what I don't care about!" Red yelled. "I do care whether it's good weather or not. But I got some logic, some goddam sense about it. I don't think a bloody piece of cardboard on a stick controls the weather."

"Oh, you know everything, I know that," says Peter, sarcastic, to him. "You know everything, you don't believe in nothin'. I didn't say this little guy controls the weather, exactly—"

Red was getting madder. "He don't control it exactly or not exactly or anyway," he said.

"Hell, I know he don't," Peter growled, "but what the hell harm will it do if I keep him in and leave the woman out like she is when it's good weather? Maybe it'll work, how do you know? Maybe the good weather will keep up."

Red grabbed his drink and gulped it down. "Oh, God!" he howled. "You half believe it! You can't get it out of your head. It's people like you has the whole world screwed up. You can't think, you're bogged down in some kind of Voodoo all your lives, you ignorant—"

Peter flew at him. "Who's ignorant?" he said, real sore, and he grabbed Red by the lapel. "I let you get away with calling me everything; now I'm ignorant!"

Suddenly Peter let go and his eyes were popping mad. He wheeled around, grabbed the whole barometer, and planked it down on the bar in front of Red. And he pushed the little cardboard guy back in with a twist that bent the pivot so he never would get out again.

"See!" Peter yelled. "He's going to stay in and the woman out. It's going to stay good weather and the hell with you and calling people ignorant. I'll bat your ears off!"

The Old-Fashioned glass was in Red's hand, and the first thing Peter knew, it whanged past his ear and bam! into the mirror. The mirror broke and big cracks ran down into the corners.

Peter rushed around the open end of the bar, at the back. But the cook had heard the racket, ran out from the kitchen, blocked him and held his arms.

Red was staring at the broken mirror. "It's all you can do," he said. "It's all you can do. Kill people as dumb as that. But instead, I busted the mirror . . . Aw, let him go," he yelled at the cook, still holding Peter. "I wouldn't stay in the joint." And he went out quick, through the side door.

The boss didn't come in until an hour afterward. "What happened to the mirror?" was the first words out of his mouth.

Peter only mumbled an answer.

"What?" the boss said.

"Red Barron done it," Peter said. "An Old-Fashioned glass."

"Why? What for?" said the boss. "The last time it cost fifteen bucks. God knows what'll it cost now, the war and all. What happen, Peter, what happen?"

"Argument," Peter said.

BARTENDER HERE TAKES DISLIKE TO "DEEP IN THE HEART OF TEXAS"

Paddy Ferrarty, the night bartender in this place on Third Avenue, lives in a furnished room. It's run by a landlady by the name Miss Myers. Paddy's single. He sleeps daytimes and reads Westerns. Everybody in furnished rooms reads Westerns and in furnished-room places there's always a pile of Westerns in the basement if your own runs out; that is, you've got it all read through.

That doesn't have much to do with what Paddy did a little while ago, except that he really likes the Old West from reading so much Westerns, even if he has never been out of New York since he landed from Ireland.

"I don't know why a furnished room gets lonesome at five o'clock nearly on the dot every day," Paddy was saying the other night, when hardly anybody was in the gin mill. "I don't like work—it's the curse of the world—but damn if I don't almost want to get to work out of the furnished room about five o'clock.

"Every day when it happens that way I begin going to work and I hope every day the joint will be livelier than home, where I'm sick of. But the same time I hope it won't get too lively with people hollering or maybe some guy reciting. Reciters are one of the terrors of tending bar. So are people striking up friendships with strangers at the bar that always ends in fights. And now they got juke boxes.

"Juke boxes are the curse of the world. They got me nuts and they got every other bartender nuts, especially a bartender that works nights.

"They first began to get me cuckoo when they had on ours 'El Rancho Reeyo Grandy.' It had a part where drunks hollered, just the same as this 'Heart of Texas' got a place drunks got to clap.

"I just thought I'd go nuts with the Reeyo Grandy one but I was sure of it with this 'The prairie sky is wide and high,' and then the goddam four claps.

"Or is it three claps? One of the things that drives you crazy is that. Some gives three claps and some gives four and they're all clapping together at the bar. Only they're not clapping together. How can they, some giving three claps and some giving four?

"One guy I see put in eighteen nickels after the other, all for the 'Heart of Texas.' He got a beer, give me a dollar, and wanted all-nickels change, which I gave him, and one by one in they went till I nearly jump over the bar.

"The hell of it is there's good tunes on there, too, and I wouldn't want it said I'm a guy hates music's guts. They got one on there a meddalee of Stross waltzes. It's Number 15. I use to be one of the best waltzers there was, only my feet are all stove down now from floors behind bars that got no give to them, like walking on cement. They're killing me right now, my feet, on top of getting mad about the 'Heart of Texas.' Thank God I got rid of that record.

"The way I got rid of it—well, I had to get tough. First I was going to ask the boss would he for God's sake jimmy that record out of there, but the boss is the boss, good enough in his way but stubborn about the customers wants this and the customers wants that. A man can't devote his life to the customers, but what sense telling that to the boss? Anyway, I figure the fox is his own best messenger, they used to say back home in Maynooth, and the next afternoon I came in myself to the gin mill about two o'clock.

"That was a Tuesday, the day the guy comes around to empty the juke box and once in a while he puts in new records.

"'Get the "Heart of Texas" the hell out of there,' I said to him when he got the front of the machine down. The boss wasn't there, lucky enough. 'You ain't running the joint and it takes in a lot of nickels,' the juke-box guy said. 'All right, it takes in a lot of nickels and it's driving me nuts,' I told him. 'Out comes the "Heart of Texas" or I'll cut the wire. I'll sabotize the whole goddam thing, job or no job.' 'I'm telling you it takes in a lot of nickels and he got to have the nickels to pay for the ice machine,' the guy said.

"I forgot to tell about how they get you hemmed in if you run a gin mill. They sell you an ice machine for the bar—costs about twenty-three hundred dollars, imagine that—and you pay for it by dropping five quarters in a slot every day at the end of the bar. Like an old gas meter. So the money out of the juke box goes into quarters to put into the ice-machine slot. The way I figure it that leaves everybody where he was, only with two machines he didn't want in the first place.

"'Get the "Heart of Texas" the hell out of there,' I told him, 'or, bejeezus, I'll screw up the icebox too.' Well, there was some more words. No fist fight, nothing.

"Sum and substance is he took it out and put in a good one. Number 17. 'Hin*doo*stan.' It's got a part at the end where a bass fiddle got a nice lilt to it. And jeez, do I get many a good peace of mind when some dame will be standing at the bar and yell to a guy, 'Hey, Eddie, put on "Heart of Texas."' I don't say anything. I just think how she'll play hell getting the 'Heart of Texas' in here."

ARGUMENT OUTSIDE A GIN MILL HERE

The doll hung above the driver's seat of the truck, which was parked outside a gin mill on Third Avenue—Fifty-first, Fifty-second Street, around there someplace. The rain had soaked the doll, but rain or no rain, it looked gay and lively, a long-legged doll with an orange belly and yellow feet. Hell of a big truck it was too, by the way.

Two guys out of the gin mill were standing there, and one said, "Goddam cute. Looka the doll hangin' up there, will yah?" The other fellow looked but didn't say anything.

The driver's foot was on the step that minute. He was just going to climb up into the seat, but he got down, and in two strides was facing the two men. "Cute, huh?" he said. "Waddayamean cute? Yah mean cute it's all right? Or yah mean cute yah think it's sissy an' yah don't like it? Waddayamean cute?"

The man he spoke to didn't take a backward step. Fairly husky man, who'd go about a hundred and ninety-two pounds, about the same as the truck driver, give or take a couple pounds. "I din say," he answered. He made a face. "Now you ast me, I mean cute yah got about an eight-ton truck there, at lease, and the doll is silly-lookin' on it, now you ast me."

The truck driver's chin came sliding out like the bottom drawer of a bureau. "Silly-lookin', huh?" he said, the words coming slow. "The doll happens to be, if yah wanna know, the doll happens to be my kid's doll. Yah wanna make somepin out of it? Howdya like to get a cute little rap on the snoot for yahself!"

"Aw, whyant you take the truck anna doll an' all an' get the hell up the avenyuh an' be done with it an' nevvamine do I wanna make somepin out of it? I din say your kid's doll look silly on the truck, did I?"

"Chry-sill mighty, yah said somepin about a doll bein' silly-lookin', an' as far as that goes I can take the truck an' the doll an' all *up* the avenyuh, *down* the avenyuh, *sideways* on the avenyuh, an' I can leave it stay where it is, an' wadda you got to do with it? Yah did so say it was silly-lookin'."

"I said a doll was silly-lookin', howmy a know it's yah kid's doll? A kid's doll looks all right an' maybe it's good luck or somepin. It's not the same thing at all as any old doll hangin' on a truck."

The driver considered. He appeared to be deciding not to give up too easily. "I got half a mine," he said, looking at both the men now, "to knock your two cute little heads togedder. You too, yah cluck, yah!"

The last was to the silent guy, who now spoke in a dreamy way. "I didn't say nothin', nothin' at all, never said a word," he said, in a monotone as level as the top of a pool table. "Holy Jeez, but it's rainin'. The 'L' is soakin' wet. Lookad the 'L,' soakin' wet."

Both the truck driver and the man he had been arguing with stared at the third guy. Then they looked at each other.

"The 'L' is soakin' wet, he says," the truck driver muttered. "Chry-sill mighty, how long this feller been livin' round here worryin' about the poor old 'L' is soakin' wet? The 'L' been there maybe fifty years, been there a hundred years far as I know. An' a dopey bottleneck standin' there inna rain sayin' the 'L' is soakin' wet!"

The big man turned to his chum. "So the 'L' is soakin' wet then. Wad aboud it? The guy onna truck is right! No wunna this country gotta snab oud of it and start getting somewheres. Chowderheads standin' around Third Avenyuh mopin' about the poor old 'L'!" He turned to the truck driver, shrugged his shoulders, and said, "You're right, Mac. Dope is right."

"The 'L' is soakin' wet," the truck driver mumbled, and climbed into the seat and started the truck up the avenue.

MAN HERE KEEPS GETTING ARRESTED ALL THE TIME

Grogan got arrested again Thursday. Talking in this place on Third Avenue Friday night, he said he was getting sick and tired of it. That's about the ninth time he got arrested lately. He seems to be having a streak.

Grogan is a nice, quiet little man. He bets on race horses and thinks about them night and day. Mostly he gets arrested in raids on puny horse rooms around Third, Second Avenue, occasionally Lexington Avenue.

Grogan's a solemn, small, scientific-minded little man, with no laughs at all written on his dead pan. He comes by being scientific-minded honestly, because in Ireland his old man was a Latin scholar just for fun. That's how Grogan got his middle name, which is Vercingetorix. His whole name is Malachy Vercingetorix Grogan, but they call him Grogan the Horseplayer. It sounds like a trade, like bricklaying.

Getting arrested doesn't bother Grogan in his pride or leave any marks on his character. He manages to remain altogether aloof from the cops that arrest him. But what gets him sore is he says you miss your dinner when you get arrested in these raids. They almost always happen half past four in the afternoon and no Night Court to stick you in front of until about ten o'clock that night.

"I don't know do they folly me around or what, those plainclothes policemen," Grogan said. "But it seems lately no sooner am I settled down nice and busy in one of these horse rooms than along about the fifth race at Aqueduct in come the policemen again.

"They're decent enough when they come in on a raid, unless once in a while somebody in the crowd of horseplayers shows signs getting tough. They have to paste them a couple then—not too hard—so everybody else will get the idea what's done is done and make the best of it and they'll know it's a raid. These couple of pastes in the jaw for somebody is what they might call in a show establishing a mood. The policemen establishes a mood that way."

This last arrest, Grogan said, just about broke the back on his camel. He got to brooding about it. Paddy Ferrarty, the night bartender, often says about Grogan, "He's Irish and he broods easy."

"It's heartbreaking the way I got to do now," Grogan went on. "They got me half scared of the little horse rooms, and I don't ketch holt of enough money for decent poolrooms. I usually got seven dollars, only, to start with. Consequence is I'm playing with guys makes book in an auto on a corner. They sit in the auto and won't let me or the other horseplayers sit in it, naturally—ain't room enough.

"No, we got to stand in the rain or doorways to look at the *Racing Form*, and walk over to the auto and make bets, or get the results that comes in over the radio. You seen that kind of bookmaking. You can tell this auto, on a different corner around here nearly every day, because it has a sign on the front, 'Remember Pearl Harbor.'

"This last raid—I don't know, it got tiresome. I make out better than the other guys arrested. I'm used to it. Like when they're going to lead you out to the patrol wagon at the curb, nobody wants to be first outside the door and pass through the crowd. A crowd always stands around as close as they can to a patrol wagon, and the cops make a space between 'em, like an aisle outside a church for a wedding.

"But I got over all that bashfulness about going out first and let the crowd gape at you. The hell with them in the crowd. You're not criminals anyway, only horseplayers meaning no harm, only want to win a couple dollars. And what the hell, the cops themselves ain't even mad at you; they got to make a couple raids every week to put in the records.

"And what I found out is you get across the sidewalk first and into the wagon and you get a seat. Why, the last time they had twenty-seven guys jammed in there, standing up, sitting on each other, piled up every which way, miserable. So I'm first across the sidewalk—let them gape—and I got a seat.

"First they took us in this last raid down to the police station on East Thirty-fifth Street. The whole twenty-seven in a big room and certainly a mixed-up bunch. They had guys like me, and wops, and some Long-champs waiters with red braids on their coats would probably get fired because it was five o'clock by then and they ought to be back to work. Three or four horseplayers had helmets on. Steel helmets. These helmet guys work in the slaughterhouse on First Avenyuh. They got to wear helmets because the big sides of beefs run along a conveyor on hooks and without the beefs the bare hooks sometimes hits the guys in the head. Therefore helmets.

"The way you mill around in that police station is an awful waste of time. Just mope there, but a guy sells coffee if you want it. That helps and he makes a handy dollar with all the prisoners dumped in there all the time.

"It's about six o'clock before they took us up to East Sixty-seventh Street, what they call Division Headquarters. They count you before they put you in the wagon and they count you up at East Sixty-seventh Street and they count you before they take you out of there. My God, you get sick of being counted! I hate cops counting me, but they have a slip says twenty-seven guys arrested and they deliver them around from station to station like merchandise. Another thing that's not becomin' at all is that in East Sixty-seventh they put you in cells. No matter who you are, getting put in a cell can make you sad, even if only for horseplaying. There's something about seeing a man walk loose by the door and you can't walk loose but got to look through bars that sinks your heart out if you let it. Only I don't let it. The thing that bothers me is why do they go through all this at all, to say nothing of making you miss your dinner? Why do they keep bothering poor, simple, ordinary horseplayers and turn them loose anyway in the finish, which they always do?

"It seems useless to me. I always thought now for years I love to study horses and bet them when I can because it is one thing you can do by yourself and harms nobody at all. I can be busy with horses, the *Racing Form* or maybe the *Morning Telegraph*, all winter nights and summer nights in Bickford's or in my room and never harm anybody, but they got to keep on arresting us. Getting married causes trouble, drinking causes trouble, working wears a man out, and I see guys all around me dying making successes out of themselves. Why can't they let me harm nobody just studying horses and playing 'em when I can?

"I almost forgot to say just before the raid I bet a horse at Suffolk, two dollars win, with Louie the bookie. But then the raid come, and of course they stopped the radio, gathered up all the *Forms* and all, and with all the moving from station to station I couldn't find out how the Suffolk race come out. None of the cops were watching me especially in the raid, and I snuck an Arlington Park part of the *Form* into my sock, folded up, and I had that at East Sixty-seventh Street. I could study that in the cell, and they run late out there at Arlington because it's in Chicago. Well, damn if I didn't find a horse in the last race out there I'd been watching for weeks. He could win easy, and luck would have it Louie walk by the cell and stopped there. He must have slipped a cop something and they broke him out of a cell and let him walk in the corridor back and forth—more comforting than in a cell. I asked Louie if he would let me bet the last at Arlington, although by that time the race was over. I didn't have money, but if the Suffolk horse had win, well, I could 'if' some money off him. That means if the first horse wins, you can bet some of the win on another one. It's like a contingency basis in the legal world, only it's 'iffing' in horse rooms. 'Honest to God, don't you know how the race come out at Arlington?' Louie asked me. 'Nobody told you, did they, in jail here?' I told him honest to God I didn't know. 'O.K.' he says. 'You're an honest guy, Grogan. You can have four win on the Arlington horse.' Then he walked away from the cell. They both win, it later turn out, and so I beat Louie for sixteen-seventy.

"I was glad I went out first to the wagon when they moved us to Night Court over on West Fifty-fourth Street. I tell you why.

"It was dark when they moved us, and of course the wagon was jammed up again. The seat I got was up front, and there's a round hole in the partition that divides the driver off from us. Well, as we drove along I could look through that round hole and see all the corners I knew. It was very interesting, just looking through that hole and seeing a particular building and figuring out 'This is Lexington and Sixty-fourth' or else 'This is Lex and Fifty-ninth.' The electric signs are blacked out, but I could read some anyway and they looked pretty through that hole and made me forget how rotten it is packed in a patrol wagon getting arrested all the time for doing no harm.

"Of course, they counted us again at the Night Court, where you stand around in a detention pen. I felt like saying, 'Stop counting me. I'm still one guy, the same as I been all my life.' But what's the use? The less said in a detention pen the better.

"The bailiff got me a little mad. They haul you up in a bunch before the magistrate, and when it came our turn, the bunch from our particular raid, what do you suppose the bailiff shouted to the magistrate? Well, he hollered, 'Malachy V. Grogan and twenty-six others!' I asked him, 'What's the idea singlin' me out?' 'Aw, you're here all the time,' he says. I let it go at that.

"They dismissed us, the magistrate did, the way he always does. We get charged with dis. con., they call it, means disorderly conduct, and there's a couple minutes' blather and they turn us loose, ten o'clock or so and no dinner yet. They hold Louie. They got him charged with main. nuis., which is maintaining a nuisance, probably meaning Malachy V. Grogan and twenty-six others. It all seems useless, and I don't know why they got to keep arresting us all, not doing anybody a bit of harm but finding an interesting way to put in all the days and nights.

"Louie give me the sixteen-seventy after we got out. He got bailed in no time. I knew he would because Louie's the kind nobody pends him up very long and so I was waiting in Fifty-fourth when he come out. He bought a *Telegraph* at the stand there at Fiftieth and Broadway and we found out how the races we missed in jail come out."

DON'T SCRUB OFF THESE NAMES

If a wife could be as patient as Grogan the Horseplayer's landlady, there would be hardly any old guys living alone in furnished rooms the way there are hundreds of them now. One time Grogan owed his landlady ninety weeks' rent. That will give you some idea about Grogan's landlady. She got more tolerance than you can shake a stick at and she certainly is a fine woman. She's an elderly woman, seems to understand horseplayers and not be bothered by them as much as other people are.

This rooming house where Grogan lives is quite a place once you get to understand it. It is an old brownstone house, once upon a time worth forty thousand dollars. That part of it comes in to what happened with Grogan, how much the house was worth and all. You wouldn't notice this house among thousands of houses like it in different parts of Manhattan. It's just a four-story affair, with a stoop, and a gate door under the stoop, the kind of door you used to go through into hundreds of speakeasies in the old days.

Grogan's rent got piled up to ninety weeks that time because he's the kind of old guy you trust once you get to know him. He is quiet and more than fifty and wears glasses. He clears his throat before he talks, and when he does talk it is mostly about race horses. A gin-mill man that knows Grogan for years said one time about him, "Grogan is so goddam honest he don't *have* to pay you." What he meant was that there are a lot of guys, if they borrow five bucks, let's say, why two minutes afterward you begin worrying are they going to cheat you out of it and never pay you back. But with Grogan, if he borrows anything and a couple months goes by, even a couple years, you still got confidence that as soon as he can get around to it Grogan will pay you back.

That accounts partly for Mrs. Benoit, that's Grogan the Horse-player's landlady, letting the rent run up to ninety weeks. In money it was two hundred and seventy dollars, because he has a rent of only three bucks a week. That's all out of kilter with rents now, but Mrs. Benoit decided years ago that Grogan's rent was three bucks a week and it never changed. Anyway, Grogan just kept putting it off week after week, sometimes being in the hole on account of horses, sometimes having to buy some shoes or something, and there was never enough left for the rent, so what he owed piled up. Never once did Mrs. Benoit bother him. She knew Grogan would pay up sometime. Then he went to Mexico. Some cousins took him, and he was gone a year and a half, and back he comes, walking into the rooming house and saying "Hello, Mrs. Benoit," after he cleared his throat. And he paid her sixty bucks on the two-seventy. He got the sixty bucks selling a bishop's ring which a Mexican family gave him for a goodbye gift when he left Mexico City. They were very fond of him.

Grogan's got an ace in the hole to keep up to, or at least not too far behind, the horses. He is a crackerjack commercial artist, drawing pictures of hams and bacons and, at Thanksgiving, Puritan girls carrying in turkeys, for the ad agencies, but he usually works at it only to get money for horses. Well, he had a fit of working as hard as you could imagine right after he came back from Mexico and he paid off the two-ten. It was working money, earned from working, not from horses, and how Grogan paid the landlady with it so steady was a surprise to those that know him and realize he'd rather put every cent on horses than do anything else with money. Here's how he did it.

In the afternoons, Grogan would sit around in Mrs. Benoit's basement apartment calling bets on the phone to a puny kind of bookie. The bookie is a Greek runs a flower store, but he watches the entries and results more than he cares a damn about the rhododendrons.

These afternoons would show you how patient Mrs. Benoit is. With Grogan studying the *Racing Form,* then telephoning to the Greek every couple of minutes, and the radio going steadily all the time, it would make anybody jumpy, but not Mrs. Benoit. She would stand there ironing perhaps, just pushing the iron back and forth and now and then reaching for something else out of the clothesbasket, while Grogan rushed to the telephone or turned the radio up louder so he wouldn't miss a result coming in.

This basement apartment is Mrs. Benoit's own, and it is the only one with a telephone in the house. Grogan and the others got an arrangement they leave a nickel down on a plate by the phone every time they use it, so as not to cost Mrs. Benoit anything for horse calls or any other kind. To her it must be a nuisance, but away back she is a woman of French descent and she does not seem to get mad at the things that Americans get mad at. That is, she does not get mad at people being peculiar, but seems to figure everyone has his own way of being and there's no sense trying to change it.

For example, over the telephone in her apartment, written on the wall, it says this:

Don't Scrub Off
These Names

And underneath that are some names written out very plain. They need to be explained. These names are there because one of the guys who lives in the house is Clancy. You might call him an Irish gigolo. That's the way he gets along without working, he preys on women. But it is only fair to say he doesn't hurt them any. They are all elderly women that Clancy makes a point of striking up an acquaintance with in cocktail bars.

Clancy is a terrible fake of a guy, but in a way harmless. He plays up this "Dublin Irish" stuff and can talk pretty fancy in a Dublin way. He wears shirts that have high soft collars, with tabs in them, they call them tab collars. They're the kind of collars Englishmen wear, and they give Clancy a high-brow kind of look. He borrows suits from nearly everybody in the house. It's a remarkable thing, but everybody's clothes seem to fit Clancy and he is a very persuasive talker, can talk everybody into lending him suits, so much so that often he gets to borrow a new suit before the guy who owns it has it on twice himself.

Anyway, Clancy looks good dolled up, and he talks fine, and his regular routine is meeting these lonesome old ladies in the cocktail lounges and shining up to them. First thing you know, they're having him to dinner at their apartment, and he talks about money coming from the old country, and after a couple of dinners he tells them his money didn't come and he is hard pressed, and he borrows fifty or a hundred. That's boiling it down pretty much, how Clancy works, but that's the guts of it. He's such a faker he lies about nearly everything, more or less to keep in practice, and to each new old lady he gives a different name. He gives names he thinks are fancy, and they're so much so they're almost silly. But silly or not, he comes back and writes the latest name down on the telephone list on the wall. The idea is, known to everybody in the house and above all to Mrs. Benoit, that when there's a telephone call for a strange name, why you look at the list and if the name is there you say, "Yes, he's home. Just a moment, please, I'll call him." Then you holler for Clancy, being sure to keep a hand over the transmitter, because you know that Clancy has given this name to one of his old rich ladies. Five of the names that were written on the wall all together lately were these:—

Mr. Cavendish
Mr. Lancet
Mr. Morency
Mr. De Courcey
Mr. Baltimore

That Mrs. Benoit puts up with such nonsense as Clancy and his names is another instance what a patient woman she is. To say nothing of Mallan. He's another one lives in the house, and he's an out-and-out drunk. Like all the others except Clancy, this Mallan is past fifty, and he's still getting drunk somehow every night, until he has a rum blossom for a nose and purple veins on his grinny face.

What would make Mallan annoying anywhere but at Mrs. Benoit's is the habit he has of getting a *Daily News* when the bars close up at 4 A.M. He gets a *Daily News* without fail, reads it as best he can, although drunk, in a Shanty near the rooming house. Then at half past four in the morning, in he goes to the house, stomps up the stairs, and wakes up Grogan, then Clancy and a couple other inmates, one after the other.

"Come on, sit up!" he always says. "Sit up and take the Intelligence Test! Wake up and take the Intelligence Test!"

And then he reads out the questions in the Intelligence Test, loud, and shaking Grogan, or whoever it is, while he reads off the questions, that are always something like this: "Astigmatism refers to a disorder of which organ?" Then Mallan will continue to read, loud and slow, the list of organs, while Grogan blinks in bed:—

"Liver? . . . Ear? . . . Heart? . . . Eye?"

And Grogan, or whoever it is, will want to get it over with and get Mallan out of the room, so he'll say "Eye!" if he knows that's the answer.

"Right!" Mallan will holler. Then he'll go on to the next question, which might be this: "A statue inscribed MCCCCXCII would probably represent Julius Cæsar, Columbus, Washington, or Lincoln?"

It turns out to be, in this instance, Columbus, but hardly anybody could wake up and answer one like that. Just the same, Mallan teeters on the edge of the bed until Grogan gets the right answer, and then he hollers "Right!" And after Mallan has given the Intelligence Test to Grogan and Clancy and maybe a couple of others, why he staggers to bed himself, and that's that. He's gone through that rigamarole hundreds of times, and it goes to show you how much patience Mrs. Benoit has to let a guy like that keep on living in the house.

Well, to get back to Grogan, and the afternoons down in the basement apartment, betting the horses while Mrs. Benoit does her ironing. Grogan used to run completely out of money doing that. But somehow, when he came back from Mexico and started paying up the remaining two hundred and ten dollars after he paid the ring money, why he cut down on betting, until gradually it was mostly mind bets. He'd pick horses but not call the Greek, and he'd listen to results. Sometimes he'd be furious he didn't bet one that turned out to be a winner. More often he'd be tickled to death he didn't bet, because it was a loser. "I save two bucks on that one," Grogan would say. And to make a game out of it, why he'd hand Mrs. Benoit the two bucks and say, "Take that off what I owe you, will you please, Mrs. Benoit?"

"Yes, Mr. Grogan," Mrs. Benoit would say, putting down the flat-iron, or whatever she was using at the moment. "Thank you. I'll mark it down."

Well, in only a couple of months, Grogan was in the clear on the ninety weeks' rent. And the funny thing was, he kept right on going on with the same scheme after he got the rent paid off. In a few more weeks, he had nearly a hundred and fifty "on deposit," you might say, with Mrs. Benoit. She never said a word to egg him on, except in her own way, perhaps, of remarking, "That's very good, Mr. Grogan. You have fifty-six dollars"—or whatever it was—"now. I'll mind it for you."

Grogan acted as if this was the first time, and him past fifty years of age, that he ever heard of saving money. He got fascinated by the idea and when the money Mrs. Benoit had for him got up to three hundred and sixty, he told her one day what was in his head. He cleared his throat, the way he always does, and he said, "That's a great spot, that Mexico, Mrs. Benoit. And I'm going to go back down there, only this time with dough. For a little while, I can be a rich American. It'll certainly be something, walking in on that Mexican family I know. They were swell to me when I was down there broke, and here I'll come walking in to them, take them to the bullfights, the best seats, not out in what they call the *sol*. That's the sun seats, you know, what we call at a ball game the bleachers. And I can buy them stuff knock their eye out. When I get a thousand bucks, just a little more than a thousand, so I can get there at the Mexican house with the whole even thousand after my fare, why off I go to Mexico!"

That was quite a speech for Grogan, but he was hopped up with the idea. He told his plan later to Clancy. Fake or no fake, Clancy was a guy Grogan liked, and he told him stuff like that.

It's funny, too, in a place like Mrs. Benoit's, that even accidents works out good. You could take for example about the chimney. What happened about the chimney was that it gave out too much smoke. O.K., only nearly next door is a hotel, higher than Mrs. Benoit's place. And when the wind blew right, the smoke went into some of the hotel rooms. The guests kicked and wouldn't stay there and it was a ticklesome situation. Problem was, you couldn't deny the rooming house had to have heat—that's human. And there's laws against smoke, but they're tricky laws, and it wasn't too much smoke legally, you might say, and so here was a hell of a situation, an accident, too, the whole of it, not planned by anybody, but the situation worked out good. The hotel men tried to bully Mrs. Benoit first, but she wouldn't scare. So the upshot was that the hotel men came to Mrs. Benoit and they put up this proposition: "Say we hook up the heat from the hotel into your place, will you shut off your furnace, Mrs. Benoit?" That would be O.K., she said, and no sooner said than done. So the accident of the smoke saved Mrs. Benoit the coal money, to say nothing saving the trouble running the furnace. There never was a time when she didn't have to skimp to run the place. The finances of it was that when Mrs. Benoit's husband died years ago he left her money and she bought the house with it. It was supposed then to be worth forty thousand, but nowadays, why nothing like forty thousand. And the mortgage, even lately, was only down to nineteen thousand dollars. You couldn't get that for the house if you wanted to sell it, is what Mrs. Benoit said.

She said that one afternoon only lately. Grogan had shut off the radio because the races were over and the announcer had slumped into talking about Warsaw and Pisa. Clancy was blathering his way through making some tea. While he made it on a little stove in Mrs. Benoit's apartment, he said for the thousandth time in a year, "I have this tea sent to me specially from Boston."

And Mrs. Benoit said in her soft voice, "I know you do, Mr. Clancy. It's very nice." She knew and Grogan knew, sitting there, you could get the same tea anywhere, but Clancy went to great trouble to have it sent from Boston anyway.

Well, after that, Clancy poured out the tea, talking in big words all the while, and Mrs. Benoit went on talking about the house. "The bank told me a funny thing. I couldn't believe it," she said. "It didn't sound like something a bank would say."

Grogan cleared his throat. He'd been talking about Mexico again and he thought he was talking too much about it, although he was going there soon and it was all he could think of. "What did the bank say?" he asked, after a swig of the tea.

"They said that if I put up two thousand dollars, they'd cut the mortgage down to twelve thousand dollars, instead of it being nineteen thousand dollars the way it is now. Does that sound like a bank?"

"The financial situation in these times is extremely unorthodox," said Clancy, swinging into the big words, as usual.

Grogan cleared his throat again. "Do I get it right? They said if you put up two thousand dollars, they'd cut it down by seven thousand?" he asked.

"That's it," Mrs. Benoit said. "If I put up the two thousand, which I can't because I only scraped together a thousand dollars in all these years—well, if I put up the two, then they'd take off seven thousand off my shoulders. Then the interest would be a lot less and I could really make a little money on this house."

"Seven thousand for two thousand," Grogan said. He put down his cup and meandered out the door to the stairway. "Excuse me," he said over the banister as he went up to his room.

Clancy told about it later. He said Grogan come down again in a few minutes.

"I kept track upstairs in a book," he said to Mrs. Benoit. "Is it a thousand and seventy, exactly, that I got for Mexico?"

"It's more than a thousand, I know," said Mrs. Benoit. "Without looking in my book, I know that."

Grogan stared her in the eye, Clancy said, and then he says, "Look, Mrs. Benoit. I don't have to go to Mexico yet. You take my thousand and your thousand and give it to the bank. Look! I don't want a lot of talk and guff about it. Give them the two thousand quick and get credit for seven thousand. Seven to two on a mortgage! Jeez!"

"Oh, no, Mr. Grogan!" Mrs. Benoit said, and she turned pale. "It's for Mexico."

"Look," Grogan said, mad. "I don't want any guff about it. I never had a thousand bucks before and I don't know that I like it. It makes me nervous. It don't feel like me. Mexico will be better next year. Clancy, come on to the delicatessen with me."

And out they went, Clancy and Grogan. The way Clancy told it later, after the whole thing got straightened out and the mortgage cut down to twelve thousand, he got Grogan sore on the sidewalk outside the delicatessen. He did it ribbing him. Clancy said to him, "You chump, you couldn't resist the price, that's what happened to you. Once you heard it was seven to two on a mortgage, and a bank the sucker into the bargain, why you couldn't resist it!"

Grogan burned up. "No such thing," he growled at Clancy. "It's a question of a room. How many years is three hundred and thirty-three and a third weeks? That's how long I got a room paid up. It's a matter of a room. No seven-to-two stuff or what they call sentiment. Just cold-turkey business, you lousy faker!"

A MAN LIKE GRADY, YOU GOT TO KNOW HIM FIRST

Some of the people that inhabits this saloon on Third Avenue requires explanation. Grady the Cabman is one of them, and the other night, for want of anything better to do, Paddy Ferrarty was trying to explain him the best he could and make talk anyway for a while while there was hardly anybody in the place.

"A man like Grady, you got to know him first," Paddy said. "Else you won't make any headway at all understanding a man like that. Grady befuggles even me sometimes, and I know him since they said then he was only about seventy. Some around here says he's around a hundred, putting it on a little perhaps, but he's anyway old. Maybe he's sixty-eight, but God knows. And God'll tell you sooner than Grady.

"The thing about Grady is he seems to be always doing two things that works opposite each other and spending all his time doing it. Like he takes a cab out of the garage every night and then he spends half the night trying to keep people from getting into it and making him take them someplace. If he don't want to have people in the cab, and God knows he don't most of the time unless he can pick out who gets in his cab, well then why does he take out the cab in the first place? That's the part about Grady, you got to know him first. And even then it ain't any too clear what Grady's all about. Maybe it ain't important.

"He only wears a wig when he goes to court, or did you know he's as bald as a banana? Well he is, but how hardly anybody knows that is he wears that cabby cap night and day, wouldn't take it off for anybody. You'd get him raving mad if you yanked it off his head. Never takes the cap off even if he goes into somebody's house—I mean into a friend of his's that's drunk and got to be carried in and help the wife get him into bed and his collar unbuttoned and his shoes off so he won't choke and can sleep easy.

"One day Grady come in here in the middle of the afternoon, which was surprising to see Grady in daylight ever. I happened to be here on account a cousin of mine was with me at a funeral and I had to get up in the daytime, and after the funeral I brought my cousin in here to show him where I work because he beeslong in Brooklyn and don't get around much. Anyway, there was Grady wearing the wig and his cap off sitting at the end of the bar. He claim he found the wig one time in the back of the cab off a customer and it fit him, but so help me God I think he bought the thing. He explained why he had it on after he had to admit it was a wig, couldn't fool anybody any more than a wax apple. He got into some kind of traffic trouble, which don't happen often, I'll say that for him, and he had to go into court. He knew there's no getting away with keeping your hat on in court. Grady or no Grady, lifelong custom or no lifelong custom, take off your hat and no goddam arguments. So he wore the wig. The wig's unimportant anyway, but it's one of the things you got to understand about Grady and I'm only starting with the wig. It's hardly anything at all.

"The funny part is Grady got his own way making about three bucks a night with the cab. Even if he don't, he don't worry. You take the start of a nice summer night for instance here around Third Avenue, say take six blocks up from here and say five blocks down from here. Well, that makes eleven blocks in all and in eleven Third Avenue blocks it stands to reason they got a slather of saloons.

"Well, we'll say it's the start of a fine summer night around here. Maybe seven o'clock and the 'L' is roaring down from time to time and some kids standing in a bunch on a stoop on the side street and singing 'Don't Sit Under the Apple Tree with Anybody Else but Me Till I Come Marching Home,' and the little guy, they call him Shorty, smoking a cigar on the corner, God knows where he gets all the cigars, and everything like normal for the start of a fine summer night and along comes Grady.

"He starts sizing up the terrain as they say. He puts the cab at the corner, facing the wrong way chances are, and he walks a ways smoking that dudeen of his.

"Calm enough, he goes into this saloon and he goes into that saloon along the line. Maybe he'll see Junior Connors lined up at the bar in the first saloon. He's a big fat guy with a fine rum blossom for a nose and looks nothing at all like a junior so they call him that. He's a regular customer or ward, or whatever it is, of Grady's. Wards is better. They're more like wards than customers. Grady chooses them, they don't have hardly any hand in picking Grady for a cabman, he takes care of them year after year. Anyway, Junior is like most of the guys Grady'll allow in the cab, you might say. They're nearly all fellahs that have good enough jobs to keep them in liquor money, works regular but mostly devotes themselves to drinking and singing and arguing. Not rum-dumbs but warmin' up to be rum-dumbs.

"Anyway, to get back to Junior, Grady takes a look at him beginning to drape over the bar. Grady got little squint eyes and some says he doesn't see good, but I think he can. He can spot Junior and the rest of them. A man that claims Grady can't see good any more claimed to me one time Grady drives up and down Third Avenue by memory and don't see much ahead of him. This man claim that's why Grady don't like to drive on the West Side, because he can't remember it and don't see it, and the same guy claim it's a terrible thing for Grady they're tearing down the Elevateds because the way Grady drives he counts on the 'L' being there and it'll ball up his driving if the 'L' ain't. I think the man was exaggerating about Grady. He sees well enough I believe.

"When Grady takes a look at Junior, Grady says nothing, don't even say hello, but in his own mind Grady says to himself, 'Connors'll be ready by ten o'clock.' In other words he kind of make a mental note of Connors and the shape he's in figuring like an estimate the shape he'll be in by ten o'clock probably ready to be taken home. Then Grady leaves that saloon for the next saloon that's only no distance at all.

"In the next saloon we'll say Grady spots another regular of his, maybe Shauno Haggerty that already, and it's only ha-past seven, is standing there reciting 'Dawn on the Coast of Ireland'—I'm so goddam sick of hearing about dawn on the coast of Ireland from Shauno. 'Oh-oh,' says Grady to himself, making a mental note of Shauno, 'he'll be the first, he's almost ready already. I'll get him home first, soon as I take a look around the other places.' Out goes Grady and to the next adjoining gin mill.

"That's the way Grady does. In a half hour after he gets the cab parked on the corner, and a trip made into the saloons, he's kind of got himself booked for the night. You know how I mean—he's got to take Shauno at eight o'clock and steer him into the cab and home, then Junior at ten o'clock, and some other guy he's spotted will be drunk and ready at one o'clock, and so on.

"When these times come it sometimes gives me the shudders to see Grady circlin' around the guy he got picked to take home soon. He looks like a buzzard closing in on the guy sagging over the bar, but when all is said and done it's a good thing. Somebody got to take them home or God knows where they'd wind up and Grady takes care of them like a mother you might say. But a pretty tough mother it'd be running up nickels on a taxi clock taking care of her son, now wouldn't it?

"You can see in the meantime between these guys to be taken home at certain times Grady got fixed in his mind why he don't want a lot of strangers climbing in the cab. Grady gets into the euchre game, and the hack out at the curb bold as you please. I seen guys, strangers, push the horn and push the horn, trying to find the driver, and finely come in and say, 'Where's the guy drives this cab out here?,' and all the while Grady'll be whispering loud out of the corner of the mouth, 'For God's sake don't tell him. Don't tell him for God's sake.' That's what he'd be saying to me, in deadly fear he'd be cornered into carrying a stranger around in the cab. You got to know Grady first to understand a man'd act like that.

"It ain't that he's surly. I seen him kindhearted often. One time I had to climb in the hack, run an errand around Fifty-ninth. It was about seven P.M. and when I got into the cab what was in the seat but a scooter, two dolls, and three tops. 'What the hell is this?' I says to Grady. 'Oh, never mind them,' he says, 'the McNally kids were playing house in the cab, leave the kids' things alone.' Grady wouldn't stop kids playing house in the cab. He's kindhearted.

"But Grady's even worse than I told you about regarding the cab as a private affair of his own and not something for every Tom, Dick, and Harry to get into that's got a couple bucks and wants to be taken someplace. I've seen guys get into the cab while Grady was sitting in it, dopey, and not seeing them get in, and you ought to see Grady then. He steps on the starter without turning on the switch and it make a discouraging noise, whirrrrrrr, and of course the engine don't start. Grady looks around his shoulder at the stranger while he does this a few times and the stranger finely gets out and looks for another cab. Grady's tickled to death and turns back to reading the Intelligence Test in the *News*. The Intelligence Test is a favorite of his, especially if it's got geography in it.

"Grady claim he been everywhere but you can't tell where lies start in and the truth leaves off but you can be sure it's early in what Grady is saying because he's an awful liar. He claim he worked in shipyards everywhere. Whenever there's a war comes up, Grady's bragging about how he makes ships in the old days. Nobody knows, but this I do know. He disappeared one time four years. Four solid years. The way it happened Grady thinks nothing of it, but some would think it was mystifying. He sometimes takes little rides for himself to look at things, the way an old gentleman might take a ride for a whim to look at something. This day, it was years and years ago, Grady druv himself down to the Battery, he wanted to look at some ships going by, he thought at the moment he needed to see some ships for a change.

"Well, he went down there and four years later he came into the house up in the Bronx where he lives, and his wife and his kids were still there. One of the kids had growed up, you might say, in the meanwhile because this kid was fourteen when Grady took the ride to the Battery and he was naturally eighteen when Grady come back. That's the growing-up time, between fourteen and eighteen.

"Grady's wife seem a little surprise to see him, he told me later on, but no great fuss made. She must be quite a woman, or at least she know Grady. He said it was just dinnertime and one more for dinner in a house like that makes no difference so he pull up a chair. He told her he was working those four years in a shipyard in Clyde that's in Scotland, and that's all there was to it, those whole four years.

"I remember asking him what the hell he thought the wife and kids would do when he just plain left the cab at the Battery, abandoned it, and saunters over, maneuvers himself onto a ship and to the Clyde. 'Aw,' says Grady, 'the wife have a rich aunt. They was nothing to worry about with the rich aunt sure to take care of them all soon as it dawn on them I'm gone for a while.' A guy like that Grady, how you going to understand him without knowing him first?"

CLUNEY McFARRAR'S HARDTACK

The only trouble with this coffee pot around a Hundred and Sixty-eighth Street is it's practically one whole war behind the times. Dozens of guys who go in there off the Fifth Avenue buses are old Sixty-ninth men and they keep some track of the war in the *News* every morning. But no sooner do they talk ten minutes about this war then back they hop into the other war because it is still more familiar to them. The result was they got this war into France before it really got there. They're always talking about Looneyville—that was a spot in France in the other war—and about LaFurty Millon, they call it, that was also in the other war.

They're bus drivers and conductors on the buses, and this coffee pot is a hangout for them. Sometimes they get talking the other war and they get carried away by their own talk so that once in a while it makes quite a story they tell, in its own way. The other day it was

Cluney McFarrar talking. He just finished up work on the Burma Road line, they call it, because it's the Number Two that goes through Harlem.

Cluney McFarrar was a sergeant in the Sixty-ninth and it is practically a miracle how he weaves around in traffic with that big bus, considering the right arm he got. It was hit by a machine gun in a wheat field and later on he developed a thing in it called osteomyelitis. He knows the medical name for it because he heard the doctors in the hospitals talking about it a million times. But osteomyelitis or no osteomyelitis, he can jockey that bus around O.K., and not only that but with his bum arm he can maneuver the door open and shut in traffic in the twinkle of an eye, so that he can spit tobacco into the street as he goes along. One conductor that works with him says McFarrar is a marvel of timing, opening and shutting the door for this purpose.

This day, a couple days ago, McFarrar finished on the Burma Road, had a slug or two in a place next door to this coffee pot, then came in for coffee and to sit around talking. One thing led to another and McFarrar told about one time in a woods in France—still back a whole war, into 1918.

"There was no more trenches than a rabbit," McFarrar said, "because it was July, around that sometime, and we were chasing them but still plenty of our fellers getting killed. You don't know really what's happening in a war like that until a couple years later when you come home and read in a slow-written book just what the hell was going on that time, like for instance the day I'm talking about.

"We couldn't go up the road, so we were going ahead the best we could through a woods, the woods on both sides the road. They were shelling the road so you couldn't go up it.

"Guys would see Germans here and there ahead of them in the woods, so the way you'd have to do is stand behind a tree and fire a few, then run up and get behind another tree like the goddam Indians they used to have here in this country, except the only Indians most of us knew was those cop-shooters and wild men used to be around the West Side, Tenth Avenyuh and around there.

"That was the best way to do it, behind trees, everybody separated, but it's hell to keep soldiers separated. Or deployed, if you want to call it that. The toughest thing a sergeant has to do is keep the troops spread out, because as soon as there's shooting, they bunch up, usually around the sergeant, which'd make a fine target out of him.

"We kept separated pretty good through that woods, though, going ahead a little at a time. I come across McElroy, from Eighth Avenyuh, behind one tree, smoking his pipe and shooting one shot after the other. He says to me when I bunched behind the same tree, 'Have you got a match, McFarrar? This pipe keeps going out, and I ought to hold up a minute for a smoke anyway. The bolt on this rifle is getting hot, so help me God.'

"All that has no bearing on what I was going to say, I mean about the hardtack. Well, after I left McElroy and ran for another tree ahead a little bit and McElroy found *himself* another tree, I saw something out of the corner of my eye while I was running up to this other tree.

"What I saw was a nice new can of hardtack lying there, and jeez, was I hungry. I forgot to say the chow wagons didn't get up, and everybody was hungry. And there was this can of hardtack some poor guy dropped. He was dead near it. I had to run past it, but I never saw anything so clear as that hardtack.

"So when I got behind the tree I says to myself, 'I'll come back and get that hardtack if I ever live through this day.' And to make sure where I was, I mean where the hardtack was, I took a good look around. I looked up at how the trees set with regards to the road, and how if a man was walking on the road he could look in and tell this part of the woods exactly. Like distinguishing marks, I mean, that you'd see from the road, how the trees grew and the like of that. 'If it's the last thing I ever do, I'll get that hardtack tonight,' I says to myself.

"Well, the day come to an end, and us maybe two miles ahead of where McElroy and me was behind the tree and the hardtack was."

Then McFarrar said they had a funny thing about that other war, compared to this war they got now. He said in some ways that other war was a union war, like. In some places, anyway, it seemed to have regular hours.

"Near this woods was one of those places where the war kept regular hours," McFarrar went on. "It seemed to stop almost altogether at night, even before night. What you might call twilight, it stopped, only the way I remember it, this twilight come at pretty near ten o'clock. Not dark yet, only getting gray and birds going to bed in the trees.

"The birds were funny. I remember them because when everything come to a halt and I was still alive for the end of that day, I says to myself, 'Now I'll go back and get the hardtack.' And I started all alone back down the road. They wasn't shelling it any more, because whether it seems logical or not, the war come to a stop, I tell you, right about that hour. Not a stop for good I don't mean, but a stop for that day. And I walked back down the road toward the place where the hardtack was. Jeez, I was hungry—no chow wagons yet.

"About the birds. While I was walking back the road, I could hear them loud and busy, getting ready for the night. Banging and shooting sounds all the day, and there were the birds singing or at least talking, at this kind of twilight, as if nothing happened. It seemed funny, and it was that quiet I could hear my feet scrunching the gravel down the road.

"Of course I kept glancing into the woods, so I wouldn't pass where the hardtack was. It got silenter and silenter except for the birds, and gradually they started to shut up and it got a little darker, only not what you'd call dark. For some reason there was nobody on the road but me. The stuff like camions and chow wagons wouldn't come up until real black dark.

"There was beginning to be a little smell from the woods. They were the quietest woods I ever seen then, even though they was certainly noisy all that day we just pulled through.

"I come to the place I marked in my mind's eye, and my stomach give a jump because I knew the hardtack was right in there. Honest to God, I was near starved. I stood a minute in the road and checked up. I wanted to make sure by the shape of the trees I was right and that was the place. And I started to go into the woods after the hardtack.

"Then the silence come over me. Every bird quit all to once. My feet stopped going into the woods. It come over me how in there was all the guys, some of them I knew, would never come out of those woods again. Some of them from New York. Most of them, you might say, because don't forget this was the Sixty-ninth. I thought how they'd never walk around on the New York streets any more, Ninety-sixth or anywhere, and not ever get drunk in New York on Saturday night the way you do. And on top of all that, this silence I got to explain to you but I can't.

"And that was the last step I took toward that hardtack when I thought all that. I turned around and went up the road again.

"I couldn't have gone in those woods if there was Fig Newtons in there."

THE SLUGGER COMES INTO HIS OWN

The Slugger had the good fortune to break his right leg one winter day. This started a chain of circumstances that made the Slugger a man among men. Not that he wasn't before that, because he was.

The Slugger is physically a small man. He is spiritually a large man. He is imaginatively a prodigious man, because he imagines himself, at times, to be able to conquer the most rugged wrestlers, to knock cold the most hardened prizefighters, and to cow the boldest employers.

The Slugger is a handyman, casually working first for this one and then for that one along Third Avenue between Forty-second and Fifty-ninth Streets. He works casually because that is his nature and because the kind of work he does is casual anyway. He might wait on table a little, he might cook a little, he might sweep up a little, he might do anything that does not require too constant application.

This winter night, the Slugger was making his way from McCarthy's, at Forty-fifth and Second (a block to the east off his beat), over to the home region of Third Avenue. Without assistance from himself, he stumbled and fell over a grating that was jutting up on the proper sidewalk. That was the beginning of his luck. When Joe, the policeman on the beat, picked up the Slugger a few minutes later, his right leg was all out of shape. Joe told him to sit there in a doorway while Joe called the ambulance from Bellevue. When they got him there, they found the Slugger's right leg was broken.

The Slugger took great joy in it. His friends heard he was in Bellevue and, learning upon further inquiry that he was not in there with the creeps but with a broken leg, they became very solicitous about him. They came to visit him one after the other. One brought a pint and stuffed it under the pillow, one left him two dollars in cash, another made it a point to bring him the *Daily Mirror* every day. The Slugger was a moderately big man right away.

When the Slugger got out of Bellevue, he was limping very picturesquely and walking with a cane. He had an expression of fortitude on his face when he got back to the old neighborhood, and everybody asked him how he was making out and told him they were sorry about his misfortune.

"Oh, it's all in the game," he would say, "it's all in the game. But, God, it hurts terrible in the damp weather."

It was getting on spring and April then, so there was lots of wet weather and the Slugger had opportunity enough to look up at the sky when he said how the damp weather made the pain worse.

One day, a lawyer came looking for him, not long after he got out of Bellevue. The lawyer went into Mat's saloon, which the Slugger had given as an address when "admitted," as the saying goes, into Bellevue. "Admitted" is a fine word for such a place; the way it sounds, a person would think it was an exclusive club. Anyway, the lawyer got the address of Mat's and came in there asking for Carroll M. Holligan, which was the Slugger's right name, although hardly anybody knew it but the Social Security people and the place in Ireland where he was born, baptized, and confirmed. That town was Ballyhaunis, in the County Mayo.

"I don't know where he is this minute," Mat told the lawyer, "but if you tell me what it's about, I might be able to find him in the next day or two."

"That was pure negligence, the occasion on which Mr. Holligan suffered a fracture of the right leg," the lawyer said.

"The Slug—I mean Mr. Holligan wasn't the least bit negligent," Mat said. "He was going along minding his own business and it was slippery and that grating stuck up unbeknownst to him."

"I mean it was negligent on the part of the city, not Mr. Holligan, of course," the lawyer said. "I think the city should not go unpunished for such negligence."

"Oh, I see what you mean," said Mat. "I'll try and find him in a day or two."

Mat found him, and they sat in a booth together, the three of them—the lawyer, Mat, and the Slugger.

"It was pure negligence," said the lawyer.

"I wasn't doing anybody any harm," said the Slugger. "I was walking along and I bunked into this here thing and down I went—"

"Shut up, Slugger. Let the lawyer talk," said Mat.

"I have seldom heard of a case of more obvious negligence," the lawyer continued. "A stormy night, a citizen on his way home, and the grating sticking up as a menace to each and every taxpayer. The most reprehensible thing I've ever heard of. Have you any money saved up, Mr. Holligan?"

"Who, me?" said the Slugger.

"Shut up, Slugger," Mat said. "What size of money are you talking about, sir?"

"I was trying to estimate if Mr. Holligan could stand the cost of a lawsuit, in the event it would be unsuccessful, but I don't see how it could be when the negligence is so apparent," the lawyer said.

"Mr. Holligan is a workingman," Mat said, "and with the cost of living what it is today, he hasn't been able to set much aside."

"And by this broken leg this honest workingman has been deprived of a chance of a livelihood all these months," the lawyer chimed in.

"It hurts worse in the damp weather," the Slugger said.

"Shut up, Slugger. Let me handle this," said Mat. "Now, is there any way you could treat this on a contingency base? I heard there was times a lawyer would take a cut of what he gets for the man he's speaking up for, and let that be his end of the deal. Could we work it out that way for the Slug—I mean Mr. Holligan?"

"The Bar Association does not approve of such arrangements," the lawyer said.

"But Mr. Holligan doesn't happen to have any money at this time," Mat said.

"It is possible that Mr. Holligan may come into some money, however," said the lawyer. "In which event he would be readily able to meet my fee."

"That is possible," said Mat. "Keep quiet, Slugger."

"We shall proceed on that basis," the lawyer declared. "I am suing for thirty thousand dollars for gross negligence. Carroll M. Holligan versus the City of New York."

"He has my real name, Mat," said the Slugger. "Can you beat that, the way these fellows get to know things. My real name, Carroll M. Holligan!"

"All right, Slugger, go up to Jimmy there at the bar, and tell him I told you to have a drink," said Mat.

"Thanks, Mat. Thank you very much," said the Slugger. "Glad to meet you, sir." This last was to the lawyer. He went out of the booth on his cane and bad leg, and started over to the bar, glancing back at Mat as he did so. Mat signalled O.K. to Jimmy the barkeep. The Slugger, by no means as dumb as he seems, walked proudly forward and asked for rye-and-water—plain water, if you please. "They're going to get me thirty thousand dollars for me broken leg," he said. "I'll square this drink up with you when I get it. And it's many a drink you'll have on me after that. You're a good boy, Jimmy, and don't think I won't take care of you after I get my money. I'm not the kind that forgets his friends, Jimmy, God bless you."

The Slugger was on the way to being a made man.

It came to be May and everything lovely along the avenue. Especially with the Slugger. The kids were singing on the stoops at evening, usually singing "Just Around the Corner There's a Bluebird on High." There wasn't a bluebird within eight miles of the stoops they were on, but that made no difference. The Slugger was a man of substance then. He was a thirty-thousand-dollar man, because his case was "pending," as they say. What did he show up in on fine sunshiny days but white shoes and white flannel pants and a blue coat, with a starched white shirt beneath the coat and a good straw hat on top of it all. He was still walking with a cane. He got the white flannels from a little store that had them left over from years ago. The proprietor had heard about the Slugger's thirty thousand dollars, which he hadn't got yet, and so the proprietor trusted him.

Down would come the Slugger, limping on his cane, and he would stand for a minute, using the cane to beat time for the children singing on the stoop:

"Just erround a corner
They's a blooboid on high . . ."

They would sing, and the Slugger would move his cane back and forth in the air. It was beautiful to see. Then he'd go away, on the route to the nearest saloon.

The Slugger was a happy man, with the phantom figure "$30,000" dancing always in the back of his head like a tiny, tiny Bill Robinson tapping out an endless jolly tune with his feet, the way Bill used to do. He had credit everywhere. He'd walk in, have a rye-and-plain-water, and they'd all say, the men behind the bar, "That's all right, Slugger, don't worry about it."

"Mark it down," he'd say with a grand air, and ask whoever was next to him to have a drink. They would.

"Goodbye, Jimmy [or Joe, or Ed]," the Slugger would say. He'd go out then, in the twilight of the avenue, and feel very good.

So would the bartender he left behind. The bartender would swab a glass under the bar, washing it out, and then he would find some pal in front of the bar and say to him, "The old Slugger. Awful nice little feller. I always liked him. He got thirty thousand dollars coming, they tell me, from that time he hurt his leg. He got it broke. He says it pains him something terrible in wet weather. Even damp weather. It's lovely out today."

The lawyer told the Slugger not to throw away the cane even if he felt he didn't need it any more. Some days he didn't need it, but he forgot the idea the lawyer had, which was to keep him on a cane until the case came up in court. So some fine days the Slugger, with a few jolts in him bought out of his merciless amount of credit here and there, would be walking around spry as anyone could be, with the cane under his arm.

"The lawyer told me never go out without the cane," he'd say. "Here it is. I never go out without it. A day like this, it doesn't pain me at all."

Mat was there, as a bystander, when the Slugger made his appearance in the court. He said it was magnificent, no less a word would do for it, magnificent. It was a damp day, as luck would have it. The Slugger's leg really pained him.

"They called him over to the witness chair," Mat said that night. "He came down the aisle leaning on the cane, and I almost felt like getting up and helping him myself. He seemed to be struggling to get to the witness chair. That's the one to the left of the judge and in front of the jury box. It was magnificent."

"What was?" Jake asked him. He was one of the men listening that night to Mat. "What was?"

"The way the Slugger came down the aisle and sat in the witness chair," said Mat. "And the only answer I remember. The lawyer asked him—and I remember this next part clearly—he asked him, 'What happened, Mr. Holligan?' And the Slugger sat there and answered him, 'I was trying to go home and this grating stuck up and I fell down and broke my poor leg.' The way he said it, you would think that the leg was not a part of him but a friend that he did not want any misfortune to fall to. 'I broke my poor leg,' he said. The lawyer—a very smart man, I believe—said, 'That's all, Mr. Holligan.' I don't remember what followed. It was magnificent."

"It was," Jake said.

It wound up that the Slugger got eleven thousand dollars. That is, the jury awarded him that. The lawyer took three thousand. That left the Slugger eight thousand. He owed $47.60 at Morley's. He owed $83.50 at Colcannon's. He owed the man for the white flannels and the blue coat and the straw hat. He owed everybody. The happy time was over. But not eternally. Because Mat took charge then.

"Will you give me the power of attorney?" Mat asked him.

"You got the power of anything," the Slugger said. "I never met a more powerful man."

Then Mat had the lawyer turn over to him what was left of the Slugger's money, and he will give it out to him twenty-five or thirty dollars a week as long as it lasts. Probably a little bit longer. Mat is that kind of man.

THIRD AVENUE MEDICINE

There's a kind of medicine practiced by old veteran bartenders among old veteran drinkers along Third Avenue, not tourists, and probably the Mayo Brothers out in Rochester have never got wind of it.

Perhaps it isn't exactly medicine, but it's medical observation, anyway, and the main part of it is summed up in two things they say at the proper times. One is "The snake is out." The other, which they say in reverent tones, is "The elevens are up." Neither of these sayings has anything to do with the ordinary, everyday bartender school of medicine, which has to do with overpowering a hangover.

First of all, about the snake. The snake is an ordinary little vein, or maybe it is an artery, that runs along the left temple of a man's head. Most of the time you don't see it, but it's there, and it runs along, a little slantwise, from up around his hair to above the left-hand corner of his eye.

Take a man gets in his late thirties, into his forties, and then, of course, as time goes on, into his fifties, and he still keeps coming into this saloon or that, wherever he always goes, and after a while this vein, the snake, gets to acting up.

One day this man goes on drinking one after the other—nobody is talking about beer but about hard stuff, and especially, out of all, brandy. No use trying to tell him to take it easy; that only gets him sore and he probably says, "Nobody's going to tell me take it easy, I know what I'm doing, I know what I'm doing," and all that kind of guff.

But after a while—and it has to be understood the bartender is his true friend—why, the bartender leans over the bar and takes a good look at him, staring.

"What's the matter with you?" the man probably says. "Have you gone nuts, looking at me like I was some kind of a bug sitting on a leaf? Give me some more of the same. The glass is empty."

"Oh, no, I'm not nuts," the bartender will say, but not for anyone else to hear. "I was just going to tell you the snake is out."

"Oh, oh!" says the man. "The little son of a bitch come out of his hole, did he?"

And he leans over the bar and stares hard into the mirror. Or if he can't see well that far, he's almost sure to go back in the men's room and study his forehead in the mirror. There will be the snake, pulsing and beating away. It must be blood pressure or something.

Time and time again this happens, in a quiet way, and it seldom fails that it halts up the man that's drinking—slows him up, anyway —when no amount of talk or lecturing could do it. Mostly, they come back from the men's room and tell the barkeep they guess they'll take a little walk, and go over to the park and sit for a while, or else they might even go home and lie down. That's what the snake coming out of his hole does, although it's probably nothing serious in the minds of regular doctors.

"The elevens are up" is as serious as anything could be, and there is no joke about it. This is not said to a man to his face at all. It comes about when there's been an old codger around for years and years, long enough to have arguments about is he seventy-one years old or is he up to seventy-eight or even more. Everybody talks of how healthy he is and he can go on for years yet, as the saying has it.

Then one time comes along and he doesn't drop in for a few days or a week. Everyone (except the tourists, of course) asks for him and someone passes word he's under the weather a little. Then he shows up one day, usually when there's only one or two in there. Such a man, in such a fix, hardly ever comes bouncing back into the place while the crowd is there. He visits for a few minutes and says he's all right, a little weak, but he'll be all right in a week or so, and then he leaves.

No sooner has he gone than those of his friends who are there—including the bartender, of course—look at each other.

"The elevens are up," says the bartender, quietly and sadly, like a priest or a judge or the like.

"They are, they are!" say the others, and they all nod their heads.

It means that the two cords on the back of the man's neck have begun to stick out, the way they have never stuck out before his illness. The space on each side of each cord has sunk away—wasted, you might say—so the two cords, from his collar to his hair, stick out like two "1"s, making a number "11." That's why they say "The elevens are up" when it happens to an old codger. It means he hasn't a chance and there's not much more time for him. They never let him hear them saying it, but the word passes around, one to another, and for a little while everyone is nicer than usual to the man, until what they're sure will happen does happen.

MRS. CARMODY'S STORE

Mrs. Carmody's corner store was the kind that widows used to run in all the little towns in the East. Here and there you'll still find such a store, but Mrs. Carmody was running hers thirty or forty years ago.

The store sold *Pluck and Lucks* and potatoes (hardly ever any more than half a peck at a time), Laura Jean Libbey novels, "16–1" chocolate bars, transfer pictures to make pseudo-tattoos on the back of a kid's hand, kindling wood tied into small bundles with very hairy cord, Clark's O.N.T. thread, cigars and tobacco, Copenhagen snuff, kerosene in small quantities, nonpareils, *Young Wild Wests* and *Work and Wins*, and the Lord knows what else.

The *Pluck and Lucks*, the *Young Wild Wests*, and the *Work and Wins* were five-cent story books that came out every week. They were hung on a wire strung across the back of Mrs. Carmody's small show window, so that the highly colored front pages could lure readers from the street.

Mrs. Carmody had two children, John and his younger, quieter brother, William. John, who was just turning nine, had his troubles with the *Young Wild Wests* and the other stories. He read all of them, but he had to do so without cutting the pages, which were uncut at the top. As soon as they were cut, they became secondhand *Pluck and Lucks* or *Young Wild Wests*, or whatever they were, and they were then worth only two-for-five. So young John developed a curious skill at holding the novels with the pages lifted up as far as they would go, uncut, and reading way up into the corners in that manner. It sounds as if it would be hard on the eyes, but it didn't seem to hurt his at all.

The nonpareils—pronounced "nonperells"—were a kind of candy, just as the "16–1"s were. The nonpareils were dark, shaped about like a button, and had a lot of tiny white dots imbedded in them. The "16–1"s were named, probably, after the political slogan of a William Jennings Bryan campaign a few years before. The "16–1"s were one cent apiece; nonpareils were five for a cent; butterballs, which were not butter but yellow candy, were four for a cent; licorice shoelaces were two for a cent; fried eggs were one cent each. They weren't fried eggs but candy in a tiny tin frying pan, the candy colored and fashioned to look like a fried egg in the pan. With each pan came a tiny spoon. Smart kids were aware the spoon had very sharp edges. The tin from which spoon and pan were made was not very heavy, and the handle of the pan or the whole spoon, or both, was almost sure to bend awkwardly when you tried to hold them and peck the candy out of the pan, a trifle at a time.

There was a whole showcase full of these candies. Young John, who helped out a little—very little—in "waiting on" in the store, knew the prices of all the candies. Occasionally, however, he would sell five butterballs for a cent, instead of four, and perhaps four montevideos, if he knew the kid who was buying the candy. He never did, at that time, get a clear picture of profits and all that, or realize how small a gain each sale meant in the little store. He was too harum-scarum to care, anyway, although Mrs. Carmody had tried to explain to him about those things, especially about when to give the candy out in a bag and when not to.

"If they buy one cent's worth, or two or three or even four cents' worth," Mrs. Carmody often told him, "just hand them the candy, nicely, of course, in their hand. If they buy five cents' worth or more, put it in a bag. Those bags cost money, John, and we'll lose if you don't do what I tell you."

John paid small attention to that or to most other things his mother told him. Mrs. Carmody herself was expert in selling the candies and she had hard-and-fast rules about "merchandising" them, as they would say now in the big stores. One of her rules was that a kid was allowed just so much time to stand in front of the candy case, trying to make up his mind what to buy. This permissible period of indecision was ticked off by a metronome in Mrs. Carmody's mind. At the end of the allotted time she would walk away without a word, and the kid, who was sure to come to a decision an instant later, would have to stand and wait a while, painfully anxious to get the candy.

Of course, there was never any announcement or any signs up about these house rules, but practically everybody knew about them. And customers took their four cents' worth of candy in their hands, or waited for the bag when they bought five cents' worth or more.

The little store was busy most of the time. People started going to it out of sympathy, and then they got used to going there and they kept on trading there for small things. Mrs. Carmody's husband had died when John was only two years old and his brother was only a few months old. Relatives had chipped in, maybe two hundred dollars altogether, to add to what was left of the insurance money after the funeral, and with this money they set up the store for the widow. She and the two children lived in the back of the store, and a bell on the end of a wire over the door rang when anybody came in. Mrs. Carmody would then come out from the back living quarters, if she was there, and wait on the customer. After a while she was able to take wonderful care of the two children, even on the small profits of the place.

Father Maurice Murphy, who was a steady customer, said she took too good care of them. He said she was spoiling them, especially John. "You do too well by those children, Mary," Father Maurice often said to Mrs. Carmody. "You give them too much and you keep them too clean and too well dressed, especially himself."

By "himself" he meant John. Now that the father of the family was dead, John was referred to as "himself," although he was just becoming nine. In families of Mrs. Carmody's nationality, they always used the word "himself" like that, whether they were in America or Ireland.

It was a habit, meaning that "himself" was the oldest male in the family. "Himself" always got the best of everything there was in the house. And he also got spoiled for the rest of his life.

For example, at the Carmodys', when there was mashed potatoes at supper, Mrs. Carmody would make a mound of them on a plate, and at the top she'd make a small indentation, into which she'd put a big chunk of butter to melt. When the two children and herself were seated, she would scoop off the first big spoonful of potatoes in such a way that the melted butter ran down all in one place. And that delicious buttery portion always went to "himself," while the younger brother looked on enviously. The little brother must have hated to see that happen time and time again but he wasn't the oldest man and nothing could be done about it.

When John got to be eight years old, he was allowed to wait on, once in a while, at the tobacco showcase. That was the more manly part of the store, on the right-hand side as you came in. Roughly, the right-hand side of the store was male, the left-hand female. There were five showcases in all—two on each side, running from the front toward the back of the store, and the fifth running partly across the store at the back, making a sort of square "U," with the street door in the opening. On the right, the male side, the first showcase was for tobacco, cigars, and cigarettes, although there were not one tenth or even one twentieth as many kinds of cigarettes as there are now; the second showcase on the right had small toys for boys, like tops, marbles, and those transfer pictures. On the left as you entered, the first showcase had cakes and pies; the second had an assortment of ribbons and women's stuff like that. The candy case was the one that ran partly across the store.

It was a kind of coming of age for John to be allowed to wait on tobacco customers. His mother, however, tried to steer him away from selling cigarettes, because in those days they were associated with a fast life. There weren't so many kinds of them, in Mrs. Carmody's, anyway—just Sweet Caporals and some called Perfections, in a red package, and some twenty-for-a-nickel brands, like Meccas and Cycles. Chewing tobacco was the popular item, and there was a simple device, a blade in a fixed frame, with a handle, to cut the chewing tobacco—B.L. and Piper Heidsieck, or whatever the tobacco was—into various-priced chunks, into ten-cent pieces and five-cent pieces. Piper Heidsieck was for the more exquisite trade; B.L. was democratic stuff.

John had a perilous pastime at the tobacco counter, a trick to be done only when Mrs. Carmody was in the back. There was a cigar cutter on one end of the counter. It had to be wound up, for it had a quick-acting spring inside. You pushed the end of the cigar into a tiny hole, a blade leaped across the hole, and neatly cut the sealed end of the cigar. John's trick was to shove the tip of his forefinger in the machine, far enough to make the spring work, and then yank his finger out before it got cut. It was dangerous, and such a feat as only somebody called "himself" would try.

Father Maurice caught him at it one day, but didn't stop him. He just watched and said, "Yuh, you *would* be doing something like that." He seemed to half approve of the trick.

Father Maurice had tricks of his own, such as making the two kids get all messed up on purpose. As he had told Mrs. Carmody, he thought she kept them too clean to be natural. They were always spotless and that irked Father Maurice.

Just behind the counter that ran across the back of the store, and before you got into the living quarters, there was a small coal stove. It was useful for making a cup of tea. There was a coal hod beside it. And if Father Maurice came in and Mrs. Carmody was in the back, he'd tell her to stay there and he'd watch the store. Then he would call the two children. "Look," he'd say, "go get this money and you can have it." And he would drop two or three pennies away down in the coal hod. John and his brother would dig into the coal, and pretty soon their hands and faces would be grimy, their clean clothes blackened. "Now you look like regular kids," Father Maurice would say, and discreetly slip out of the store.

"Himself" usually got the pennies. He got the first big possession either one of the two children had, too. That was the day of his ninth birthday. Mrs. Carmody gave him a bicycle. It was a stupendous gift. It had to be bought out of money scrupulously saved by Mrs. Carmody, and certainly she had had to plan it way ahead. She had hated to see "himself" always trying to borrow a bike for a brief ride from one of the few kids in the neighborhood who had bikes. But he was always doing that.

To get "himself" a bike of his own, Mrs. Carmody first had to have a long talk with Jim Berry, the bicycle man. The bike had to be of a smaller size than the standard, because John was only nine and most bikes in those days were made for bigger kids. So Jim Berry had to send away for it quite a while in advance. When it came, Berry brought it to the store at night, after John had been sent to bed. It was a red bike and it even had a lamp that used calcium carbide. Berry showed Mrs. Carmody how the lamp worked. The chemical was grayish stuff that was carried in a receptacle fastened on the bike. Another receptacle fed water into the calcium when a switch was turned on. That made gas, which flowed through a tube into the lamp and through a Y-shaped outlet, where it could be lighted. The whole thing smelled very scientific and slightly dangerous. Mrs. Carmody was sure John would like it. Mrs. Carmody gave Mr. Berry a part payment on the bike and agreed to pay him a dollar seventy-five every two weeks until it was paid for. They hid the bike that night in the store.

The next morning, John's birthday, John came out of the back of the store to fold the papers. That was an early-morning job for his mother, and he usually helped a little at it. They would fold the papers just before they unlocked the front door and pile the different papers at certain places on the counter, so that people hurrying to work could rush in, grab their favorite paper almost without looking, and quickly go along. It was the custom to pay for them at the end of the week. Mrs. Carmody used to open the store at twenty minutes to six and she never kept it open after ten o'clock at night. It was a long day, but then there were moments of rest when things got quiet and she could have a cup of tea.

As John started to fold the papers, he looked idly across the store. There was the bike, leaning against one counter. He dropped the paper and ran over.

"It's mine! It's my birthday!" he said, grabbing the handle bars. They felt just right. "Hurry up, Mama! Open the door!"

He couldn't get the bike out fast enough into the street. The pedal on one side caught for a moment on his mother's apron as she unlocked the door and then held it open for him to take the bicycle out. While she was looking down to see if the apron was torn, off he went on the bike, up the street. She didn't even see him start his first trip on the great gift. The apron wasn't torn and Mrs. Carmody went back to the job of folding the papers by herself.

It was summer and there was no school to go to, so John rode the bike all that morning. He didn't want any breakfast, he had said, hollering over his shoulder as he rode by the store. His mother made him eat something at noontime, after shouting at him to come in as he went by again.

He wheeled the bike all the way into the back part of the store, where they lived. In between bites of what his mother had put on the table, John pulled down the curtains on the windows. That didn't make it black dark, but dark enough so he could switch on the calcium lamp on the bike and light it. It smelled up the place, but nobody stopped him from doing it. He hated to turn off the lamp, but he did before he pushed the bicycle out into the daylight again.

He couldn't get enough of the bike that day, and he thought it would never get dark so the lamp could be used. He rode everywhere around the neighborhood, and into strange neighborhoods, into which he had seldom, if ever, been on foot. Always he'd circle back to the store, then start out again.

At about four o'clock, John was standing up rakishly on the pedals, riding the bike through a short cut. That was a path through a vacant lot. Quite suddenly, he had to stop and get off, because there were two women right ahead of him and they took up all the path. He did not want to risk riding the new bike around them, because there might be broken glass in the grass beside the path and he wouldn't see it. He got off with a flourish and, walking, pushed the bike. The women paid no particular attention to him. They merely glanced around, saw it was some kid or other and a bike, and went on talking.

"Isn't she the old miser, though, that Mrs. Carmody!" one of the women said to the other.

John heard her say it and the bike wobbled. The front wheel went over a stone and bumped, and John's face stung, and he almost could not hold the handle bars.

"Look at the way I have to carry home this candy!" the woman went on. "I happened to have just four pennies and I bought that much. To bring home to the children."

"Yes, yes," the other woman said, nodding.

"And would Mrs. Carmody give me a bag to carry it in? Not her! Not that one! No wonder she has all kinds of money. If ever there was a miser, that Mrs. Carmody is one."

John was in quick fear the women would turn and recognize him, and he was shaking and swallowing. He had an awful job turning the bicycle around and walking back to the beginning of the short cut, toward the store. He was stumbling and sick. He knew he had heard what he did, but he couldn't believe that anybody had said it.

He was still trembling when he climbed on the bike at the end of the vacant lot. The wind helped to cool his face when he raced as fast as he could to the store. Outside the store, he hastily tried to lean the bike against the curb, with one pedal catching the curb. He did it so quickly and badly it started to fall, but he caught it in time, fixed the pedal firmly, and ran into the store.

On his last two steps before the door, he seemed to catch hold of himself. He hurried to his mother, in back of the counter.

"Mama! Mama!" he said. "Thank you for the bike. Thank you very much."

TWO PEOPLE HE NEVER SAW

Eddie Casavan and Harry Marnix were walking up Fifth Avenue, around Fiftieth Street, when Christmas suddenly closed in on them. It got a tighter hold on Casavan, but the feel of Christmas clamped down on both of them. The store windows, the sharp air, the lights coming on in the late afternoon, and the couple of drinks they had on their walk must have done it.

They were turning off the Avenue when Eddie said, "I don't seem to want anything for Christmas any more."

"It's for the kids," Harry said. "It's a time for the kids, Christmas."

"Long after I was a kid I still wanted something for Christmas," Eddie said. "I'm forty-nine and it must have been only a couple of years ago that it came to me I didn't want anything for Christmas any more. I don't this year. The stuff in the windows looks nice, but I don't want any of it."

"It's mostly kids' stuff—things for kids for Christmas," Harry said.

"I know about that, but it's not what I mean," Eddie answered. "Let's go in this place. I got an hour. You going anyplace?"

"All right," said Harry. "No, I'm not. Not right away."

They weren't high. A little talky, maybe—nothing like tight. Eddie ordered two drinks. "Two Scotch highballs," he said, the more old-fashioned way of saying what practically everybody in New York now means by saying "Scotch-and-soda."

"I don't even want to go anyplace for Christmas, that's what I mean," Eddie went on as the bartender made up the drinks and left the bottle on the bar.

"I used to like to go to the six-day bike races," said Harry.

"They didn't have them at Christmas," Eddie said.

"I know it, but I used to like to go to them in winter and I don't seem to want to any more," Harry explained. "They don't have them, anyway, come to think of it."

"For Christmas I used to plan ahead," Eddie said. "Even up to a couple of years ago. And I always figured someplace to go or something to do special for Christmas. Now there's nothing I want and nothing I want to do."

"They used to yell 'B-r-r-rocco!' at the bike races," Harry said.

That got nowhere, and Eddie and Harry fiddled with the long glass sticks in their glasses.

"There *is* something I'd like to do Christmas at that," Eddie said after a while. "But it's impossible, maybe nuts."

"Christmas is nuts, a little," Harry said.

"Only way it could happen'd be an Aladdin's lamp. You rub it, you get what you want," Eddie continued. "Or if one of those kindhearted demons or something would hop out of that Scotch bottle there and grant a wish. That's kid stuff, I guess."

"Christmas is a kids' gag," Harry said. "As childish as six-day bike races, come to think of it. It felt like Christmas walking up the Avenue, didn't it? What if the gink should hop out of the bottle? What about it?"

"I was thinking that, too," Eddie said. "He could cook it up for me."

"What?"

"I'd like to take two people to Christmas dinner, a couple a people I never saw."

"Yuh?"

"One of them would be maybe forty now, a woman," Eddie said. "Oh, I don't know how old, tell the truth. Don't know how old she was when I first met her. No, wait a minute. The point is, I never met her."

"Movie star? Some notion like that?"

"No, no. Hell, no. Do you think I'm a kid?"

"No, what I mean is, Christmas is for kids. I didn't have you in mind."

"I often thought of her since. This was when I was having it tough one time, maybe fifteen years ago. Living in a furnished room on East Thirty-ninth Street—"

"And are they something, furnished rooms!" Harry put in.

"Furnished rooms are something if you've lived through and pull out of it you never forget them," Eddie said.

"I been in 'em," Harry nodded.

"God, I was sunk then!" Eddie said. "I was drinking too much and I lost one job after another. This time I was looking for a job and coming back every afternoon to the furnished room about four o'clock. That's how I never saw this girl."

"What girl?" Harry asked.

"The one I want to take to dinner at Christmas."

"If the gink comes out of the bottle," Harry said.

"Yeh, if he does. I remember I'd have a few beers after getting half promises of jobs, and I'd plank myself down on the bed in this little bit of a room when I came home four o'clock in the afternoon. It was the smallest room I was ever in. And the lonesomest."

"They get lonesome," Harry said.

"The walls are thin, too. The wall next to my bed was thin. Must have been like cardboard. This girl lived in the next room, the one I never met."

"Oh, yeh, yeh?" Harry said.

"I could hear her moving around. Sometimes she'd be humming and I could hear that. I could hear her open the window, or shut it if it was raining."

"Never see her?" Harry asked.

"No, that's the point of it. I almost thought I knew her, the way I could hear her. I could hear her leave every afternoon, about quarter past four. She had a kind of a lively step. I figured she was a waitress somewhere. Some job like that, don't you think?"

"I don't know, maybe a waitress, but *why,* though?" Harry said, and took a drink.

"Why *was* she a waitress, or why did I figure it out she's a waitress?" Eddie asked.

"Yeh, I mean why?" Harry answered in such a way that it meant how was it figured out.

"Oh, I could have been wrong. She had some steady job like waitress. She used to come home almost on the dot, quarter past one in the morning. You could set your clock on it. I used to look at my clock when she came in. Gee, her steps sounded tired when she was coming up the hall. She must have worked hard. She'd put the key in the lock and I'd hear that. I didn't sleep very good then. Worrying about a job, one thing and another. It'd be quarter past one by my clock. I hung on to that clock. I got it yet."

"Some people hate clocks in their room while they're sleeping," Harry said.

"They haven't lived in furnished rooms," Eddie said. "A clock is a great thing in a furnished room. This was a green one, ninety-eight cents. In a furnished room a clock is somebody there with you, anyway. The ticking sounds as if you're not altogether alone, for God's sake, if it's only the clock that's there with you."

"Never saw this girl—that's what you said?"

"Never saw her. Maybe she wasn't exactly a girl. I couldn't prove she wasn't a woman, older than a girl. When she hummed, though, I figured it sounded like a girl. Funny I never bumped into her in the hallway. Just didn't happen to. But I spoke to her once."

"Spoke to her?" Harry asked.

"Yeh. It was a gag. I told you I could hear everything. Well, her bunk was right next to mine—with only this wall there. And one afternoon she was getting up and she sneezed. It sounded funny from the next room. So I said very loud, '*Gesundheit!*' I remember she laughed. Her laugh sounded twenty-five."

"But you don't know, do you?"

"No, I don't and I won't. But if she was that age then, she'd be forty, around that, now, wouldn't she?"

"When was this?"

"I said about fifteen, could be sixteen years ago."

"Twenty-five and fifteen is forty, yes. She could be forty now," Harry said. "She could have been a bum. Did you ever think of that?"

"Harry, Harry, Harry, you don't get it at all! She couldn't have been a bum. A bum wouldn't have to live in such a bad room. I wanted to know her only because we were two people both having it tough together, and still and all we weren't together except when I said '*Gesundheit*.'"

Harry finished his drink and said pleasantly, "No, I don't mean it. I don't think she could have been a bum. Anyway, she would be about forty now, all right."

Eddie finished his drink and beckoned to the barkeep, who came and poured soda into the glasses. Eddie put in the whiskey, and when he put down the bottle he looked expectantly at it for a minute or two.

"And the guy would be about my own age now, about forty-nine or so, wouldn't he?" Eddie asked.

"Excuse me, but what guy?" Harry asked. "Oh, yeh, yeh, the guy."

"The one I'd like to take to Christmas dinner with her to the best place in town. Take the two of them. I've got a few bucks these days. I pulled through the furnished rooms all right, didn't I? I was thinking that, coming up the Avenue when the lights were going on."

"You're rambling, chum. Who is this feller, or maybe who was he?" Harry asked.

"It's 'who was he?' I don't know where he is, or is he dead or alive. I never saw his face. He was the soldier who picked me up in France. He picked me up off the ground, in the pitch dark, and he didn't have to."

"In the war?"

"Sure, in the war. Not this one, the other. But I bet it's happening too in this one."

"When you got hit, you mean?" Harry asked.

"That's the time, of course. You know how I hate professional ex-soldiers, guys always talking the other war. I don't want to be one of those."

"Oh, I know that, Eddie, I know it. But I know you were in the other one and got hit."

"It wasn't getting hit. That wasn't so much. It's this feller I often thought about at odd times all these years. Just to boil it down, it certainly was dark as hell, and there was no shooting going on at all. The first sergeant, guy named Baker, was with me. He got killed, I found out later. He stopped the big pieces of this shell. I only got the little pieces. We were going back through this town, going to find a place to sleep."

"A little French town?" Harry asked.

"What else? This was in France, for God's sake, so it was a little French town. Anyway, they suddenly threw one over and it hit right where we were, because the next thing I was pawing the wall of the house we were walking alongside of. I was trying to get up and my legs felt like ropes under me. When I went to stand up, they coiled."

"You were hit, all right," Harry said. "I saw your legs in swimming many a time, the marks on them."

"Oh, I don't care about that. The point is, this feller. I come to, there in the pitch dark, and somebody was prodding me with his foot. And whoever it was, he was saying, 'What's the matter, what's the matter?' I answered him. I said, 'My goddam legs.' "

"It was this guy, you mean?"

"Yes, him," Eddie said. "And then I passed out again. Well, I never saw the guy. I never saw his face. He could be black or white. He could be an angel, for all I know to this day. Anyway, he's who carried me through that pitch dark, and he didn't have to. He could have left me there. And I must have been bleeding like hell. Next thing, I came to, and I was lying on a table. It was an aid station in a cellar someplace. A doc was pouring ether by the canful over holes in my leg. That ether turns cold as hell if you pour it on anything. The guy wasn't around. Anyway, I didn't think of him then. Who the hell was he? I don't know. If it wasn't for that feller I never saw, I wouldn't be here today."

"It's a pretty good day to be here," Harry said.

Eddie took a drink and so did Harry. "That's the two of them—the ones I'd like to take to dinner when it comes to be Christmas night. But I won't."

"No, you won't," said Harry. "There's nothing coming out of the bottle but Scotch."

CAN'T SLIP ANY DRUGS TO SISTERS ON FIFTH AVENUE

A nun stumbled on the sidewalk on Fifth Avenue, near Forty-seventh Street. There was a bad place in the sidewalk and the nun had stepped on it while walking along with another nun. This happened in the middle of a busy afternoon, and the sidewalks were crowded.

A man in a yellow polo coat grabbed the nun's arm, helpfully. The other nun grasped her other arm and looked into her face, which was pale. The two nuns were not used to crowds and milling around, and both looked scared over the trivial mishap.

The man jerked his hat off before he spoke, solicitously, to the nun who had stumbled. He had a cauliflower ear and his hat was a Madison Square Garden kind of hat.

"Is something the matter, Sister?" he said, leaning toward the nun. "Something happen? You hurt yourself, Sister?"

The nun spoke so softly, out of embarrassment, that the man could not hear what she said. Another man, with his hat off, was there by then, and the two nuns and two men made a small clump in the middle of the busy sidewalk. Still another man stood still, only a few feet away, watching them.

"Begging your pardon, Sister," the cauliflower-ear man said, being very careful to use the highest-class language he could figure out, "I thought something happened you're like in distress. I mean taken or something, or hurt your foot, if you'll excuse me."

From under the black hood and starched linen of her religious garb, the nun looked timidly and kindly at him. "I—I—I slipped," she said, and looked appealingly at the other nun.

"I think Sister is all right now," the other nun said. "Her foot slipped, I think. Are you all right, Sister Veronica?"

"Yes. I twisted my—I twisted my ankle a little," Sister Veronica answered. She took a step or two, carefully. The cauliflower-ear man put on his hat, helped her that step or two, then let go of her arm, and took his hat off as the two nuns went on slowly and anxiously down the Avenue.

"I think she's all right," the second man said to him.

"Jeez, I thought something happen to her, I don't know what," said the cauliflower-ear man. He put on his hat again, looking back at the departing nuns, then started up the street, almost in stride with the second man.

At that minute, the third man, the onlooker, joined them, and the three moved along, almost as if they had known each other before this.

"Look, see what I got—amyl nitrite," the third man said, opening his gloved hand and showing a capsule in it. "I was just going to slip it to her if she—"

"Slip what to her?" the cauliflower-ear man said, almost angrily, checking his stride.

"The amyl nitrite," the fellow answered. "I have it for my old man. He gets attacks. He got a bad heart, my old man, so I have to have it, and I was right there. I thought the nun maybe had a heart at—"

"Whaddaya mean slip it to her? You ain't going to slip no amble nitrites to her," the cauliflower-ear man said. "You ain't slipping no drugs to no nuns on Fifth Avenue. Whaddaya mean?"

"My father," the fellow said, and by now all three were walking together again up the sidewalk, "he's liable to collapse any minute while I'm with him. So I got this—Look, it's to keep your heart going if you get a heart attack like my father does." He showed the capsule again, and then put it back in his coat pocket.

"Yeh, I know what he means," said the other man. "He thought maybe the Sister had a heart attack, and he wanted—"

"Oh, oh," the cauliflower-ear man said, but only partly satisfied, it seemed by the tone of his voice and the way he looked at the amyl-nitrite man.

"Oh, yes. Yes, that's what I thought. She maybe had a heart attack when I saw you two there helping her. I meant I was ready to slip her the amyl nitrite and bring her to," the man said.

"Yuh? But what if it wasn't?" the cauliflower-ear man asked, only a little placated. "Maybe something else instead of heart attack and that stuff be exactly the wrong thing to slip her? I don't like the idea, slipping drugs to Sisters on Fifth Avenue. You can't go slipping drugs to Sisters on Fifth Avenue, what I mean."

"I can tell if it would be the right thing," the man said. "My father—"

"I see't you mean, you meant well all right, but I don't like the idea slipping even well-meant drugs to a Sister on Fifth Avenue," the cauliflower-ear man said. Then, just before he turned west, he summed it up. "Anyway, the Sister made out all right. All's well ends well."

"Yeah. So long," the amyl-nitrite man said, turning the other way at the corner. "Just the same, lucky I was there, in case it was a heart attack. That stuff I showed you save my old man's life many a time. So long."

The cauliflower-ear man went west, the amyl-nitrite man went east, and the third man went straight on up the Avenue, looking back, but there was no sign of the two nuns, who were a couple blocks away by then, probably.

PEETHER IS FULL OF BLATHER

On a Sunday afternoon, a hotel room with a disattached man in it gets an empty feeling to it, even if it is small and full of things.

By three-thirty, both the *Herald Tribune* and the *Times* crossword puzzles are filled in and lying on the floor. The radio has a symphony that doesn't seem to be the right thing, exactly. It didn't to me, this Sunday afternoon, and I didn't want to telephone anyone, for fear I'd catch them with at least vestigial hangovers and they wouldn't want to talk to anyone, much less have anyone come and see them. I wanted to hear somebody talking, though—and not an announcer, either.

So I went out to get razor blades, which I always arrive at a hotel without, and a shoeshine to fill in the time.

In front of one of the closed stores on Sixth Avenue was a skinny, small man with a pipe, sitting on a pop-bottle box that had a newspaper spread over it. A shoeshine box was in front of him. I stopped there and made a little wordless signal to him that said "Shine?"

He took the pipe out of his mouth, uncrossed his legs and recrossed them, and said, with a bit of hurt pride, "Oh, no, oh, no! I'm not down to shinin' shoes yet!"

The way he said it gave me the idea that for him things were tough enough, but he still had his dignity. He was a lean man with badly worn clothes and sunken-in cheeks, and he seemed to be sitting there as a kind of observer of Sixth Avenue, doing his best to think about something or other but not succeeding very well.

A moment passed and he spoke up again, as if he had not wished to give offense in turning me down in my bid for a shoeshine. "He'll be along in a minyit, the man for the shine," he said. "He'll be along in a minyit. Sit down, if you want."

He shoved over to one edge of the pop-bottle box, leaving some room on it for me, and I sat down without saying anything.

We both watched the people passing by, most of them with an out-of-town look and walking uptown. The skinny man, smoking his pipe, was also watching me, sizing me up, out of the corner of his eye, and I knew he was holding back talk.

"Isn't it awful," he said finally, with his pipe in his hand, "the way they force a man into the saloons even if you don't want to go in there at all?"

He was very sober—I could see that—but he was not a man who had been sober every day of his life. Far from it; the lines and the look on his face told that.

"Well—" I began, not knowing just how to go further.

"Do you mind an hour or two ago?" he said, waving the pipe thoughtfully. "It began spittin' down rain a little. It din't seem it'd last long, but I thought I'd betther go in someplace anyway. I went to the Authomat. Locked! I went over to Bry'nt Park to go into the lavatory. Locked!" He looked straight at me in dismay and went on, "They'd force you into the saloons when it's the last place in the world you'd want to be going! And when I went in there, why, I wouldn't want to be standing there and not buy even a glass of beer, would you?"

"No," I said, trying to appear as thoughtful about the situation as he was.

"Here he is now, the man for the shine," said the skinny man then, pointing with the pipe to an old man coming toward us, a few steps away. The little man stood up and, putting the pipe in his mouth, leaned against the store front, watching the passersby.

The shoeshine man was well past seventy. He had a bony head, biggish, that seemed too big for the skin that covered it, so the skin seemed too tight for him.

"Hello, Peether," he said to the skinny man, and then sat down in front of me and slowly got ready for the shine. This small business was most casually run, for the brushes, most of them, were not in the box but on the sidewalk beside it, and the brush with the cleaning fluid on it looked as if it would put more dirt on the shoes than it would take off. When the old man picked up the brush and ineptly began, he looked up at me, and the eyes on him were baby eyes, set in a head older than seventy.

"Well, sir," said the old man to me as he dabbed on the cleaner—mostly on the shoelaces at the knot, and some on the socks, too—"how is the conference making out?"

"The conference?" I was puzzled for a moment; then it came to me what he meant. "Oh, the U.N.?" I said. "I don't know. Most of that is too complicated for me."

The old man dabbed away for a few seconds. "Now, I had the idea," he said, "that a man with a pair of shoes on him like these would know what'd be going on at the conference, if he had a mind to tell anybody."

"No, honest, I just don't know, that's all," I said apologetically, yet giving a proud look at my good shoes.

Peether took his pipe from his mouth and said to me, "Why do all the people want to be going up to Radio City? What do they want to be doing that for? That's where they're all going. Why is that?"

"I imagine they're out-of-town people," I said, feeling obliged to make some answer. "They read about Radio City and they see it in the movies, and so they want to have a look at it."

"Aw!" Peether said scornfully. "They don't know when to see it at all. It's when them people are all skating around on the ice up there at night and the big lights swashing down on them and some music playing they ought to see it. They don't know when to see it at all. Then it's a beautiful sight, the skating!"

The old man paid no attention as he changed brushes and went on to the polishing phase of the shine. "I'm sure, just the same, a man with these shoes would have a good notion what they're up to at the conference," he said, "and'd know if they're going good at it, or are they all balled up one against the other, or what."

Peether took his pipe out of his mouth again and, speaking past me, addressed the old man. "In India," he said, "they got a pond, or maybe it's a river, that's holy, and they be jumping into it. People that's sick in India jumps into it to get cured." He halted a moment, as if expecting signs of amazement. "And there's dead animals in it!" he went on, almost shouting. "It's full of dead animals, and them jumping into it!"

The old man stopped shining a shoe and looked up slowly at the two of us. "It's the Ganges," he said. "That's what they call it, the Ganges."

"There's dead animals in it, where they jump into it to get cured," said Peether, louder.

"I know, the Ganges," said the old man, and began on the shoe again. Then he said, seeming to address the shoes, "I been all around, a long time ago. I been in Calcutta, I been in South America, I been in Queenstown—they don't call it that any more—and I been someplace else but I forget where it was. The Ganges is what they call it. The Ganges."

Peether rapped his pipe against the side of the pop-bottle box to get the ashes out and took a step or two away.

"Where are you going, Peether?" the old man asked.

"Up to Radio City," said Peether, staring up Sixth Avenue. He looked at the sky. "And if it starts raining again, I'd have to get inside, and I'd have to go into a saloon, whether I want to or not. They force a man into them anyway!" He walked on.

The old man looked up at me as he finished the shine and clumsily shoved the rags back into the box. "Poor Peether is having a terrible time fighting the drink," he said, most kindly. "And when he's trying to fight the drink, poor Peether is full of blather."

"Oh, I see," I said. I gave the old man a quarter, although I hadn't intended to pay so much. He thanked me, and stood up as I began to leave.

"I hope they'll be all right at the conference," he said. "There's bound to be diff'rences here and there."

OVERLOOKED LADY

They took a census in 1950, as they do every ten years in the United States. This time, I hope they got it right. I happen to know that in the previous census, when they came out with the total of 131,669,275 as the population of the continental United States, it was really at least 131,669,276. I happen to know that they were at least one person below the real total. Know it for a fact.

The reason I know it goes back to the circumstance that Larry Fagan, the city editor of the Pittsburgh *Press*, was, is, and always has been a softy for two classes of people, however hard-boiled he may be in his professional relations with other classes. The two classes are Nice Little Old Ladies and Boys with Dogs.

All kinds of crackpots are always trying to get in to see city editors, so they have a reception desk outside the city room on most papers to keep out the lame-brains. Everybody around the *Press*, however, knew Larry Fagan well enough not to send away anybody who fell into the category of Nice Little Old Lady. It was the same way if a kid and a dog came around. Larry wanted to see them, because he didn't have the heart to turn them away, no matter how tough he was otherwise, as I say.

One day—more than ten years ago, it was—Tony, the head copy boy, came in from the reception desk and spoke to Larry.

"There's a little old lady out there wants to see you, Mr. Fagan," Tony said.

"Gee, Tony, I'm busy," Larry said.

"All right, Mr. Fagan, I'll tell her," Tony said.

"No, no, no. Wait a minute," said Fagan. "Bring her in. I can take a few minutes. Bring her in, Tony. Gee whizz!"

"Yes, sir, Mr. Fagan," Tony said, and he winked at me, without Larry's seeing him.

The person Tony escorted into the city room a few moments later might, I swear, have come from Central Casting if someone had sent in a call for them to send around a Nice Little Old Lady. She was carrying a small handbag with a drawstring at the top; she was only about five feet two; her hair was white and her clothes were dark and nice; and she even wore one of those jabots, a lacy thing at her throat.

There's hardly any provision around city rooms for such visitors, but since there was nobody at the desk next to me, Larry had the old lady sit down there. He threw his stogie away and sat on the desk.

"Yes, Ma'am," Larry said. "Could I do anything to help you?"

"What is your name, sir?" the lady asked in a very nice voice.

"I'm Mr. Fagan—Lawrence J. Fagan," Larry said.

It was the first time I had ever heard him refer to himself as Lawrence J. Fagan, and he knew it, because he glanced at me defiantly. He always said he was Larry Fagan if anybody asked him who he was.

"Mr. Fagan, I like the *Press* very much," the old lady said, quite composed amid the hubbub of the room. "I don't know what I'd do without it every night."

"Thank you, Ma'am," said Larry. "Thank you very much."

"I wondered if you could do something about what has happened," the old lady went on. She smiled. "Or, rather, what has *failed* to happen."

"I'd be glad to do anything I can, Ma'am," Larry replied. Anybody who gets his knowledge of city editors from motion pictures would never believe one of them could be as courteous and genteel as Larry was.

"Well, Mr. Fagan, the census man never came to see me—that's what happened," the old lady said, and she suddenly looked sad.

"I don't quite get what you mean, Ma'am," Larry said.

"Mr. Fagan, you remember you had an article—oh, you had several articles—in the paper about the census," she said. "They were very interesting. I love the *Press*. You see, I live alone, Mr. Fagan. All my children are in California. Of course, they're all married—but I don't mean to tell you about all that."

"That's all right, Ma'am. What was it you said about the census?" Larry asked.

"Yes, Mr. Fagan, about the census," the old lady said. "One Sunday, you had a long article about the census. It had all the questions the man asks when he comes around to take the census. And it told how the man gets so much for each name he takes down and answers all the questions about."

"Yes, Ma'am, I remember we did have a feature like that," Larry said.

"Well, Mr. Fagan," she said, "I thought I would have everything ready for the man when he came. That would help him get more names that day—whatever day it was he came—because I would be all ready and I wouldn't take too much of his time."

"That was a real nice thing to do, Ma'am," Larry said. He was blinking his eyes too fast. What the old lady had done kind of hit him, I could see that.

"Mr. Fagan, I waited day after day after day, and the man never came," the old lady went on. "Nobody ever came and asked me the questions about the census. I think I've been left out."

"It's all over, the census," Larry said, downcast.

"Yes, Mr. Fagan. There was an item in the *Press* two days ago that said 'Census Completed,' that's what it said. And the man never came to my house. I must have been left out, don't you think, Mr. Fagan?"

Larry fumbled around with a pencil, then automatically hauled a stogie out of his upper vest pocket, then bethought himself and put it back. "Gee whizz, Ma'am, left out of the census!" he said. "Well, now, I think I can do something. You see, Ma'am, it *is* all over, but I think those government men make some kind of allowance for going back to places they overlooked, maybe."

"I'm sure now they overlooked my house," the old lady said. "And they'll have the count wrong, won't they? Of course, one person won't make much difference, I realize, but I was all ready with the answers and everything."

"Tell you what I'll do, Ma'am," said Larry. "I'll notify the government about this, and I believe they'll send a man up to your place and fix things up right. Could you give me the address?"

"Oh, yes, Mr. Fagan," the old lady said, very much relieved. She gave Larry the address, which was in a decent, quiet part of town. She got up from the chair, and Larry went all the way out to the reception desk with her.

When he came back, he was chewing a stogie and he came over to my desk. "How do you like that?" he said. "Left out of the census! They count every cluck, every lousy heel, every gangster, pimp, and God knows what, and then they leave out a nice old lady like that! My God! Left out of the census, even!"

Larry wasted no time. That afternoon, he got Pete Botsford, one of his best reporters, and he gave him the assignment.

"Rig up some kind of a big book like a census book," he told Pete. "Get that Sunday feature we had with all the census questions in it. Have one of the girls in the front office type out all those questions, so it won't look like out of the paper."

"Yes, Larry. Then what?" Pete asked.

"Go up to this old lady's house and make out you're a government man—census man," Larry said. "Ask her all the questions and put down the answers. Look official as hell. Get the idea? Then come back here. That's all you have to do."

"Sure. But I *don't* get the idea," Pete said.

"Jeez, I forgot to tell you what it was all about," Larry said. "This old lady was left out of the census. Imagine being left out of the census, a nice old lady?"

He told Pete all about the visitor he had had, and Pete went out to the old lady's house that afternoon and did as he was told.

"She gave me a cup of tea," he told Larry when he came back with all the questions.

"Nice old lady," Larry said. "She seem satisfied?"

"Tickled to death," Pete said.

"You can throw away those questions and all, Pete," Larry said. "I suppose we wasted some time, but what the hell. What the hell."

IT'S HARD TO FIGURE HOW THEY KNOW

Yanko began first thing by revealing one of the secrets of his trade, which is tending bar in this neighborhood place, where I had dropped into at ten minutes past eight in the morning, right after Yanko opened up, because I was taking a morning walk and wanted to sit down someplace and read the paper before I went back home for breakfast.

He was standing in back of the bar with a woeful look on his face, as if something was bothering him and he hated to start work for the day. He's a large man with a belly, and is ordinarily cheerful enough, but he wasn't looking too cheerful on this particular morning.

I opened up the paper on the bar and it must have been a couple of minutes before he spoke, very weary in his voice. "Do you want to know something?" he asked.

"What?" I said.

"I'll tell you how you can tell any time, any morning, whether I went and tied one on the night before," he said. "It's a secret of the trade, you might say. Look. Lean over. Take a look down at my shoelaces."

I did as I was told, and I saw that Yanko's shoelaces were not tied. In other words, he was shuffling around with the shoes slopping along untied. "They're untied," I said.

"It'll be hours before they get tied," he said. "That's how in the future you can tell any time whether or not I got stinko the night before. Why it is they're untied on those certain mornings is I hate to bend over to tie them. If I bend over to tie them, it feels like the sides of my head's going to pop out on me. So there's how it's a giveaway if the shoelaces are untied, and don't think I'm the only one like that. I know lots of bartenders now and then in the same fix."

To make conversation, more than anything else, and keep him company, so to speak, I only said, "You got a little blotto, eh?"

"I did," he said, trying to drink a glass of water and only half finishing it. "And on top of that a guy crashes into me with a cab and busts up my fender. Not bad, that's the whole thing. But what gets me is how does my wife know practically everything I do? It's hard to figure how they know, but for once this morning I finely doped it out."

Yanko leaned on the bar and started to explain what he meant. "I'm wearing the windbreaker jacket last night, see," he says. "Well, I got the habit when I'm getting undressed I take all the stuff out of the jacket, all the stuff out of my pants, put it on the kitchen table, where I get undressed when I come in late so I wouldn't wake her up. The idea's I might not be wearing the same thing next day, so I won't forget to put the stuff like change, license, and all that, in whatever it is I'm wearing. I guess everybody does it, anyway I do.

"So all right, I wake up this morning and she's awake already, and first thing, and I'm feeling lousy, but first thing she starts in on me and gives me holy hell for drinking. We get along good all the time, me and the missus, but honest to God I wish she would let me alone for at least an hour in the morning until I pull myself together if I hung one on the night before. She don't. She starts in on me, this and that and this and that and this and that, then out she pops with the remark, 'And you had an accident with the car, too, din't you?'

"How'd she know that is the first question comes into my mind. I ain't awake five minutes, I ain't said a word to her yet, I din't talk to her when I went to bed, I sneaked into bed, and here we are and she's asking me about the accident that happened with the cab and the car. How do you like that for mystery?

"All of a sudden it come to me what might have put her wise. There's a cousin I got lives on a farm in New Jersey, matter of fact he owns this little farm, and time to time he brings in nice fresh eggs, finest eggs you could put in your stomach, right fresh from the farm. He brings them in here to the bar, and I bring them home in the car when I drive home at night. Well, I suddenly remembered I told the missus yesterday morning probably this cousin would come in yesterday and bring in some eggs. That's how I put two and two together in a flash, you might say, trying to quick dope out how she knew about the accident that busted up the fender. What I figured was she was up early and took herself down into the garage where I got the car, only a couple doors from our place, probably looking to see did the cousin bring the eggs and they might be in the car so she could bring them home we'd have them for breakfast. At lease, *she* could have them, God knows I can't eat yet this morning. Look at the shoelaces! I can't bend down, never mind eat yet for a couple hours."

Yanko stopped for breath, then turned his head and looked vengefully at the rows of whiskey bottles standing in front of the mirror back of the bar.

"Jeez, they must be putting hammers in them bottles, it's all hammering inside my head," he remarked. "Anyway, I managed to pipe up to her and I ask her, 'Were you down in the garage already?' And she snaps back at me what would she be doing down in the garage that hour in the morning. Well, trying to keep peace in the family, I said I thought maybe she was looking for the eggs that to tell the truth I did leave in the back of the car.

"So you see I was wrong when I figured it was eggs and the car and all was how she knew about the accident. Wrong. So I veered the subject onto some other subject. I asked her would she please lay off me. I asked her as sweet and nice as I could while I was feeling so bad. I asked her please not give me any song and dance so early, before I got a chance to pull myself together and face the music.

"Well, she got busy doing something, and I had another minute to figure out how does she find out about the accident and by that time I was up and getting dressed and naturally I go out in the kitchen and get the stuff, the change and the wallet and everything I left on the table so I could put them in the pants I got on today, not the pants I hung up from yesterday.

"I pick up the stuff and *bingo!* I got it figured out. Because when the accident happen, naturally the hackie that hit me with the cab got out and I got out and we swap licenses, anyway license numbers and all that. And I had it written down on a piece of cardboard from someplace, 'Sunshine Cab' and a license number, and the guy's name, I forget what it is, but I have it written down on this piece of cardboard, and there you are! Of course what happen was the missus takes a look at all the stuff on the kitchen table before I was awake, even, and there's this note I took down about Sunshine Cab and license number and all. And I say this for her, she's no dope, she simply put two and two together and she knows I been in an accident.

"I want to tell you it's hard to figure how they know, but it seems to me there's hardly anything I do, especially that's a little off the beam, that she don't know sooner or later. The only thing I'm kind of glad about is this time, at lease, I finely doped out how she knew about the accident. For once I know, anyway. Most the time I can't figure it at all."

HANDS NO GOOD

The big, husky man standing at the bar didn't belong in this saloon any more. There was a time when he might naturally have been there, straggled in like anybody else, but the way this saloon had changed, he didn't fit into it now.

This saloon used to be ordinary enough and on the level. Neighborhood people came in and had their drinks and fights and arguments and talks, and most of them knew one another, and nobody was acting roles like actors. Whatever was wrong with this one or that one, nobody paid any attention to it, because everybody went his own way and was himself, or herself, and let it go at that. Then the place got its name in the paper, and gradually a new kind of people came there—people from fancier neighborhoods and from fancier jobs and business buildings that are full of advertising agencies and the like. The old kind of people felt out of place, and they gradually went somewhere else. The new mob spent more money, and the grogshop got famous. It was always full of people who were trying either to be picturesque themselves or to find other customers who were picturesque, and succeeding in neither. Anyway, few natural people like the people who always used to be in there were ever in there any more.

The big, husky guy might have fitted into the place the way it used to be, but he didn't now. He had broad shoulders on him, made broader by padding. It wasn't a real Billy Taub suit he had on, the kind that Taub makes for leading prizefighters—a "draped" long coat with big shoulders, and flowing pants that taper down to the cuffs—but it was a kind of imitation Taub suit.

The husky ordered a beer, and as luck would have it, there was one old-timer who was standing next to him, an old-timer who had been around a lot and who came in once in a while despite this new mob that was like people wrapped in cellophane.

Even if he was big and battered, the big guy had a sad face on him. His face looked as if it couldn't figure out where the guy would be taking it next.

The old-timer was tight enough to talk to anybody. "You a fighter?" he asked the big man.

"Yeh, a kind of a fighter," the man said. He had a crumbly voice and spoke with queer spaces between the words, as if his throat hurt.

"Was you any good?" the old-timer asked.

The big guy looked down at his hands, folded on the bar in front of the beer glass. He had taken only a little dab of the beer and didn't seem interested in it. He didn't seem interested in anything, only puzzled about everything. "No, I wasn't," he said, crumbly-voiced. "I wasn't much good. I was just a fighter. Club fighter, they call them."

"You ain't old," the old-timer said.

"I'm thirty-three—wait a minute—thirty-four now. I near forgot that birthday I had—I didn't get nothing. Nobody gave me anything for my birthday," the big guy said. He picked up the beer but took only a little sip of it, then put it down and folded his hands on the bar again.

"How the hell could you be a fighter? Look at them hands!" the old-timer said. "I never see such little, skinny hands on a grown-up guy."

"What's the matter with them?" the big fellow asked, as if he were trying to be resentful but couldn't. "Never mind," he went on before the old-timer could say anything. "I know what's the matter. They're no good, my hands. I know it. They used to hurt me when I hit anybody."

"Could you hit at all?"

"I could hit pretty good. Only, my hands hurt. Sometimes I pulled back after I got one sock in on a guy. My hands hurt."

"Whyn't the manager do something?" the old-timer asked. "They're little, but maybe he coulda toughen 'em up at that. Soak 'em in salt water, maybe brine them tough, something like that."

"I never told him they hurt," the big guy said. "He didn't care a hell of a lot anyway. He just threw me in there with different guys. I think sometimes he thought I was yellow. I don't know, though. I never talked to him about it. I can't fight any more anyway. My cousin says maybe he can get me an ordinary job. I'm living with my mother. She didn't want me to be a fighter."

"Them hands is wrong for a fighter," the old-timer said.

"That's what I say," the big guy said. "But, say, you ought to see my kid brother's hands. Jeez! Big as hams. He can box, too. Maybe he'll be a good one. He's a good kid. I got an idea he'll be a hell of a fighter. You ought to see his hands!"

"Have another beer?" the old-timer asked.

"No, I'm going home," the big guy said. He looked into the mirror as if he couldn't understand his own face, and then he went out.

THE FIGHT IN THE HALLWAY

Leo was sitting at the bar in our neighborhood place with a tall beer in front of him when I went in, eleven o'clock in the morning. First he showed me his left hand, the back of it all swollen, and he asked me to have a drink and I told him too early, and then he announced, in so many words, "I'm waiting for the police to come and get me."

That was a fine thing to run into on such a nice Monday morning —Leo, my friend, sitting there expecting the police. It *was* a nice morning: sun shining after a night of soft rain, everybody busy around, flowers in front of the flower shop, vegetables, naturally, in front of the vegetable shop, Jimmy, the shoemaker, tapping shoes in the window of his place and spitting nails into one hand like clockwork, with him and the shoe and the hammer all parts of the clock—everything just as it should be, a neighborhood morning in summer near where

I live and everything all set for a pleasant day. Well, maybe the niceness of the morning had to be balanced up by somebody being in a jam in the middle of it, as things usually get balanced up like that.

"You bust somebody in the snoot?" I asked Leo.

"Big fight in the hallway outside my door," he said. He was twisting and turning his left hand around and looking at it from every angle, as if it was a present somebody gave him and he didn't know whether he wanted it or not.

"I think the guy made a charge," Leo went on. "They tell me somebody said they see him go to the station right after this happen yesterday, and walk in sore. O.K., no use running away. I'm waiting for the police. I'd bust him again. Nobody going to call Joey my 'goddam kid' and tell me keep the carriage the hell out of the hall."

While he was saying this, there were only the three of us in the place, including Yanko, the barkeep, and it was all Greek to me, except that so far I knew there had been a fight in the hall of Leo's tenement. And before I could get it straightened out by listening, Yanko had to go and complicate it by bringing up a fine point of law.

"A cop can give you a ticket for a baby carriage, how do you like that?" Yanko piped up. "What's more, unless I'm mistaken, even a uniform fireman can give you a ticket for a baby carriage, pervided you got the carriage stuck out in the hall, how do you like that? It's a fire law, that's what it is."

Leo got mad for a minute. "This had nothing to do with a fire," he barked out. "Who said anything about a fire? First this guy said something about my 'goddam kid,' that's what he called him, and then started yapping about get the carriage out of the hall. How does fires get into it. Are you nuts, or what?"

"Now, listen, Leo," Yanko said. "You better slow down on that beer, you're getting quarrelsome. That's about eight beers, and it's only five minutes past eleven. I'm not nuts."

"Since when it's your job making remarks how many beers somebody had that comes in and pays for everything they get?" Leo snapped at him.

"Well, all right, Leo," Yanko said. "All right, Leo. All's I said was there's some kind of fire laws that if you leave a baby carriage in the hall, a cop can give you a ticket. I happen to know a friend it happened to personally. He forgot the carriage, left it in the hall, and either a cop or a uniform fireman come prowling along, and he got a ticket. I don't remember exactly, but I think it was a fireman gave him the ticket. That's why I say a fireman can give you a ticket in this case."

I asked them both, Yanko and Leo, would they let the points of law go by a minute or two and clear me up on what happened, what was this fight in the hall. While I was telling them that, in came a woman from the neighborhood with a big basket of what they call damp-dry laundry, and plunked it up on the bar with a big heave. Yanko greeted her by name, and she asked for a beer. Yanko drew her a beer.

"Thank you," the woman said. "We got an icebox full of beer at home but His Nibs calls it his television beer. If he comes home and gets ready to settle down in front the television, first thing he does is go to the icebox, and if a single can is missing, he hollers bloody murder, like 'Who's been nipping at my television beer? I got that beer for television only.' It's a joke he has, but here I am, lugging laundry and drinking beer in here, with an icebox full at home."

"Was you up at the laundrymat?" Leo asked her.

"Look at the laundry I done," the woman said.

"Was my wife up there? This is Monday. Was she?" Leo asked.

"I was talking to her, Leo," the woman said. "She's up there now. Did you want her?"

"Last thing in the world I want," said Leo, and then turned back to Yanko and me. "Did she give me hell for busting this guy! Ought to be ashamed of myself, she said. But I told her, I asked her was that a nice way to speak about a man's little boy, call him your 'goddam kid,' the way this guy did? She seemed to think that was nothing, nothing at all. Last thing in the world I'm going to do, go chasing up to the laundrymat after her! Anyway, I'm sitting here nice and calm. I'm waiting for the police."

That very instant, Yanko suddenly looks at the door and says, "Oh-oh!" Then he puts his hand up to his mouth and says, a whisper, "Mention the devil!" A cop was coming in.

He was a young cop, a dark-haired man, had a paper in his hand, and he had a friendly walk. He walked in easy, no bullying walk.

"Leo Molik," he said when he came up to the bar. "Anybody here by the name Leo Molik—M-o-l-i-k? Leo Molik?"

Yanko took a swipe at the bar with a rag, never said a word. Naturally, I said nothing. The woman hoisted the laundry off the bar and carried it out, looking back over her shoulder at the cop.

"That's me," said Leo. "I'm Leo Molik." The way he got up off the stool, hitched up his pants, and smiled at the cop, anybody might think he'd been waiting for the cop to come in and give him a season pass for the Giants.

The cop was certainly friendlier than most. He smiled, too. "You don't need to jump up," he said. "Not yet. No hurry. Finish your beer." Leo sat down on the stool again, but nervous. "There's a little something I want to go over with you, Molik," the cop said.

"Yuh?" Leo said.

"Yuh," the cop said. "This man that says you belted him one yesterday has filed a charge against you, claims you let him have one on the jaw, no provocation."

"No what?" Leo said, trying to gulp the beer quietly, as if he weren't nervous, which he was indeed.

"No provocation," the cop said. "He claims he didn't do anything to you, and you let him have one on the jaw, that right?"

"He didn't do anything but call my little boy my 'goddam kid' and start shoving the baby carriage down the hall, that's all he did," Leo said. "I ain't going to deny I socked him. I did sock him. Look at my hand, all swoll up."

"I wouldn't brag about it if I was you," the cop said. "Let me see that hand."

Leo held his left hand out, and the cop felt the swollen part and pushed down on it a little. Leo didn't yelp, although it must have hurt. The cop looked at him. "What you ought to do is get some Epsom salts—you can get it at the drugstore—dump a whole box into some real hot water, and soak that hand for a half hour at least," he said.

"That good?" Leo asked.

"Best thing in the world," the cop said. "You don't know how to hit, you realize that? Else your hand wouldn't get all stove up like that."

"It was what he said about my little boy, that foreigner!" Leo said.

"What are you talking about, 'foreigner'?" the cop asked, stern all of a sudden. "Where were you born?"

Leo was all fussed up. "Well," he said, "it's true I was born in the old country, but I'm only a baby when we come here. Look, I been living right here, right in this neighborhood, thirty-four years. The guy in the hall only over here four or five years! He don't even speak English right. Broken English he talks."

"I wouldn't go hollering 'foreigner' about people if I was you," the cop said. "I happen to be a Syrian boy myself."

Leo didn't answer him. He got up off the stool again, hitched up his pants, and said to the policeman, "You got to take me in? All right, then, let's get it over with."

The cop ignored him and looked at Yanko and me. "You know this man?" he asked me.

"Yes, I know him," I said. "He's all right. Leo has a few snifters once in a while, that's all."

"You know him, of course," the cop said to Yanko.

"I tell you, Officer," Yanko said. "Leo got a real good reputation around here, Officer."

Yanko called him Officer twice. Fellows who are not exactly new at explaining things to policemen fall into the habit of calling them Officer every couple of words.

"Thing is, Officer," Yanko said, "Leo here's crazy about that little boy he got. He's what they call an only child. Me, jeez! I got six! Kids ain't any novelty to me, Officer. But Leo here, why he even parades that little Joey in here every couple days, show his new hat, show his new suit or something— Meaning no offense, Leo! Meaning no offense!"

"He seems to go around smacking neighbors in the teeth," the cop said, as if Leo weren't standing right there. "Has he got a chip on his shoulder, or what?"

"No," Yanko said. "It's being daffy about the little boy, Officer, that's the way I'd size it up. I don't know the guy he hit, only of course I seen him around, know him by sight, kind of."

"Look, Molik, I got something to tell you," the cop said, finally. "You realize it's a serious thing have somebody put a charge against you? You could go to jail for a little while, anyway, you realize that?"

"Yes, sir," Leo said. What Yanko had been saying about him seemed to have impressed Leo himself, and he began actually acting like a nicer guy.

"Well, what I got to tell you is this," the cop said. "I have this man outside, the one who made the charge against you. The man you hit. It was him told me I'd probably find you in here."

"He would!" Leo said, surly again.

"Keep your shirt on," the cop said.

"Let the officer talk, Leo," Yanko said.

"I'm not stopping him," Leo said.

"Look, Officer, would you like a beer?" Yanko took a chance and said. "I know you're on duty, but sometimes—"

"No thanks," the cop said. "Molik, you're right, this man outside doesn't talk English too well at all. He can't help that. Barkeep, you know what language that man talks, the one got hit? You claim you know him a little."

"Yuh," Yanko said. "I can talk to him his own language. I got parents the same nationality."

"Well, the thing is this," the cop said. "I figure this a little neighborhood mix-up. I talked to this man, and, best I could figure that he was saying, we can straighten this out. I'm going to bring him in, Molik, and if you get tough, in you go, and I might bust you in the teeth into the bargain. Hear me? Can we sit down someplace?"

"Sure, back in the booths," Yanko said.

The policeman told Leo to wait; then he went outside and came back in a couple of minutes with the other man. He was a little older than Leo, very nervous, had a look somehow like a professor but husky enough just the same. He was very nervous.

"Come on, Molik," the cop said, and then asked Yanko if there was anybody could tend bar, because he needed Yanko to talk to the man in his own language.

"I get the guy out of the kitchen," Yanko said, and he went back and sent out an old man who helps out in the kitchen. The old man could fill in for a few minutes, anyway, behind the bar. The cop said I might as well sit with them if I wanted to, and so I did, all of us in the booth.

The man that got hit had only a small swelling on his jaw. Leo's hand was hurt worse than the man's jaw was. The man got more and more nervous every minute. All of a sudden, he pawed at all his pockets, and finally found a handkerchief and pulled it out, because he was crying. Big tears.

"What's the matter with him?" Leo piped up. "What's the matter with him? It's me that's in trouble for socking him. What's he crying for? He's in the clear."

"Take it easy, Molik," the cop said. "*You* ask him what's wrong, what's he crying for, Barkeep."

Yanko spoke to the man in whatever language it was. He seemed to be asking him a long question, a lot of words. The man aimed all his answers at Yanko, and he didn't stop crying but he talked and talked and talked, none of us except Yanko knowing what it was all about. Then, little by little, Yanko would hold his hand up and stop him and tell the cop and Leo and me what he said.

"He says he was sorry all night and couldn't sleep," Yanko said. "He says he cried at night, too, on account what happened. He says he don't want no harm to come to anybody, and where he got hit don't hurt any more."

The man talked some more and more and more, and every once in a while Yanko had to stop him and explain.

"He says he forgot himself altogether, that's how it happened he said bad words, that's what he said, bad words, about Leo's little boy," Yanko explained. "Here's what he says. He has a wife and a little boy in the old country and he come over to this country try to make enough money bring them over here to be with him. But he says he can't make the grade. I mean that is what it amounts to in English, he can't make the grade."

The man talked some more, very intently, to Yanko, as if the rest of us weren't there.

"He says it's true he had a few drinks himself before the fight they had in the hallway," Yanko said. "He says it's true he did. He says when he drinks, all he thinks about is how too bad it is he don't have his wife and baby here like everybody else has their wife and baby. He says he don't know why he got mad and called him 'goddam kid,' he says, except he says everybody got a wife and little boy except him. He's very sorry all night last night and can't sleep because the fight happened."

The man broke in on Yanko. Putting his handkerchief away, the man said to the cop, in English not too bad at all, "I don't want anything should happen with the police to Mr. Molik. I am sorry I go to the police station. I forgot myself altogether, and I tell Mr. Molik before you this little boy is a good boy. He is not goddam kid, like I said when I forgot myself. He is a good, nice little boy, like my little boy used to be. I do not want anything should happen to Mr. Molik with the police. Is all right, sir?"

"Everything's O.K.," the cop said.

He asked Leo and the man if they would shake hands. Leo didn't say a word. They shook hands, and the cop got to his feet. He and Yanko and I went back to the bar.

The cop stood there a minute. "Hard luck, the man having his family stuck on the other side," he said to Yanko.

"Yuh," Yanko said. "You still don't want a beer?"

The cop said no and started out.

"Before you go, Officer," Yanko said. "A cop can give a ticket for a baby carriage in the hall, can't he? It happen to a friend of mine."

"Yes. It's a fire-law violation," the cop said.

"How about a uniform fireman, he can give a ticket, too, for that?" Yanko asked.

"The inspectors usually report it and something's done," the cop said. "Well, I got to get going. So long!"

EIGHT TO FIVE IT'S A BOY

It was to be expected that there would be betting on Rolfe Packer's baby at the Broad Street brokerage office where he worked. The men at Carton, Dasherman & Monks bet each other on practically every uncertainty, either casually or earnestly. They bet on tennis matches, fights, ball games, basketball, elections, everything.

Packer told about the coming baby one day at lunch. At the time, his wife, Marnie, was about five months pregnant. He had had a difficult time keeping his mouth shut that long. And when he blurted the news out as he sat with Eugene McCarthy and Karl Stanner, two other C.D.&M. men, having a second coffee after lunch, he found it wasn't news at all. Their wives had known about it for a couple of months.

"Well, he's not going into this high-toned bucket-shop business," Packer said. "I can tell you that this far ahead."

"How do you know it's going to be a he?" McCarthy said, and laughed. "I suppose you've had some of these new tests taken, and all that. They're the bunk. Nothing but tabloid-newspaper science, that's all."

"We haven't had any tests—I mean outside the regular ones. No trick stuff," Packer said. "He'll be a boy, though."

"You betting on it?" asked Stanner, half kidding.

"I haven't *been* betting on it," Packer said. "You people are the first I've told about it, practically."

"Give me a nice price and I'll bet you it isn't a boy, long as you're so sure about it," McCarthy said.

"Wait a minute, Mac," Stanner interrupted. "You're betting against the best available dope. Seems to me I saw in the *Information Please Almanac* that there are about a hundred and one boys born to every hundred girls—something like that. More boys than girls, anyway. I have a habit of thumbing around in that book, and I saw something about the ratio of boys and girls."

"Where would *Information Please* get any inside dope on the forthcoming Packer offspring?" McCarthy put in. "I said I'd bet him no boy, if he makes the price right. That's what I said, and I mean it."

"I didn't tell about this to start you dice throwers gambling," said Packer with mock righteousness. "I'm merely telling you this child of mine is going to be a boy. Marnie says so, too. Marnie's got a hunch. I got a hunch."

McCarthy said, "Trouble with you, Pappy Packer, you've been playing that record from *Carousel* too much. You know the one—'My boy Bill, he'll be tall and as straight as a tree.' You're just talking yourself into a sucker bet. What price, Packer, my fine, aged sire? What price it's a boy?"

"Lay off that 'aged' stuff, McCarthy. You're no kid yourself," Packer answered, a little peeved. "I told you I wasn't betting."

"Oh, sure—too sacred a subject for gambling," said Stanner. "First-time fathers always get holy about babies."

"No, no, no," Packer said. "I realize people's wives have babies every day. I mean somebody's wife has a baby every day. I mean I'm going to have a baby, that's all. Nothing remarkable about it."

"Except biologically, that's all," McCarthy said. "Stop beating around the bush. Do I get a bet or don't I? What price a boy?"

"All right, wise guy, I'll give you eight to five it's a boy," Packer said sharply.

"You've got a bet!" McCarthy snapped. "Eight to five for how much?"

"Oh, well, I want to go a little easy," said Packer. "I'm sure about it being a boy, but this baby business costs money. I'm learning that. Make it for twenty-five. Let's see, that'd be I'd give you forty to your twenty-five. Right?"

"Make it eighty to fifty. It's simpler," McCarthy said.

Packer hesitated a moment, and then said, "O.K., you're on. I give eighty it's a boy, you give me fifty it's a girl. Right?"

"Right—eighty to fifty it's a boy. When's the payoff?"

"About four months," Packer said. "And the payoff's right after my boy weighs in."

"At eight pounds ringside," said Stanner. "Give or take a pound, of course."

After Marnie had become pregnant, Packer often thought about how they had met, in the office, and how they had gone to dinners and shows, and fights in the Garden, and how, almost imperceptibly, they had eased into marriage.

That had been in wartime, and in wartime marriages between men and girls considerably younger than themselves were not at all uncommon. Packer had been thirty-six then, and Marnie twenty-five. The difference in age had bothered Packer in his mind sometimes, but he had taken what he thought was a bold way out of it. That is, when they went places, it was he who always made cracks or pulled gags on the old-guy-young-girl theme. To himself, he reasoned it was better for him to beat anybody else to the punch on that kind of stuff.

Marnie had stopped him from that. "Not very subtle," she had said. "What makes you think eleven years is anything? You're only thirty-six. A stripling, practically."

"Maybe you're right, Marnie, maybe you're right," he had said a little sheepishly. "I'll cut out the cracks."

Nevertheless, he had thought about the eleven years' difference occasionally. More than occasionally, now that there was going to be a baby. Packer was forty-two now; Marnie was thirty-one.

He was thinking about that while he wandered around the apartment they lived in, on East Fortieth Street, the night after he made the bet with McCarthy.

Marnie, as usual lately, had gone to bed early. Packer had made a fruitless search of the bookshelves, looking for the *Information Please Almanac*.

"No *World Almanac*, either," he said to himself. "I ought to buy more books and less *Racing Forms*. Fine house, no almanac at all. Packer's haven for the ill-informed, that's what I'm running here."

Nearly four months later, the basketball games and the winter's fights at the Garden and the other betting milestones had been passed, and again Packer was with McCarthy and Stanner at lunch.

"When do I pick up my eighty bucks, Packer?" McCarthy asked, in connection with nothing at all. "You know, I forgot to tell you that when the husband is the dominant character in the household, why, it's bound to be a girl."

"So?" Packer asked.

"So Marnie always struck me as a nice, mild-mannered lady," McCarthy continued. "And you're a pretty arrogant guy sometimes."

"So what do you road-company obstetricians make out of that?" Packer asked.

"Nothing on earth, except that you two are bound to have a girl," McCarthy said with an air of finality. "When's the payoff? I haven't had a look at Mrs. P. lately."

"Nice, delicate guy, that McCarthy," said Packer, with a nod, to Stanner. "Well, it's pretty close now, pretty close, Dr. Fisher says, but those guys don't seem to ever know exactly when. I can't pin him down."

"Real close, though?" McCarthy asked solicitously.

"I say I can't worm it out of that doc," Packer said. "Any time now, though, he seems to think, but he won't come right out and say."

"Well, good luck to Marnie," said Stanner. "You, too. Need a lot of luck, you first-time pappies."

"Oh, I'm all right. I'm not nervous," said Packer nervously. "He'll be a boy all right. I've got a lot of plans for him. I'm going to take him to the fights on Friday nights at the Garden and then over to the Philharmonic on Sunday afternoons."

McCarthy and Stanner looked at each other and reached for the coffee.

"You know, make him a mug and a gent, nicely blended," Packer went on. "A man can like symphonies and fights, too. They're not mutually exclusive. That's why I'm taking him to the Garden and Carnegie both."

McCarthy and Stanner laughed, not too derisively.

"Let's see, now," Stanner said to McCarthy, as if Packer were not present. "Is that the twelfth or ninth prospective pappy we've heard with the well-rounded-man plan for his son?"

"What son?" McCarthy barked. "Don't jinx me, Stanner! I'm betting fifty clams that this brat will be a girl! Don't put the whammy on me!"

A few days later, Marnie phoned Packer at his office and told him that Dr. Fisher was on his way to the apartment to drive her up to Harkness Pavilion.

"Nothing to worry about, darling," Marnie said. "We'll be here at the house for a little while, and if we've gone by the time you get here, you can come up to Harkness by yourself."

Packer laughed nervously at Marnie's solicitude for him at that moment and said he'd hurry home. But when he got outside, it was raining, and it was also around four-fifteen, the time when many cabbies are turning in from the day shift, and he had to take the subway to his apartment. He let himself in, found nobody there, and hustled back out into the rain.

Still no cabs, of course. He started west on East Fortieth Street, up the incline toward the Murray Hill Hotel, or what had been the Murray Hill Hotel. Right now, they were running up the steel for a new building on the old hotel site. It *is* a hill, he thought as he hurried. He was puffing, rather suddenly, although the incline was so gentle people hardly thought of Murray Hill as actually a hill.

Packer waited on the corner. No cabs—no empty ones, with the lights on top lighted. He realized he was pretending to himself that the object of the wait on the corner was the search for a cab when in reality he was waiting to get his breath back. It dawned on him that hills and stairs were bothering him lately.

He started briskly uptown on Park Avenue, toward the subway. That was downhill, easy. Didn't bother him at all. "Aw, what the hell!" he said to himself. "Everybody's heart pounds when he's going to have a baby. Old proverb I should make up right away: 'Oncoming babies make pounding hearts.' "

He took the crosstown shuttle and was hurrying through the underground maze at Times Square when he noticed the pounding again. Not bad, just a little. He was glad when he managed to get a seat in the uptown train.

He found himself looking at a family group in the train—two boys and their father and mother. Father and mother just the same age, I bet, he thought as he looked at them. The softball game last summer, at the C.D.&M. picnic, popped into his mind. All at once, he was panicky. He remembered how he had pulled up at second base in the game, all out of puff. Standing on the sack, he had thought for a moment he was going to fold up. Then he thought of last Saturday. That afternoon, he had quit in the middle of a badminton game, pleading a hangover. Truth was he'd felt he couldn't breathe. "Forty-two years old, and me with a brand-new baby," he said to himself, almost aloud.

At 168th Street, Packer hurried through the train door. He stopped once, halfway up the subway stairs. "Take it easy," he said to himself.

On the sidewalk beside the subway exit, he looked at his watch. It was nearly two hours since Marnie had phoned. Packer crossed Broadway, in the direction of Harkness Pavilion.

I'll be fifty-two and he'll be ten, he thought, hastening over the long block to Fort Washington Avenue. He'll be with me in the country and he'll throw a ball. Or he'll want to bat out some fungoes and have me chase them. I won't be able to do it. He'll see me all out of breath. He'll want to go swimming at the beach, and I'll do nothing but wade around. My own kid'll laugh at me.

At the desk inside the Pavilion, the woman clerk smiled at Packer's puffing haste as he gave his name and said to her, "My wife is having a baby, and I—"

"Yes, Mr. Packer, that's on the ninth floor," the woman said. "Take the elevator right there."

In the elevator, Packer stood at the back, and the operator couldn't see that his lips were moving. "Holy Pete!" he was saying. "Let McCarthy have the eighty bucks, and I hope it chokes him! Lord A'mighty, make it a little girl for Marnie and me! A little girl won't notice that I'm fifty-two when she's ten. Please make her a little girl!"

ELEVEN DOLLARS A DAY

The man, dressed in plain light blue pajamas, a striped seersucker bathrobe, gray woollen socks, and flat slippers, the leather kind held on by straps crossing up near the toes, sat near the west window. The nurse, in her white uniform, sat across the room, beyond the bed, at the window that faced the north. Each was reading a book, and the room was warm and peaceful.

The man, Tommy Wade, stopped reading for a few moments and looked out across the rooftops as he took a cigarette from the package on the window sill. He picked up the book of matches and read, on the cover, "PIPERS CLUB." Before he pulled out a match, he stared for almost half a minute at the book of matches. The nurse did not look up from her book.

As, finally, he lighted the cigarette, Wade spoke. "I made a fool of myself there, too, for a couple of days. I forgot to tell you that," he said.

"Where is that?" the nurse asked, closing her book. She was small and pretty, with blue eyes, and a mole on her right cheek like a beauty patch worn at a costume ball, and her ankles were slim.

"The Pipers Club," Wade said. "Pretty fancy club, in its way."

"Oh, I don't think they'll mind," the nurse said. She seemed interested.

"Not fancy in a snooty way, you understand," Wade said. "But they like to have you kind of stay on your feet no matter how many slugs you've been pouring into yourself. Good club. The way I remember it, I slept on the couch in the library the last night before I got here. Made a fool of myself before that, though. Pretty fancy club. This is a pretty fancy hospital, too, isn't it?"

"Some big people get here from time to time," the nurse said. Her voice was gentle, her accent more than a little British, and her smile was easy, yet not overdone.

"Any big people here now?" he asked.

"There's a lady who used to be a big star in the room a few doors down," the nurse said. "She's quite handsome."

"What's the matter with her—operation?" Wade asked.

"I think it's sleeping pills," the nurse said. "Of course, I don't know. Overdose of sleeping pills."

"They're a terrible habit," Wade said. "I've always been afraid of them myself. Never take any."

By that time, he had opened his book again, and the nurse had opened hers. He was reading *The Last Puritan,* and she was reading Philip Wylie's *Opus 21.*

The man and the nurse went on reading, and the room was warm and peaceful. The silence continued for ten minutes or so.

"I've been meaning to read this book for about thirteen years," Wade said then. "Never got around to it. This is a good chance here, isn't it? I couldn't concentrate on reading anything yesterday. Did nothing but talk to you, did I?"

"The things you said were interesting," the nurse said. "Don't forget, I did some talking, too."

"It was all right, wasn't it?" Wade asked.

"I don't mind it," the nurse said.

"Don't know how I managed to get this book here with me," he said. "I must have grabbed it from a shelf before the doctor came and brought me up here. He said it was the only thing to do, go into the hospital for a few days and get straightened out. My wife's away, you know. She went out to Sun Valley, skiing. Won't be back until next week."

"You told me about that—remember?" the nurse said.

"The doc was right," Wade went on. "I couldn't have stopped all that drinking by myself. Getting to be all right now. I feel pretty good this afternoon."

"You're not eating enough yet, though," the nurse said.

"I can eat tonight, I think," Wade said. "What are we having—I mean what am I having? I told you to fill out the slip."

"I ordered a slice of roast beef, with some chicken consommé first, and a salad, and some browned potatoes and beets—you said you liked beets," the nurse answered. "Ice cream afterward."

"Sounds O.K.," Wade said, and turned back to his book. The nurse began reading her book, and, as before, the room was warm and peaceful.

Wade wasn't really reading this time. His eyes were on the book but they weren't taking in anything. He was thinking that the thing of being there in the hospital because he had been drinking too much had swiftly, and by imperceptible means, turned from being a distressing and sorrowful, almost shameful, thing into an idyll. Of sorts, anyway. The nurse was one of three. To go around the clock. Each worked eight hours, for which the fee was eleven dollars. The two other nurses were all right. They did their work. This one had become a lovely little lady sharing his idyll with him.

It should be like this, he thought, with his eyes on the book. He lifted them for a moment and looked steadily at the nurse's quiet profile as she read. I must try to remember how things are this minute. Her eyelashes are long, and her nose turns up a little. There are the faintest hollows in her cheeks, and she is young. Her upper lip sticks out a little bit.

And, Wade went on thinking, we only talk to each other when we want to talk. Come to think of it, I always start the talk, don't I? But all those things she told me, in bits and fragments, were each a thing that had a sharp, definite interest for me: From Norway to boarding school in England at thirteen, she said, and never back to Norway again. She became a nurse in London, and she nursed there in wartime. Still, she is so young. She never told me how old. Twenty-eight, maybe? It should be like this. Her sitting there in the chair, me in mine. Nothing can happen to us in here. No drinking for me. Reading. And she'll take care of me if I want anything, but still I'm not really ill. She's lovely, and every time I talk she seems interested. She *is* interested. We've talked a lot in three days. Three eight-hour days, that is. I feel bad when she has to go home at four o'clock. I miss her right away. Just the same, she'll be back at eight o'clock tomorrow morning. We were strangers a few days ago. We still are, too. And at the same time we are not strangers, we've talked so much, each about ourselves. She knows how I miss my wife. Her husband must be a swell guy, from what she told me. He had been in the Pacific.

"Yeh, these are wonderful hours," Wade found himself saying, "and by all good rights they should be tough to bear."

The nurse looked up. "Did you say something?" she asked. "I was quite wrapped up in this book." Her eyes were alert, and she put the book over on the table by the bed.

"No, I didn't say anything," Wade said.

"What would you think of going up in the solarium?" the nurse asked. "It's such a lovely day."

"I didn't know they had a solarium," he said. "But I'd like to go up, if you want to."

"It's nice there," the nurse said.

"O.K., let's go," said Wade, and he put his book aside. "I'll go in the bathroom and put on my pants, and we'll go to the solarium."

"I'll get your trousers and things," the nurse said, and she went to the closet and gave them to him, along with a shirt.

Wade came out of the bathroom dressed, after a fashion.

"Do you know where my belt is?" he asked. "Or suspenders?"

The nurse smiled. "I'm afraid you didn't have any belt when you came in," she said. "Nor braces, either."

"Holy Pete!" Wade said. They both laughed. "No belt or suspenders," he said, "but I grabbed *The Last Puritan* somewhere along the line. I must be nuts."

With the nurse by his side, Wade, still in his slippers but more publicly attired, with his trousers and shirt on beneath the seersucker robe, walked down the hall toward the elevator.

"I don't think you're nuts," the nurse said.

"Thanks," said Wade.

There was nobody else up in the solarium, and the sun truly splashed all over them as they sat in chairs side by side.

In a room down the corridor, someone was playing a phonograph, and the tune was "Bali Ha'i." That's what it is, right here and down in the room, Wade thought—Bali Ha'i, N.Y.

The nurse asked him if he had seen *South Pacific.*

"Yes. It really is a knockout," Wade said.

"It must be," she said. "I read the *Tales of the South Pacific*. That one called 'Fo' Dolla' ' is the best, don't you think?"

Her British accent was comically assertive when she tried to say "Fo' Dolla'," Wade thought. "That's the one they took the show from, mainly," he said.

He looked directly at the nurse again, as he had so many times in the last three days. Suddenly, he saw she wasn't listening.

Nothing had happened. No disturbance anywhere, in the hall or here. She wasn't listening, that was all.

Wade looked away. He stared out into the sun until it hurt his eyes. He was hurt inside his head, too. Because in those few seconds the smashing thought had come to him: She has been listening because she had to; she listens for eleven dollars a day; oh, what a louse I am! Making somebody listen to me for eight hours a day by paying her for it! What a heel indeed! Bali Ha'i my eye! A guy getting over a binge, and for days he pays a lovely lady a lousy eleven bucks a day to listen to his twaddle!

"I think I'd like to go downstairs," he said to her.

"All right, Mr. Wade," the nurse said. It didn't sound the way all her other talk had sounded. This thing was over, so they went downstairs and in a half hour the nurse's day was up. They hardly said anything that half hour, and their goodbyes were courteous and meaningless. The doctor came in and said that Wade wouldn't need anybody around after that day, so that was the last he saw of her.

SLIGHTLY CROCKED

John Fowler sat on the porch of the beach club at the end of the day, thoroughly pleased with himself and his surroundings and life in general.

During the afternoon he had been in swimming three times, and he had been to the bar just enough times. That is, he had maintained a proper balance—the sting of the rye at the bar and then, a few minutes later, the salt water washing away the taste of the rye. Each swim had made him feel that he had cancelled out the harm of the whiskey and kept the fun of it. For a man who tended to go overboard on drinking, that was the ideal, seldom achieved.

So, sitting alone on the porch, he looked at the sea gulls walking purposefully at the edge of the water and thought to himself what good luck he had had with whiskey and waves that day. He was pleased that he could think of one dignified old sea gull as a bishop, and the sea gull who followed in matronly style as the bishop's lady. Without the drinks, thought Fowler, I wouldn't see a couple of old sea gulls in that light, and if I did, why, I'd be ashamed of it. They *do* look like a bishop and his lady, he said to himself.

From up the beach there came a lovely young girl riding along the sands on a horse. Fowler thought that that was a fine sight. The girl wore overalls rolled up to her knees and a gay shirt, and she sat nice and loose on the horse, with her back straight, as she should. Against the background of the sea, horse and girl were perfect. Fowler watched them as they approached and then passed him and finally passed out of sight, and again he was warmly delighted at his awareness in the twilight. He was thankful that he was slightly crocked.

Just then some music drifted down the easy sunset wind. Fowler knew that it was canned music from the carnival, a quarter of a mile, maybe three eighths, down the road in back of the club. (He had passed the carnival lot early that afternoon, walking from the hotel to the club. They were just putting up the stuff then—a Ferris wheel, a merry-go-round, a half dozen booths, a sadly small menagerie.) The distance softened the brazen crackle of the loud-speaker, and the music was clear and admirable to Fowler. A march tune, "Under the Double Eagle," was being played, and as Fowler listened, he looked at the darkening sea and beat time gently with one hand. He kept his feet up on the porch railing. He didn't want any more drinks. The sea gulls, the girl on the horse, the music borne on the wind—everything was perfect.

"Da-*da*-da-de-da, da-de-*da*" went the tune on the air, very gay and beckoning, and Fowler took his feet down from the rail and was surprised to note that he was speaking out loud, but not very loud, to himself. "I guess I'll go to the carnival," he heard himself saying. "Just take a walk there for a look at it."

He nodded in friendly but slightly aloof style to a few friends in the club bar as he passed through without stopping, on his way to the outside door, and in a minute or two he was out on the road. There's a pleasant walk ahead, he thought. And it was, with the darkness coming down, the sound of the sea on his left, and the growing sound of the carnival ahead, and a nightfall scent of sea, and sweet grass, and —oh, yes—iodine, over it all.

I wouldn't have thought of that iodine without the drinks all day,

Fowler thought, and quite proudly. The sea is full of iodine, and the seaweed, too, and not everybody knows that.

Fowler turned into the carnival lot, and the trampled-down grass felt springy under his feet. The brightness of the spottily lighted booths, merry-go-round, Ferris wheel, and the popcorn stand was dazzling. "In a brave little way," Fowler murmured. Again, as a few times before in his usually steady life, he felt a childlike admiration for people of carnivals and the courage they have in going always to unknown towns.

It had been more than an hour, nearly an hour and a half, since his last drink, but Fowler was still just right when he stopped at the last booth on the lot. What caught his eye there was the shining stacks of silver dollars. There were two such stacks, each as high as a man's hand from finger tip to wrist, and they were standing there on the table at the rear of the booth.

The guy running the little stand presided over the dollars, and he was running a kind of dice game. How many dollars, Fowler wondered as he stood there a minute with other carnival visitors, watching the play of the game. He tried to count them, but the coins blurred in the light. Was it twenty-four in each pile? Hard to count, because the carnival man kept jingling the top coins up and down in the stacks as he talked to the small group playing the game.

He was a tough-looking guy, but Fowler saw a kind of gaiety in his eyes, a look of what-the-hell-difference-does-anything-make.

It was a simple game they were playing, simpler than a crap game. The players put their quarters, half dollars, dimes, or, rarely, dollars on squares on the surface of a counter which had built-up sides. After all the bets were down, the guy threw the dice for a point. If he threw an eight, all those who later threw higher than an eight, on their turn to throw, were paid off. Some winners got silver dollars, others got smaller coins. Those who threw an eight or less lost their money. The guy won on the ties. He got his percentage that way. Also, he threw a lot of nines, and they were hard to beat.

Fowler was playing almost before he knew it, and winning. He had a handful of silver dollars in no time, maybe fourteen, and he was happy at how much more like money they felt than bills. And every silver dollar was new, untarnished. That was part of the lure, the way the dollars gleamed.

Fowler lost a couple of times, then won again. He was jingling the dollars in his hands when the guy said, "Wait a minute, boys, wait a minute."

The guy was looking down at a little kid, maybe six or seven years old, who had strayed around to the back of the counter, where only the guy was supposed to be. He halted the game, leaned over, and spoke to the kid.

"Here, Johnny," he said, "go on over to the merry-go-round." He handed the kid a dime. Then, he smiled and said, "*Is* your name Johnny? Anyway, beat it to the merry-go-round, like a good kid. This is no place for you, Johnny."

The boy looked up and grinned, and stayed where he was. The guy looked at Fowler, who was a bigger, older man than any of the other players, and shrugged and laughed.

At that instant, the drinks, and the fun of the waves, and the pleasant walk down the road all surged up in Fowler. He took a silver dollar and spun it in the air over the table to the kid, so that it almost landed in his hand. "Go on to the merry-go-round!" he said.

The carnival guy looked at him, and there was a kind of gay and reckless challenge in his eyes. "Wait a minute!" he said. And he reached to the pile of dollars, picked one off, and tossed it to the kid. Then he looked at Fowler and grinned.

Fowler threw the kid another dollar. The kid scrambled wildly for it, picked it up, and stared at both men.

The guy threw him another dollar. "I'll keep it up as long as you do, Mac!" he said, and Fowler felt then that the guy was from New York, where the name of every encountered stranger is Mac or Chief.

The contest went on—a silver dollar from Fowler, a silver dollar from the guy, the kid scrambling, the dollars glinting in the air, dollar, dollar, dollar, and the kid was dizzy with delight, both hands full of coins.

I think that's nine from me, thought Fowler, and he saw he had four more. "I quit," he said.

"I'll always top you," said the guy, not surly but confident. "Here, Johnny, go to the merry-go-round." He threw the kid another dollar, then still another. Then he turned back to the players. "All right, boys," he said as he picked up the dice again. "Let's get going. All you got to do is beat me."

Fowler turned to watch the amazed kid, clinging to his wondrous handfuls of bright silver dollars and running through the crowd. He saw him stop before a man and woman, somber folk who were staring idly around, as townspeople do at carnivals. Their eyes popped as they saw their son and the dollars. Then they grabbed him and hustled away—all three.

Fowler threw the rest of his silver dollars on the counter, pleased to let them go. On his turn at the dice, he lost them.

Wasn't it a great day, thought Fowler as he left the brightly lighted lot and started walking back to the club. Everything was just right. I think I could stand another drink now. But I got to be careful. I don't want to spoil everything.

BACK WHERE I HAD NEVER BEEN

My wife and I recently returned from a sentimental excursion to Ireland. All my life, friends have called me "Irishman," because of my name, McNulty, and since before this summer I had never been in Ireland and knew little or nothing about the Irish, except those of Third Avenue and Boston, I felt like a fake. Now I have spent a couple of months in Ireland, and while I still am no Irish authority, a few small things did happen to me there that recurringly please my mind, and I feel better for having gone there.

How we came to go was that we had a windfall of about four thousand dollars. The money was so unexpected that we had a joint impulse to waste it. Perhaps not to waste it, exactly, but to spend it on unnecessary things rather than put it aside in fearful anticipation of a disaster, four-thousand-dollar size. "We'll dribble it away," I said venturously, "with an automobile here and a new suit there, and a television set we don't want, and, first thing we know, it'll all be gone and nothing to show for it." "We could go to Ireland," my wife said, and I was astonished. "I have an idea you've always wanted to go to Ireland," she went on, "but when I think of it, I don't ever remember your saying so in so many words." This was a joyful surprise to me, because my wife is only a small part Irish, the other parts being New England Yankee and English and French.

I myself am what the Irish call a Narrowback. The term is neither praiseful nor disdainful. It is merely a sorrowful truth about us American men who were born here of parents who came from Ireland. In nine hundred and ninety-nine cases out of a thousand, our fathers came to this country with small education but broad backs and strong muscles, prepared to do such work in the United States as called for this equipment. Succeeding here to a greater or lesser degree, they gave us, their American-born sons, as much schooling as they could, and with some education we turned to less laborious means of earning a living. So, figuratively or literally, through an accelerated process of evolution favored by the Irish, our backs grew narrower. It is my belief that every Narrowback is pleasurably haunted by the notion that someday he will go and see about Ireland for himself. When my wife said what she did, I replied, "That's the thing to do—go to Ireland. And let's have no more concern over what happens to our little box of money." "That's right," she said. "The hell with it." A strange thing for a wife to say, but a most pleasant thing to hear.

The trip decided upon, my first impulse was to noise the news modestly around our neighborhood, at Seventy-second Street and Second Avenue. Everybody knows Ireland is only twelve or thirteen hours away by plane, but a trip to Ireland seemed to me a sizable project. Besides, I didn't want to go by plane. I wanted it to be farther away than thirteen hours, and we'd go by ship and have a lot of talking about it beforehand. Our neighborhood, which comprises a certain few blocks where we know each other, by sight anyway, is small and nicely gossipy. I started the news around by going to Maxie Slavin, the tireless little hundred-and-fourteen-pound man who runs the newsstand at the corner of Second.

"I want you to stop sending the papers to the house, Maxie," I said.

"What's the matter?" he asked. "Any trouble?"

"Oh, no, no," I said. "We're going away for a couple months. We're going to Ireland."

Maxie smiled a big grin. He comes from Minsk. I noticed an odd thing in the next few weeks: when you tell people you're going to Ireland, they smile almost as if they were going themselves. I imagine that if you say you're going to Paris, people say something like "Oh boy, oh boy!" with the implication that you're going to polish off all the women and drink up all the wine. When you say England, maybe they say "Yeah?" When it's Ireland, they smile. I don't know why this is.

"Gee whizz! Ireland!" said Maxie. "Galway Bay! Blarney Castle! Going to Ireland, huh? You're a lucky guy! It's a great spot, they say. When you going?"

"I don't know yet. In a few weeks, maybe. Just beginning the arrangements," I said.

"Well, why am I going to stop the papers so soon?" he asked. "You could tell me just before you go away'll be time enough."

"That's right," I said. "I'll let you know."

It was probably a bad way to start the news around the neighborhood, but it was the only one I could think of.

The news got around. I went to the shop of Mark Tribus, the Jewish barber who always cuts my hair. "I hear you're going to Ireland," Mark said. "You going to Dublin?"

"Sure we'll be in Dublin," I said.

"Right away I'll write a letter to my nephew," he said.

"In Dublin?" I asked dubiously.

"A man's going to Ireland, will I write a letter to a nephew in Chicago?" Mark said. "Certainly in Dublin! He got a big furniture business. A big man in Dublin, my nephew. Right away I'll write him."

"Do that, Mark," I said.

Part of the pleasant preparations was having a talk with a friend who was born and brought up in Ireland and in whose counsel I have great confidence. He is Timothy Athena Costello, who runs what he calls a "store," or saloon, at Forty-fourth Street and Third Avenue. (The "Athena," his confirmation name, was given him in honor of a nun in Ferbane, County Offaly, where he was reared.) We spread a large map of Ireland on the bar and together scrutinized it, I with the eyes of a greenhorn, he with knowledge harking back to the period years ago when he was the driver of cars rented to visitors in Dublin.

"It'll be raining most of the time," Tim said. "Do you have only a skimpy raincoat, or have you something with a little weight and warmth to it?"

"Skimpy," I said.

"Then first thing is get a raincoat," he said. "It'll rain every day, and it'll be cold in the mornings and evenings, especially cold for Americans. A hefty raincoat, the first thing."

He took a pencil and made rings around four or five places on the coast. Then, with an appalling gesture of dismissal, he swept his hand down through the whole middle of Ireland. "This," he said, "you can skip. You'd find it very tiresome and dull. The coast is grand." It was as if on a map of the States he had eradicated in one motion all America between the Rockies and the Appalachians.

"Tell me this," Tim said, dropping his pencil near Cork. "How do you feel about Blarney Castle?"

"I am determined to avoid Blarney Castle at all costs," I replied. "I'm sick of hearing about it and I think it's the bunk. That isn't the Ireland I want to see."

"Ha-ha!" he said. "Then you'll have a glorious time in Ireland. The place is not all Mother Machree and that sort of thing."

"I don't want it to be Mother Machree," I said. "I don't go at all for Mother Machree. Don't misunderstand me, now. She's probably all right in her place, but on all those Saint Patrick's Days, all those years of meeting synthetic Gaels around saloons, I got terribly sick of Mother Machree. I hope there'll be very little of Mother Machree on this trip."

"I don't misunderstand you," said Tim. "A minimum of Mother Machree is what you mean, a minimum of Mother Machree. Will you do as I tell you and go get a warm raincoat?"

"I will," I said.

So I went over to Brooks Brothers and bought a handsome raincoat for seventy-five dollars. Ordinarily, I would never dream of buying that class of raincoat, but that's the way I felt, and I even bought a detachable woollen lining, which cost fifteen dollars. The rain that makes Ireland so green also made this coat a good investment.

A night or so before we were to sail, my wife put our guidebook down on the arm of her chair and said, "I was thinking about the drinking. I don't want to be a dry blanket, but don't you think you might really enjoy it more over there if you did no drinking? I have the impression they do quite a lot of it over there."

"I've always had the same idea," I said. "Probably you're right. No doubt you're right. And I've been thinking about their complicated politics, too. It certainly would be unwise for a stranger like me to go talking Irish politics in Dublin, or wherever we might be."

So I made two resolutions for the trip, as follows:

1. No drinking in Ireland.
2. No talking Irish politics in Ireland.

As it turned out, it was quite some time before I began talking Irish politics in Ireland.

On board our ship, the *Britannic*, we became friends with a six-foot-three American, David Mellor, who comes from Natick, Massachusetts, and was on the Dartmouth crew in his college days, which are only a few years back. Mellor told us that he did not have one drop of Irish blood in him but that since boyhood he had read everything Irish he could get his hands on—poetry, history, plays, stories—and that this had aroused in him an irresistible desire to visit Ireland, which he was about to do. He planned to bicycle all over the place for two or three months. Mellor could recite Yeats by the half hour, and his fervor for Ireland was amazing. It is hard to believe that any returning Irishman could be as eager to reach Ireland as Mellor was.

When the tender that took us from the *Britannic* at last touched the dock at Cobh, Mellor was way up front, anxious to be among the first passengers to step on Irish soil. In Ireland, flowers seem determined to grow. They pop up out of crevices in the flagstone walks, they peek out of soil-filled cracks in ancient walls, and they even blossom, unasked, out of the roofs of cottages. So it was that bright, yellowy blooms were growing in a tiny space at the edge of the dock, in the cracks of the stone walks. Mellor's foot touched the dock, and his eyes widened as he looked down. "Jeepers cripes!" he said. "An Irish dandylion!" And he leaned over and examined it with delight, as if it were something new and strange, something he had been waiting a long time to see, and here it was at last. "An Irish dandylion!" he said a few times more.

In Counihan's snug, near the Imperial Hotel, in Cork, the Corkonian next to me at the bar was reading the *Irish Times*. "Did you see this?" he asked, looking at me over his spectacles. He pointed to a story about the Minister for Agriculture, who on the evening before had said in an address that the farmers were doing fine with the cattle and fine with the pigs but that they would have to do better with eggs. More and more eggs must be produced to be sold to England and other countries, to bolster the finances of this beginning republic of Ireland.

"I read it this morning," I said.

"That's the latest scheme they have around here now," he said, and a glint came into his eyes.

"What's that?" I dutifully asked.

"Drown the English in a wave of eggs!" he roared. "It's a horrible death! Drowning in a wave of eggs! I doubt the English deserve such an end as that!"

Most mornings, at the Gresham Hotel in Dublin, we were awakened early by sea gulls and "Buttons and Bows." Every morning, I thought about how we have sea gulls back home in Manhattan, too. There were hundreds of them over around First Avenue and Forty-fourth and Forty-fifth Streets when the slaughterhouses were on the spot where they're building the United Nations Headquarters. But our sea gulls seem to keep off the main streets. In Dublin, they wheel ceaselessly over O'Connell Street, dipping down from time to time onto the River Liffey, and every morning they are screaming as they search for breakfast. Invariably we would hear, mingled with their screeches, the sound of an early worker hustling along the street whistling "Buttons and Bows." It was not an unpleasant awakening at all, and each morning it fell into a pattern, part of which went like this in my train of drowsy thought: There go the sea gulls, over the Liffey. Oh, yes, the Liffey: O'er the Liffey's swell. . . . Now, how did that song go?

> And the Angelus bell
> O'er the Liffey's swell,
> Rang out in the morning dew. . . .

That is a song I had often heard in the bars-and-grills of Third Avenue. The Angelus bell o'er the Liffey's swell was the signal for the Easter uprising of long ago, according to this song, the singing of which was once forbidden in Ireland, and that made it a very popular song to sing. And now, I would think, I am in Dublin, and not far from the Liffey. In a couple of minutes I can walk down to the General Post Office and see, on the great pillars before it, the marks of the bullets that scarred those walls during "The Trouble."

Nobody in Dublin took me around to see such things as the bullet marks. Nobody, of all the Irishmen I met, conveyed any impression of hatred of the English, with whom those battles on the streets of Dublin were fought. It was back on Third Avenue that I had heard such things—had heard long-distance Irish patriotism expressing itself in great blasts (verbal) against the English. On Third Avenue, many is the time I had heard the phrase "the goddam English." Never once did I hear it in Ireland. For one thing, it seems to me that I heard mighty little swearing in Ireland anyway, and when, in a pub or some such place, I dropped a few profane words into my speech, from force of habit, I had a sense of being offensive, and I soon learned to curb myself. And, for another thing, the feeling distinctly came to me in Ireland that this struggle against the English has been going on too long—eight hundred years or so—to be encompassed in any superficial loud talk belittling so steadfast an enemy.

Enemy? Yes, I suppose so. Yet I heard in Ireland frequent expressions of sympathy for the English in their economic plight, their dire need of a varied diet. Ireland is full of English families seeking food. In talks with visiting Englishmen, I learned that the austere diet of England makes parents worry about the health of their children, even when they can overlook the wearying effect a meager allotment of meat has upon themselves. Many fairly well-to-do English families arrange to spend a week or so in Ireland every once in a while, so that they can "feed up" in a country where meat and butter are abundant. That is good for the economy of this new republic of Ireland, because when an Englishman goes to Ireland, he may take an unlimited number of pounds to spend, even though if he is going elsewhere in Europe, his limit is fifty pounds.

One morning, I sat at a table next to an English family of four—father, mother, young son, and young daughter—and I gathered from their easily overheard conversation that they had arrived the night before and this was their first meal in Ireland. Here is what each of them ate: a large dish of oatmeal and cream and sugar, a mackerel, three or four slices of cold roast beef, bacon and eggs, plenty of buttered bread, with marmalade, and, of course, pots and pots of tea. They ate ravenously.

Their waiter was also mine. In between his servings, he stood by in his tail coat (in Ireland waiters often wear tails even at breakfast) and with a gentle, thoughtful look on his face watched the English eat. When the bacon and eggs were finished, he went to the table, and I heard him say, "Could I get you some more eggs, sir? The children seem to be hungry still. Let me run out and get you some more eggs." And he did. Afterward, he came over to my table and said to me in a low voice, "It's pitiful to see them so hungry, now, isn't it, sir? The poor children seem starved with the hunger. D'ye know, sir, I'm really sorry for them!" The waiter was old enough to have been in The Trouble. I had a feeling that he had been in it, fighting the English on the streets of Dublin, or maybe of Cork. Now he was sorry for them. It wasn't at all like Third Avenue, there on O'Connell Street.

Trinity College is right in the middle of Dublin, on College Green. To the same extent that I did not want to see Blarney Castle, I did want to see Trinity College. So here I was, standing across the street from it. Beyond the open gates were two statues, which I knew to be of Oliver Goldsmith and Edmund Burke, both graduates. In the middle of the street, like a tall rock, was a cop around whom an endless flood of bicycles swirled. There were lots of times in Ireland when I was conscious of not wanting to barge into places. I never wanted to barge into a countryman's white cottage, however appealing it was as we passed in our rented car. I didn't want to barge into Trinity, either. I went out into the street and spoke to the cop. He took his arms out from where they were folded majestically under his cape and saluted as I approached. "Would it be all right for me to go into Trinity?" I asked. "I'm not a student. I'm an American visitor."

"Ho, ho!" the cop said. "That wouldn't be my business at all. That's private property, sir, and, of course, I have nothing to do with it at all!" He smiled, yet he conveyed the idea that he was imparting a piece of valuable knowledge. He waved a bevy of bicycles by.

"Oh," I said.

"You understand, sir," the cop said, in more patient explanation, "I would not have a thing to do with a place that is private property. You could go in there as far as I'm concerned, and they could hang you if they felt like it, and do you understand, sir, it wouldn't be my place to lift a hand about it? Private property."

"I guess I'll go in," I said, and started toward the gates.

"Very well, sir," the cop said, and quickly blocked off a surge of bicycles for me. An instant later he shouted after me, "I don't think they'll hang you!"

At the gate there was a porter in a uniform that included a Prince Albert coat, and he told me that it was perfectly proper for visitors to go in and wander about. "Be sure and see the Book of Kells," he said. It was sunny, but the gray walls of all the old buildings around the quadrangle looked chilly, the way a gray sea can look chilly even in summer, with the sun beating down on it. Trinity is a busy and peaceful place, both at the same time. Students wear black gowns to classes, and sometimes go by on bicycles with their gowns flying behind them, like the robes of Bedouins on horses.

The Book of Kells has been described as the most beautiful book in the world, and all my life I've been hearing about it. The attendant in the library, which is upstairs in an aura of lovely mustiness, took me over to the Book, along with an elderly English couple, both of them tall and tweeded. The Book was under glass, opened to a breathtaking page. The attendant held a magnifying glass over it, so that we three could see the marvels of it, the fineness, the unbelievable beauty of the gold and rich blue and deep green of the coloring, so enhanced by the kindliness of a dozen centuries. The attendant explained that the Book was illuminated by the monks of the town of Kells in the eighth century or thereabouts. It is the Gospels.

"Quite good, quite good!" the Englishman said when the attendant paused. The Englishman did not mean the slightest harm. But is that a thing to say of such a wondrous work—"Quite good, quite good"? No harm in him, I repeat, but he managed to imply that if the Book had been done in England, it would have been done slightly better. The attendant, surely an Irishman, looked at me wordlessly, and I at him. It was one of the few times in Ireland when I felt like a thorough Irishman. The attendant and I smiled at the Englishman. "It *is* quite good," the attendant said.

I walked away and for a few minutes stood by myself in the library. This room has a feeling of bold serenity, you might say. Only one other place I've ever been felt like it—that room in Philadelphia where the Declaration of Independence was signed. I rejoined our group, and the attendant showed us a Bible printed in Ireland centuries ago. A small thing was the most interesting thing about that Bible. Others say "There is no balm in Gilead," but this early Irish Bible says "There is no treacle in Gilead."

I gave the attendant half a crown before I left. He took it and said, "Is there anything you fancy at the Phoenix Park races this afternoon, sir?"

Does a two-dollar horseplayer wear a neon sign on his forehead that says HORSEPLAYER?

"I haven't even looked at the entries yet," I said, and I went out through the gates and, crossing the street, passed the cop.

"Did you see the Book of Kells?" he asked.

In a public square in Galway City there is a statue, modestly done, of a compact little man. He is sitting on a wall, with a bucolic hat on, an angular, countrified suit, and common, thick-soled shoes, and he is in a contemplative pose, his eyes looking down, and a quiet air about him. This is the statue of a storyteller. That's what he did; he went around the country with an ass and a cart, telling stories. His name was Padraic O'Conaire. His was a simple yet noble calling, I think, and they must have thought so in Galway, too, for there's the statue, and while I am not much of a traveller, and so do not know for sure, I doubt if anywhere else in the world there is a statue in tribute to a man who merely told stories to those who would listen.

I had heard that back in the mountains, away from the cities, in small, Gaelic-speaking communities, there are still storytellers, men locally famed for their ability to sit by the fire and entertain their neighbors with narratives. So every now and then I would make an effort to find one. In Waterville, which is a seaside resort on the southwest coast, in County Kerry, I spoke to the barmaid in the Butler Arms Hotel about this matter. (That's a good way to begin any quest in Ireland, I learned—speak to the barmaid about it.)

"I am sure, sir, that Tadg Murphy would know about things like that," she said. "He's on the Irish Folklore Commission, and he lives just up the road a way."

The barmaid went back to humming "*Mañana*," with no more thought for Irish folklore, and after a Guinness I went on out and found Tadg Murphy's house. His first name is pronounced "Tige," as if it were short for "Tiger," and it is the Gaelic version of "Timothy."

He is a soft-voiced, scholarly man, whose wife's brother lives in the Bronx. Murphy, who speaks the Gaelic language, has spent years going about in the rural parts of Ireland, seeking to preserve the vanishing lore and making written records of ways of life that are disappearing. He promised to find an Irish storyteller and take my wife and me to hear him.

A day or two later, the three of us met at noon and drove for an hour or so, to the foot of a mountain by the sea. Then we walked up past a farm on the slope, through mist and rain, to a fine, substantial cottage. Two dogs came out to wag us in. Within—and it was warm after the chill rain of the mountain outside—was the scene so well known to millions who have never been in Ireland—the whitewashed walls, the turf fire burning, the dogs and the children at their ease upon the floor, the furniture simple and scrubbed, many holy pictures, pictures cheaply made but sincerely revered, on the walls. An old man was seated by the fire, his back as straight as the haft of a T square, his cane in his hand, and his eyes as young as if he were twenty-five; they were not the blue Irish eyes, but gray-green. He was, we were told, eighty-one years old, and his name was O'Connor, the English form, coincidentally, of "O'Conaire," of the Galway statue.

Murphy explained to him that the Americans wanted to hear him tell a story, and he demurred, only slightly, on the ground that if we did not understand Irish, what would be the sense of his telling a story in that language to us, and it the only language he ever told stories in? Murphy offered to translate from the Irish to us, and the old man began.

"I will tell you a story of a young man who let a great anger be born inside him against the sea and what happened by reason of that," he said, according to Murphy. "He was strong and bold, and there was a great deal of goodness in him, even though he had the mischief that has to go with sailing on the sea, which he did; and he was a fisherman."

This was the first time I had ever heard the Irish language spoken at any length. It did not seem to me a melodious language; it seemed guttural. Every once in a while—and there is no foundation for the resemblance in philology, of course—it sounded like Yiddish.

"Now, I will not tell you of their courtship," the old man said, "because that was a matter between the two of them and not for us at all, but in time the young fisherman married the most wholesome, handsome young woman of his village, which is not far from where we are all sitting, by this very fire, although the village is down by the edge of the sea itself. God sent them a lovely child, and the two of them were happy with the little one, and the father, home from his fishing, would carry the baby in his arms, with his wife walking behind them, on the two streets of the village, so everyone could see—back and forth, back and forth, on the two streets, of a Sunday or even in the twilight on other days."

The children were quiet as he told his story, and so were the rest of us. His daughter-in-law was attentive, and yet all the while she was baking bread. A large iron kettle sat on the burning turf. Upon its heavy lid, four or five oblong pieces of glowing turf had been placed, and so an oven had been made of the kettle. From time to time, but without interrupting the story, the daughter-in-law would go to the fire and deftly lift the lid—burning turf and all—with tongs, and reach in and move the large loaf baking inside, then replace the lid. She was smoking a Sweet Afton cigarette.

"The young fisherman went to sea in his boat, and his comrades with him," the old man said. "And his beautiful wife and his dear child were down by the water's edge to watch the boat go farther and farther away, and at last they could see it no more. Now, that was the time an evil sickness put its cold hand on that village. One after another of the people died, young and old alike. It was only four days the young fisherman was away on the sea. All the same, in that short time what happened was so bad there was nobody in that village had the courage to meet him, when at last his boat came in, and tell him. His darling wife and the child were dead. He went home alone, nobody to meet him, and he found out in that minute he was always going to be alone—no more wife and child for him. The young fisherman was swallowed by sorrow and madness.

"Now, I will not tell of the wake and how deep-stricken the young man was, because you know that and you can think it more truly than I can tell it in my poor way. What you do not know, and I'll tell you, is that when his dear ones were buried and him alone, this terrible anger against the sea came on. One day not long after, when he had the drink taken, he was seen by his friends on a lonely part of the strand, standing with his feet in the water, and he was shaking his fist at the sea and roaring curses upon it. They heard him say this to the sea—they heard him say, 'I hate you and hate you and hate you, and so I'll beat you always. I'll go back upon you and I'll beat you. You'll try to take my boat, and I'll beat you and bring my boat home to the land again. You'll try to take me and you'll try to drown me, but you'll never have me, because I'll beat you, and I'll walk the land alone until I die in my bed. I hate you and hate you and hate you. You kept me away while my dear ones were dying, and if I had been here, I would have saved them and not let them perish.' That is what the poor, unfortunate man was roaring at the sea, and who could blame him for that?"

As the storyteller went on, his words took on a discernible rhythm and cadence. His dramatic pauses were magnificent, and now and then he would strike his cane vigorously upon the hearth, and the children by the fire would look up and stare. I tingled with the anger imparted by the storyteller as he repeated the young fisherman's mad talk to the sea.

"Away he went, back to his fishing," the old man continued. "But that is not the end of my story. A big storm came in two days and the village was full of fear. And it was rightly so, because all of them were drowned, the young fisherman and all his comrades. In a bay far away, his body was washed up not long after, and it had not been touched by the monstrous fish that commonly devour the drowned people in the sea."

Two Irish words became familiar to me as I listened to the old man talk. One was *agus*, which means "and." Many sentences, coming after pauses, began with *agus*. I had noticed that before, in translations of Irish stories. The other word was *seadh*, pronounced almost like "sha," and it means "yes" or "so." It also began many sentences.

"They brought the young man's body back to his village and they buried him in the cemetery there," the storyteller said. "Now I must tell you how it was with this cemetery. A finger of land stretched out into the water. Now, on the side of this finger of land that was farthest away from the sea was the most peaceful place in all that village. And so it was there that for centuries and centuries the dead of that village had been buried. Never in all the time there was an Ireland had the waters been any other way than most serene there where the cemetery was. Not a handful of land had ever been stolen away by the sea coming in, although the cemetery spread quietly down to within a few feet of the water. So, nine days after the young fisherman was buried, in the grave nearest by the water, the most terrible storm in all memory arose. Three days it went on, and never had anybody seen the like of it. For the first time ever, it happened, the monstrous waves reached over the finger of land. All the people stayed far back from the sea and prayed for the end of the storm. So, the storm ended at last and the people went out. And they stood silent when they saw the great havoc the sea had brought about. It was not at the bigness of the damage that they were frightened and struck silent. It was at this—it was that the mountainy waves of the storm, the clutching hands of the sea, had reached in and torn away one grave. It was the grave of the fisherman who had shaken his fist at the sea, and his coffin was gone and never again was it seen."

Slowly the old man swept his keen eyes around at his listeners to signify the end of his story.

We thanked him and got up to go.

"You'll have some tea?" the daughter-in-law asked timidly after she had lifted the kettle of bread from the fire. We said that it would be too much trouble for her and anyway our dinner was waiting for us back at the hotel.

"You'll not leave my house without having a cup of tea and some bread and butter," said the old man sternly, in English. We had it, and it was fine tea and fine bread and butter.

We bade the daughter-in-law goodbye at the door and started to go out into the rain, the two dogs wagging farewell as they had wagged a welcome. Suddenly, the old man, who had remained seated, appeared at the door. He took me by the arm and addressed me in his slow, halting, but precise English. "Do you see what I have done?" he asked softly. "Without passing a solid thing from my hand to yours, I have put words into your head, and they're the words of a story. Now you will carry the story back in your head to America, and perhaps you will tell the story, too, or perhaps you will write it down. And after a while I will die, but over in America will be a story of mine going around, without ever stopping from going, one to another, and so I won't be dead at all, in one way of thinking it. That's what I have done this day. God bless!"

When anybody asks one of us Narrowbacks why we are going to Ireland, we usually say we want to see the little village our parents came from. That was one thing in my mind when my wife and I were planning our trip. My father came from County Clare, from the region around a town whose name does not sound or look Irish to an American; it is Lisdoonvarna. My mother came from around Ballyhaunis, which is a town in Mayo. (In Gaelic, the prefix "Bally-" means "town of.") Now, to come right down to it, I've never known much more about their birthplaces than these names. Other Narrowbacks I've talked to are in the same fix; we're pretty vague about background. Vague or not, there's quite a pull back to those places. Over the years, in the rare times when my eyes fell on a map of Ireland, two names stuck out from the hundreds—Lisdoonvarna and Ballyhaunis.

But on the *Britannic*, going over, I began to shy away from Lisdoonvarna. The guidebook described it as "renowned for its Spa," and said: "Attention centers on the recent analysis made by Dr. Monroe, F.I.C., of Bath (England), an acknowledged authority of spas, who found that all the waters of Lisdoonvarna contain the very valuable therapeutic element iodine, in addition to their other constituents."

My people were of the soil, and I never connected them with spas and the resorty air that goes with them. This bit of prose about Lisdoonvarna was far from the white-cottage, burning-peat reveries of years; so, as I say, I began to shy away from Lisdoonvarna. We never did get to Lisdoonvarna. Ballyhaunis was something else again. I really wanted to go there, and one day when we were in Mayo, fairly early in the morning, we headed for the town my mother came from. As we got near Ballyhaunis, it was evident that it was a market day. Many donkey-drawn carts were on the road, going toward the town, and we passed several caravans of tinkers—Irish gypsies—in their covered wagons, their numerous children happily sprawling over these wagons or trudging along the road. In one wagon, we counted fourteen children. "It's no wonder people used to believe that gypsies stole children," my wife observed. "It doesn't seem reasonable that they would have so many of their own."

The square of Ballyhaunis, a small place, was busy and crowded with pigs and people. This was the day, luckily for us, set aside each month for the sale of pigs to the agents of big bacon firms and pork-butchers. Well, the great thing for me about those few hours in Ballyhaunis was that the minute I got away from the automobile, purposely deserting my not-wholly-Irish wife, I felt at home, felt just right, felt as if I belonged there. It smelled right, the faces looked right, and I, the fellow from Seventy-second and Second who seldom, if ever, sees a pig, suddenly had the notion that I knew quite a lot about them as I wandered by the carts and peeked in at the small pigs, and stared down at the sows lying on the cobblestones beside the carts.

I stopped by a young farmer in his late twenties who had a litter of pigs in his cart. He didn't speak to me, but he seemed friendly as he waited for a buyer to come by. "How much would all the pigs bring you, do you think?" I ventured to ask him after standing around a while.

"I'm wanting twenty-eight pounds," he said. "Tell me, sir, do you think I should go to Milwaukee?"

For a while I had almost forgotten I was an American. My clothes and my tongue, evidently, hadn't forgotten what they were. "I don't know," I said. "Do you have a little place of your own here—a little farm? And how are you getting along? I imagine you have relatives in Milwaukee, and that's why you ask."

"I have a cousin there, and he's after asking me to come over," the farmer said. "Do you think it's the wise thing to do, sir?"

"I was wondering if you had a little place of your own here, as I said," I replied.

"I do," said the farmer, "and it's comfortable. In our own way of comfort, I'd want to explain to you."

"Then, since you asked me, I'd say to stay here," I said. "It isn't all like the movies, back in the States."

"That's the way I've been thinking myself," he said. "The cinema does be painting it up a glorious place, sir. Still and all, they're not picking the money up in the streets, I know."

"They're not," I said.

Up came a buyer, brisk and fat, a pad of paper in one hand, a pencil in the other. Buyer and seller greeted each other like old acquaintances; the buyer looked at the pigs and scribbled some figures on a sheet of his pad and handed it to my friend. But the farmer put his hands behind him. The buyer shoved the piece of paper in the breast pocket of the farmer's homespun jacket and walked away with lively formality. The paper stuck out of the jacket, and I was standing close enough so that I could see the figure "27" on the paper. I was tempted to start talking, but then two other men came up to the farmer and I realized that a ritual was going on, too important to interrupt. These two men, as I found out later, were the "middlemen" traditional in Irish market transactions. They asked the farmer if he would "split the pound," and although I failed to catch an answer, they must have caught one, because up came the buyer again. He flicked the paper from the farmer's pocket and wrote on it. I peeked, and he had made the "27" into "27/10," or twenty-seven pounds and ten shillings. The farmer's right hand came out, the buyer took it, and one of the two middlemen gave a slap to their joined hands. The pigs had been sold for only ten shillings less than the farmer's asking price.

"Will you come along with us, Yank, and have a drink?" the farmer asked, smiling, and he and the middlemen and I went into the pub so miraculously handy. The buyer didn't come. He was busy. The middlemen and I ordered Guinnesses, and the farmer ordered a "club orange," a kind of pop. It wasn't until then that I observed that he was "wearing the pin." In his lapel was a small green button that means that the wearer is a member of the Pioneers. This is a total-abstinence society, and I was told that it is a matter of national honor never to ask a man wearing the pin to have a drink of liquor. Nurtured on the notion that Ireland is a place of extravagant drinking, I was amazed at the hundreds of men I saw wearing the pin. The pub, a simple one, with a bench against the wall across from the bar, was full, and the barmaid knew everyone except me. I noticed how low the voices were, as I had noticed before in pubs. I had to be careful to keep my voice under control, lest it brash out over the soft ones I heard around me. The barmaid made jokes, my friends of the moment talked local gossip, everyone drank much more slowly than we drink at home, and I felt fine, there in the town some of my people came from.

"The mother's a Yank," a man next to me said after I'd talked with him awhile and had a couple more Guinnesses.

"Born in the States, you mean?" I asked him.

"No," he said, "but she worked there for twenty-five years. I've never been there myself. The mother says it's a grand place."

"It's O.K.," I said. "In many ways, it's O.K."

After some more talk, mostly about how good the prices for pigs and cattle were, the man said, almost bashfully, "Would you have time to go with me and see the mother? She'd be greatly pleased to see someone from America. But then you'd have to be moving along, wouldn't you?"

"Tell the truth," I said, "I'm expecting my wife to come in any minute and haul me away. Is your house far from here?"

"Ah, it's only a minute or two," he said. We went around the corner and up the road a piece.

He opened a gate and we walked up to the house—a small, tidy one a few steps away—and, inside, "the mother" was sitting reading a newspaper and drinking a cup of tea. Her eyes were like those of the storyteller I met down in Kerry—gray-green. She was a tiny, neat woman, and the look in her eyes was steady, serene, and keen.

"I see Mr. Forrestal ended his life, poor man!" she said as she put down the *Irish Times*.

I was shocked. I hadn't seen the paper that day.

"And who is he?" the son asked me.

"He'd be the Minister for Defense in America, the same as Dr. O'Higgins here," the little woman explained to her son before I could answer him.

"Oh, then you two Yanks have a talk together," said the son, smiling. "I'll not bother the two of you. I don't know what you'd be talking about, the two of you."

We all had tea, and my hostess told me that she had worked in Westchester for a long time, and we talked some more, about one thing and another.

When the visit came to an end, the son and I left the house together. As we walked to the gate, the mother stood in the doorway, and as my hand was on the gate latch, she said, "Give my fondest regards to the United States!"

I said I would.

Sometimes the thought occurred to me in Ireland that what frequently made me happy there was this: In Ireland, they do the things we used to do but don't do any more. This idea came to me when we visited a family named Walsh, near Navan, in County Meath, which is not far from Dublin. They live in a lovely Georgian house, of God knows how many rooms. "Lovely" is a word I fell into the use of in Ireland, for it is one of the most used words there. In the United States, "lovely" is a woman's word, I think; you don't hear men saying it much. That's not so in Ireland. Once, in Dublin, on a Sunday afternoon, after thousands of Dubliners had marched and sung and shouted, and speakers had made orations against the Republic of Ireland bill, then in the British Parliament, I heard a man say, "Wasn't it a lovely protest?"

Mr. and Mrs. Walsh greeted us with tea and richly buttered bread and several kinds of cake, and their two daughters, children of six and eight or so, stood courteously by, not at all ill-at-ease. Finally, Mrs. Walsh said to the smaller one, "Won't you recite for our visitors from America?" The child made a curtsy, advanced with immeasurable poise to the center of the room, and, moving her outstretched arms as if she were a ship on the rolling sea, recited:

> I saw a ship a-sailing,
> A-sailing on the sea,
> And it was heavy-laden
> With lovely things for me.

It was so many years since I had heard anybody, child or grownup, recite anything that it was a quietly wondrous thing to hear. I suppose children still do recite things here in the States, and that probably it is because I haunt Seventy-second and Second Avenue and Madison Square Garden and Aqueduct race track and places like that that I don't get to hear them any more. At any rate, children recite in Ireland, and sweetly, too. And people take long walks, and they sit by the fire and talk without a radio going, and do all the other things we used to do but don't seem to do any more.

They had been having trouble with an electric lamp at a country house we visited in Tipperary. There appears to be something in the Irish atmosphere that makes all mechanical things work less well than they do in the air of the United States. This lamp was exasperating. Sometimes the string would have to be pulled a half dozen times before it would light, and sometimes it wouldn't light at all. The lady of the house told us about it and about turning it over to Thomas, an old fellow who for a couple of generations had been around the demesne for the purpose of having such things turned over to him. "I'll fix it, milady," he said.

More than a week passed and the lady of the house heard nothing from Thomas.

"About that lamp, Thomas," she said to him one day when she came across him cutting the nails of one of her greyhounds. "Have you fixed it yet?"

"It's a good thing you mentioned that lamp," he said. "I've been meaning to speak to you about that lamp. I'm after studying that lamp this long while, and you'll have no more trouble with it."

"Good, Thomas!" said the lady.

"But I want to tell you," Thomas went on. "You'd want to be very careful with that lamp. If you're to have that lamp be lighting up grand for you, here's the thing. First, take a soft holt on the string. Then give it three long, slow pulls. Then one quick, little pull on it, and after that two fine, gentle, long-drawn-out pulls. Do that and you'll have no more trouble with that lamp."

Our last days in Ireland were spent at Crosshaven, which is near Cobh (pronounced "Cove," and still called Queenstown by the crew of the *Britannic*, on which we were to sail back to the United States). At odd times during those days, I recalled the dreamy notions I had had of what was ahead of us before we left East Seventy-second Street. My head had been full of all the things I had heard about Ireland from the time I was a kid, at wakes and in songs about white cottages with thatched roofs, and the smell of burning peat. (I learned within a week or so to call it turf, not peat.) After landing there and riding around the little island, only a couple of hundred miles from north to south and less than that from east to west, I always had a feeling that Ireland wasn't exactly what I had dreamed it would be. Yet it was—in a sentence or a phrase dropped by a passerby, or timidly passed to me by a man next to me in a pub. Often I felt that these were my people, although they did not know me any more. At those times—oh, how lonely I was there! At the hotel we stayed at in Crosshaven, there was a little boy, the son of Walter Macken, the actor and writer. The father was down for a couple of weeks from the Abbey Theatre, in Dublin, to play in Cork, which is about fifteen miles from Crosshaven. The name of the little boy was Ultan. That is a name you never hear in the United States. It is pronounced "Oolthawn," with the accent on the "thawn." It is an old, old name, older than Patrick or Michael in Irish use, and to hear the little boy's mother, Peggy, say it was to hear a caress. The place where we were staying was the Bunnyconnellan Hotel, nestled on the side of a hill from which we could look out upon the splendid harbor of Cobh. Sitting on a bench in front of the hotel, in one of the bursts of sunshine that space out the rain in Ireland, the little boy and I were looking out at the sea. Ultan, who is only five, was born on the coast of Galway, where they say the sea in a rage can be a most terrifying thing. Before us, there was the empty sea, where tomorrow the ship would be. "Out there will be the *Britannic,*" I said to him, "and if you look out tomorrow, you will see her. There will be no way of seeing us—it's too far to see—but we will be there, heading back to America."

Ultan walked away and plucked idly at a flower in the border of the path. Then he came back to me, the stranger he had known for only seventy hours or so. He, too, was groping, as I had long been, because he put his little hand on my arm and he said, in his beautiful Galway speech, "We'll be terribly froightened for you tomorrow whin the loiner, and you on it, starts out into the big sea."

A stranger I was, in a country I felt was my own, and a little bit of a boy, with a single sentence, ended all my groping—"We'll be terribly froightened for you tomorrow . . ."

It was our last evening in Ireland. We were staying overnight in Cork. As with all holidaymakers nearing the holiday's end, I had sorrow and eagerness blended, a sorrow that came with leaving Ireland and an eagerness to feel East Seventy-second Street again and to find out what had been going on in our neighborhood, around Maxie Slavin's newsstand, at Second. I wanted to hang on to Cork and the scenes in its streets, and at the same time hear the kids singing of a summer evening on the stoops of East Seventy-second. It couldn't be done. By telephone, the Cunard Line told us that we would have to be at the dock back in Cobh at seven o'clock in the morning, to go through the customs, board the tender, and go out to the *Britannic,* which would be at anchor in the harbor, after the overnight trip from Liverpool. That meant getting up at five and having a taxi at the hotel door at six. My wife had to do some shopping—handkerchiefs, last-minute gifts, and so on. While she did that, I dropped into the Swan and Cygnet, which is near the Old Bridge across the Lee and not far from the statue of Father Theobald Mathew, the great apostle of abstinence from liquor. In the Swan and Cygnet, one Guinness led to another, discussion of one horse race of the day led to discussion of the next, a few pleasant words were offhandedly spoken about Partition, and a few hours passed. One man quoted the *Dublin Opinion,* which had said, "Partition is like the ones landlords put up to divide houses into flats. You keep on hearing voices through it."

At nine o'clock, while it was still light in the streets from the long twilight, I was walking along thinking about those last Guinnesses and the coldness and dampness of five o'clock the next morning. In such a frame of mind I entered a wineshop, or what we would call a package store, and was greeted with a "Good evening, sir" by a tall, dignified, white-haired clerk, alone in the small shop.

"Good evening," I said. "I have something of a situation before me."

"Sit down, sir," the white-headed man said.

"I'm a visiting American," I explained.

"I thought so, sir," he said. "By the hat, you know. Bigger than ours, do you see?"

"Yes," I said. "Well, we're sailing tomorrow for America, and we have to get up at five o'clock to go down to Cobh and the dock."

"Five o'clock?" he said, unbelieving. "A shocking hour! A shocking hour! I thought we were supposed to encourage you fellows. That's no way to do it. Five o'clock in the morning! A shocking hour!"

"I'm afraid it might be cold at that hour in the morning," I went on, moving into the heart of the matter.

"It *will* be cold," he said definitely. "Where are you staying, sir?"

"At the Metropole," I answered.

"Oh, Lord!" he said. "A timperance hotel. They have no license."

"That's it," I said.

The clerk thought for a moment before he spoke. "Now," he said, "you wouldn't want to be drinking brandy at that hour of the morning, would you, sir?"

"Oh, no," I said. "That wouldn't be it."

"Tell me, sir, how long have you been in Ireland?" he asked. "Have you had time to get used to the Irish whiskey?"

"Nearly a couple of months," I said. "I think the Irish whiskey is all right. A little better than all right."

"Then that's fine. Irish whiskey's the thing, then," he said. "Could you wait a moment, please?"

"I could," I said. "Take your time."

He went out into the stockroom and came back with a small bottle of Paddy's, an excellent brand. The bottle was of no measure familiar to me but about the size of two or three of those small bottles that are sold on American trains. The clerk held the bottle up before me and pointed to its top. It was one of those screw tops.

"Now," said the clerk, "the beauty of this is, do you see, that it can be opened without the aid of a corkscrew. Is the Missus with you?"

"She is," I said, studying the top of the bottle.

"I thought as much," he said. "Now, frequently enough the Missus does not approve of drinking at that hour of the morning, no matter how cold it is."

"You hit the nail on the head," I said.

"It's odd, but they're like that," he continued. "Well, do you understand the point I'm making about this Paddy's? The point I'm making, sir, is this. The top of this bottle may be removed *in secrecy, if necessary!*"

It was necessary, as things turned out.

WHERE THE GRASS, THEY SAY, IS BLUE

Like many other people who have a durable fondness for betting small sums on horse races, I have always been quite remote from the horses themselves. Occasionally, I do see them at the race tracks, but even then it is from some distance. Gradually, over the years, I have been forming the ambition to close this gap between the horses and me. So this April I packed a bag and went down to the Blue Grass region of Kentucky, the heart of the horse country, to visit for a couple of weeks. I chose April because more race horses are born in that month than in any other. Since my aim was to make the personal acquaintance of the runners, I might as well begin at the beginning, I thought.

Animals were to be the focal point of this holiday, and, by chance, an animal became the topic of talk on my train journey to Lexington, Kentucky. It was not, however, a horse but a chimpanzee—a chimpanzee of uncommon aptitudes. The train, the George Washington, had just sauntered into the State of Kentucky when I found myself in the smoking compartment listening to the conductor, who had no duties to perform at the moment. It is noticeable that tongues are loosened by the vibration of trains, and the conductor was chummily conversational. "I've been on this train, Number One, for years," he said. "Funny things happen on it. Like the time the fellow I took over from for the night run, another conductor, never told me anything about what was in the baggage car. Never said a word. I went into the baggage car to sit down and eat my lunch that I always bring from home. Well, sir, I was sitting there eating the lunch and all of a sudden I looked down and there's a kind of a big chimpanzee sitting beside the crate I was on. He was looking up at me as calm and as natural as you please. About four feet tall, he was. Very quiet. Sitting there watching me eat. By that time, I had reached what you might call the dessert course, and I was eating a banana. This damn ape could almost talk. I wasn't the least bit afraid of him. He practically told me, the way he looked at me, that he could use a little lunch, too. So I handed him another banana I had, and he sat there and peeled it and ate it exactly the way he saw me do it. The two of us sat there like old buddies, having our lunch in the dead of the night. I had a cup of tea and poured him one, in a paper cup. He held the paper cup of tea without squashing it and he looked up between sips like he was thanking me.

"We finished our lunch, me and the ape, and I still had nothing to do. Some baggage cars got iron bars running along the walls. For fun, I went over and began grabbing the bars on the wall, walking the length of the car grabbing one bar after another. I used to see monkeys swinging from bars in the zoo up at Cincinnati, and I wondered if he'd get the idea. He sure did get it. I unloosened the leash around his neck, and, sure as you're born, over he went—jumped up and grabbed a bar on the wall. In a jiffy, he went swinging down from one end of the car to the other, never touching the floor. I swear to God it was just like he was saying, 'If this is what you're trying to do, old man, here's the way to do it. You're doing it like a rank amateur.'

"He was a family pet of some rich New Yorkers that were passengers. They were taking him to Hot Springs with them. I had to go back through the train once in a while, doing my work. I'd fasten the leash each time I left and unfasten it when I came back. Each time, the monk would show me how to swing on bars. He seemed very disappointed that I didn't catch on to the trick and go galumphing along the wall like him.

"Him and me had a very pleasant night in the baggage car. At odd times that night, I got the notion that I was showing him how to be a man, like showing him how to eat, and at the same time he was showing me how to be a chimpanzee, like showing me how to swing on bars. Neither one of us made much headway winning the other over, but it made quite a night."

Any man who lives on East Seventy-second Street, as I do, has a black curse on him if he is habitually unable to sleep after five-thirty or six o'clock in the morning, because this is an unusual affliction in the city and the man is therefore bound to be lonesome by seven o'clock, since he has nobody to talk to. In Lexington, however, a man finds early rising a pleasure. As a chronic early riser, I certainly found my first morning in Lexington to be just that. I was stopping at the Lafayette Hotel. Up at five-thirty, I dressed and went down to the lobby, where a large oil painting of Sweep, the famed race horse and sire, hangs over the reception desk. In fact, paintings of horses adorn every wall in the Lafayette lobby. It seems a fitting *décor*, because Lexington has no other industry to compete in size and interest with the business of breeding, raising, racing, and selling Thoroughbreds. (So respected is the running horse in the Blue Grass region that "thoroughbred" is invariably spelled there with a capital "T.") That first morning, I found three Kentucky horsemen seated under a blown-up photograph of a fiery stallion, the great Bull Dog. The men had presumably breakfasted, although it was not yet six, and had already begun their day's chatting. It was about horses and kindred subjects, naturally. All three men were in their sixties, surely, and obviously healthier than many a twenty-year-old. Their complexions were brown, clean, and seasoned; the texture of their skin made me think that they had washed every day for years with saddle soap. They had keen eyes, with wrinkles around them, no doubt the result of their having laughed a lot in their time, and of their having squinted a lot as they peered across broad country paddocks or into the distant reaches of race tracks. I could not resist sitting within eavesdropping distance of them for a few minutes before going out for my coffee. (The dining room doesn't open until the leisurely hour of 7 A.M.)

"Man alive, grass is the most important thing in the world!" one of the men said. "Ain't nothing anywheres near as important as grass, Jody."

"Maybe," the man called Jody answered. "But I can't eat it. No, Jud, I can't eat it."

"Course you can't eat it," Jud said. "Neb'ch'nezzar in the Bible got down and started nibbling on it and they damn near put him away for doing it. Just the same, Jody, grass is pretty important to you. Ever stop to think what a cow is, Jody?"

"What's cows got to do with it?" Jody asked. "We're talking horses, ain't we?"

"Let me tell you something, Jody," Jud said. "A cow ain't nothing but a machine that makes you and me able to eat grass. That's an idea stuck in my craw ever since I read it somewheres. You can't eat grass. All right, a cow can eat grass, and plenty of it. So the cow eats the grass and turns it into beef and turns it into milk, and we eat the beef and we drink the milk, don't we? Cow ain't nothing but a machine that makes grass fit for us people to eat. Listen to me, Jody, and you're bound to learn something every day."

"All I just learnt is cows eat grass and I eat meat," said Jody. "I knew that long ago."

"I'm proving to you grass is the most important thing in the world," Jud said.

"Mightn't be most important in the whole world," Jody said, "but Lexington, Kentucky, sure would be in one hell of a fix without it. That I *do* know."

Later that morning, I went out to the Coldstream Stud Farm, which is a few miles from Lexington, on Newtown Pike. Coldstream was the main objective of my trip. Before leaving New York, I had arranged to spend most of my time there. One of the first subjects I took up with Charles A. Kenney, Coldstream's manager, was grass, and especially Kentucky grass.

"The Blue Grass country really consists of a thirty- or thirty-five-mile circle centering around Lexington," Mr. Kenney told me. "We figure it's the best grass there is for raising Thoroughbreds, or any other kind of horse. Suitable to their stomachs and the ground is full of limestone, which puts calcium in the grass and makes good bones. Got more vitamins in it than you can shake a stick at, too."

"It looks thoroughly green to me," I said. "I've often wondered why they call it blue grass. Now that I'm walking through it, I wonder all the more."

"Everybody does, including me," said my host. "And I've been looking at it all my life. They do say, though, that a certain time of summer, when there's a kind of tiny, pinhead-size blossom on it, there's a bluish tinge to it. That is, if the wind is blowing it at just the right angle and the sunlight is striking it just exactly right. Between the two of us, it always looks mighty green to me, except when it's brown in the late fall and winter. You've got to have special Kentucky eyes to see it blue, and I reckon I haven't got them."

As we walked around that morning, getting a preliminary view of Coldstream, Mr. Kenney told me a few things about himself and the place. He is a tall, strongly built man, of pleasant manner and wide vocabulary, with an easy courtesy in his friendliness—a gift I later found not at all exceptional in the Blue Grass country. Mr. Kenney was born forty-eight years ago in Paris, which is in Bourbon County, about eighteen miles from Lexington. (The prevalence of French place names is conspicuous in this region. The town of Versailles—pronounced "Versales"—is only a short distance from Lexington.) Coldstream is owned by a man in his early thirties—the only man I met in Kentucky who can sport four initials. He is Elmer Ellsworth Dale Shaffer—pronounced "Shay-fer"—and the farm was left to him by his father, a Pennsylvanian who made his fortune in gas and oil in the West. Coldstream is about nine hundred acres, on which there are no fewer than eight barns; the farm is divided into dozens of fenced fields, or paddocks, each serving a specific purpose in the plan of operation, which calls for, among other things, raising thirty-five to forty baby race horses every year. These, of course, are in addition to the yearlings—"last year's crop," they are called—and the mares, numbering forty-five or so, and the six or eight stallions that constitute the rest of the farm's Thoroughbred population. Then, too, there is a herd of Aberdeen Angus cattle. "It's good stock but doesn't pretend to be prize stock," Mr. Kenney said. At the time of my visit, the herd numbered exactly a hundred. "And, oh, yes, I almost forgot," he said. "We also raise about two hundred turkeys every year. We give most of those away at Christmas to friends, from one end of the country to the other." In the world of horses, "from one end of the country to the other" means from Santa Anita, in California, to Belmont Park, in

New York, to Hialeah Park, in Florida, with all the eighty or ninety race tracks in between.

A breeding farm the size of Coldstream costs between $250,000 and $300,000 a year to operate. It is not nearly the largest farm of its kind in the Blue Grass, but, as I gathered from various people during my visit, it is a farm with an enviable reputation. Its live produce is of the best, I was told by Kentuckians, and in support of this, they pointed out that last year Coldstream sold seventeen yearlings at public auction for a total of $228,208. The average price was $13,424, one of the highest averages in the country. Unlike certain other breeding farms, some of them larger, Coldstream is a paying proposition. Some of the others are rich men's pastimes, operating at annual losses of a half million or more. Coldstream has not always run a racing stable, but nowadays it does. It races nothing but fillies, and is the only stable of its size in the country to do so.

One thing that I was determined to see while I was in Kentucky was the very earliest hours in the life of a race horse, and I told Mr. Kenney so.

"That's not too much to ask," he said, "even if these mares don't always co-operate with us in the matter of foaling. Most foals are born during the night—did you know that?"

"No," I said. "I don't know anything about it, tell the truth."

"Well, it's so," Mr. Kenney said. "I've often thought about that fact, and I reckon it's something that goes back centuries and centuries—thousands of centuries. As far back, maybe, as when a horse was an Eohippus and was only about eleven inches high. It was advantageous to give birth in the dark of the night, I figure, because then the mare's enemies wouldn't have so much chance of catching her and her baby at a bad time."

"That could be," I said.

"Anyway," he said, "Herbert Barnes, our foaling man, will let us know about the mare we have closest to foaling time. That's Fille d'Orlean. She's an American mare, but several of her ancestors had French names. And, by the way, that Orlean is spelled without an 's' on it. Ought to have an 's,' but, as you probably know, the rules for naming race horses allow only fourteen characters and spaces in a name, so we chopped the 's' off."

"Well, how soon is she going to have a foal?" I asked.

"Any time now," Mr. Kenney replied. "The sire is Goya II, a pretty famous French horse. We have good hopes for this foal. Hope he's a colt."

That very night, at the Lafayette, I got a phone call from Mr. Kenney. It was about ten-thirty. "The foaling man just phoned me to come over," he said. "That mare's about ready to have her foal, he says. I'll come into town and pick you up, if you'd like." I told him I'd wait for him in the lobby.

As Mr. Kenney and I rode out along Newtown Pike through the quiet night, there wasn't much talk. We were taking in the lovely cleanliness of the miles of white fences, immaculate stripes against the darkness of the fields beyond. I looked at them happily as a stranger, Mr. Kenney with the familiar liking for a land he had known all his life. (Those white fences are a badge of the Blue Grass region. Later on, I was told that one farm, Calumet, spends at least thirty thousand dollars a year on painting alone, to pridefully maintain the beauty, as well as the usefulness, of fences and barns.) And as we rode the four miles or so to Coldstream, I mused on how far this experience—a nighttime ride to be present at the birth of a racer who, at best, will not be seen at the tracks until 1952—was from standing out of the rain in a doorway on Second Avenue conferring somewhat stealthily with a bookmaker over a two-buck bet on Mangohick in the fourth at Belmont.

One of the barns at Coldstream is a foaling barn, and it was brightly lighted when we arrived. Ordinarily, it is lighted only dimly at night; on this occasion, it had a festive brilliance—the kind one might imagine a castle would have on the night a royal heir is to be born. "Let's go inside and see the foaling man," Mr. Kenney said as we got out of his car. A big red dog named Coldstream greeted us at the door of the barn. When we reached the stall of Fille d'Orlean, on the half door of which was a typewritten card bearing her name—along with Goya II's—Mr. Kenney glanced in, then turned to me and said, "Look!" Over the half door I had my first sight of a newborn Thoroughbred.

"It's a colt, Mr. Kenney, sir," said Mr. Barnes, the foaling man, who was standing with watchful and kindly eyes in a corner of the big stall, ankle deep in straw.

"Just how old is he now?" I asked.

"Let me see," said Mr. Barnes, taking a thick, old-fashioned gold watch out of a pocket of his white jumper. "Now it's eleven-forty-two. He was foaled at eleven-thirty. He's twelve minutes old. Fine, big colt, isn't he?"

The baby was lying in the deep straw, close to his mother, who was also lying down. To me, he looked strikingly beautiful—never mind the gauntness of his body, the incredibly stiltlike legs. He seemed all legs, face, and eyes. He was lying where his mother, without rising or even moving very much, could turn her head, stick out her tongue, and lick his face and neck, smoothing down his coat, which was awry.

"At this point," Mr. Kenney said, smiling, "I often wonder if the mother knew ahead of time what it was all about. Or does the whole thing come as a delightful surprise?"

The colt looked inquisitive but sleepy. In answer to my questions, Mr. Barnes said that the birth had been an easy one, both for the mare and for him. "I didn't need to help her hardly at all," he said. "I'm waiting now for the colt to get up. Often, they're on their feet before this—sometimes less than ten minutes after they're born. Usually fall down the first time they try it, but they make another try at it in a couple of minutes. Second try, they usually make it."

I had never seen Fille d'Orlean race, but while keeping her company there in front of the stall, I could well imagine her—sleek, shiny, keyed-up, in racing trim—as she must have looked mincing to the post. Now she was before us in the far different role of mother. She was tired, fat, still weak, and serenely full of concern for the small colt leggily sprawled so near her, close enough to feel the warmth of her breath and her caressing, reassuring tongue.

The baby was forty minutes old before he decided to try to get on his feet. At ten minutes after midnight, we watched him most awkwardly unlimber those bony, disobedient forelegs and plant two small, perfectly formed hoofs on the floor. Then we saw him adventurously arrange the two rear hoofs in similar manner and get up. For an instant, he wavered. But he was for that instant triumphantly on his pins, in brave ridiculousness. Then he tumbled into the straw, unhurt, and our friendly laughter was one of the first sounds he heard in the big world.

A minute or two passed, and then he was up again. It was amazing, the skill he had acquired in his single previous try. This time, he stayed up, looking around him cautiously to be certain that the process of getting up had not removed him too far from that warm, protective body of which he had been a part only an hour before. The colt remained standing for ten minutes or more, once in a while taking a few tentative steps around the stall, nearly always with an eye on his mother.

"How much do they weigh, as a rule?" I asked Mr. Kenney.

"I don't know," he answered. "How much does a foal weigh, Barnes?"

"Mr. Kenney, sir, I don't know either," the foaling man answered. "Never have weighed a foal, and I've been a foaling man for more than twenty-five years. Too much else to do at this stage of the game to fool around weighing 'em."

The newborn son of Goya II and Fille d'Orlean seemed to grow handsomer as he moved around. Awkward though he was, there was a graceful flow to his movements. He was a fine, healthy colt, and his color was a sort of tawny chestnut. Down the center of his face was a broad white streak—a blaze, it's called. The white terminated in a point, distinctly decorative, between his nostrils, which were wide. I made a remark about the blaze.

Mr. Kenney had been sizing up, with expert eye, every feature of the colt, and seemed more than satisfied with his appearance. "That's good, those big nostrils," he told me. "They can scoop up plenty of air. A day will come when this little fellow will be racing down the stretch—I hope—and he'll need plenty of air in his lungs. Let's go and have some coffee."

As we started off for a small room farther down the barn, from which came the smell of fresh coffee cutting through the unforgettable odors of a racing barn—hay, medicine, ammonia, the sweat of animals—the little colt lay down. I glanced back at him, and his eyes were closed as if he were going to sleep. He'd been up and around, and, after all, there wasn't much to see in a world made up of just one stall.

At six the next morning, when I went down to the lobby of the Lafayette, the three mellow horsemen were again in their cozy corner. What was more noteworthy, they were again, or possibly still, talking grass. This time, it was the one called Jody who was holding forth, and the long-talking Jud was listening.

"Limestone, limestone, limestone!" said Jody petulantly. "I'm sick and tired of hearing about limestone in the grass. Dammit, if they was nothing in the grass but this here limestone, the stuff would be white. Wouldn't be green, or blue, or yellow with pink polka dots, or anything else. It'd be white."

"There's other things in it besides limestone," Jud said, with surprising meekness.

"But all you hear about is the damned limestone," Jody asserted. "For me, I figure they must be plenty of limestone in the water, and it's the water around here that makes the bourbon so good. So I figure I'll get my share of limestone in the whiskey. Best way to get it."

"Listen, Jody," said Jud. "You said at breakfast you weren't feeling so good this morning. And I noticed you were giving that bourbon a good going over yesterday."

"Now, now!" Jody said. "It wasn't the bourbon made me feel a little off-color this morning. I know what happened to me. What I done last night is run into a batch of stale ice cubes. That's what done it, stale ice cubes."

At breakfast, I kept thinking back to Mr. Kenney's remark that nearly all foals are born during the nighttime. It had not taken long in Lexington to learn that when a person there is wondering about any facts or statistics having to do with Thoroughbreds, the thing to do is go and ask Mr. J. A. Estes. Of Mr. Estes, a scholarly graduate of the University of Kentucky and now contributing editor and research director of the *Blood-Horse*, a learned magazine published weekly in Lexington, a Kentucky acquaintance had said to me, "I honestly believe that if you went up to Joe Estes and asked him how many bay horses with three white feet had won six-furlong races on Thursday afternoons during 1934, he wouldn't blink an eye but would give you an answer without even looking it up." So I was not in the least astonished at the readiness of Mr. Estes's reply when I went to his office and asked him about the hours when foals are born. "It so happens that I made a study of that back in 1935," he said. "We'll look it up in the magazine." The Estes study covered the birth of 376 foals. The figures showed that the vast majority of these were born during what Mr. Estes calls the "dark hours"; that is, between 6 P.M. and 6 A.M. "To be exact," said the great figure man, "of the foals I tabulated, 83.22 per cent were born in that period. Between 7 P.M. and midnight, 55.7 per cent were born. The peak hour was between 9 P.M. and 10 P.M., for which the figure is 13.03 per cent. The smallest number were born between noon and 6 P.M. None of the 376 was born during the hour between 2 P.M. and 3 P.M. That answer the question?"

"It does," I said, and immediately I wondered if a similar study had been made of human babies. Later, I found that of a thousand children tabulated at the Chicago Lying-In Hospital, 507 babies were born during the "dark hours." That is, of course, 50.7 per cent. And it was revealed that, just as with the horses, the smallest number of babies were born between noon and 6 P.M. What all this proves, I haven't the slightest idea.

Out at Coldstream at ten o'clock that same morning, it was a delight to look into the paddock next to the foaling barn and see Fille d'Orlean and her foal walking around as big as life. The colt was now only ten and a half hours old. Yet there he was dutifully following his mother around the field, nuzzling her to get something to eat whenever he thought of it, which was often. He was never more than three or four feet away from her, and every once in a while, between snacks, he would move up beside her and rub his downy nose against her muzzle.

"Does she know him from any other foal who might be around?" I asked Mr. Kenney, who had joined me at the paddock fence, his morning's work finished.

"For today, she probably does, by the smell," he answered. "But in a couple of days she probably won't know him from any other foal. They're kind of dumb that way. The foal knows his own mother, though, as long as he's getting milk from her."

Mr. Kenney and I got into his car and drove over to the stallions' paddock. There are seven stallions on the farm now, four of them wholly owned by Coldstream, and the others either the property of syndicates in which Mr. Shaffer is a member or owned by friends of his. "There's the greatest of them all," Mr. Kenney said soon after we reached the paddock. He pointed to a big, dark horse. "That's our Bull Dog. His hundred and ninety-five sons and daughters had won $4,964,564 at the end of 1949. Bull Dog's twenty-three years old. He's retired from the stud now. Finished a couple of years ago. I don't need to tell you he's the sire of Bull Lea, and Bull Lea is Citation's pappy."

The active sires owned by Coldstream are Heliopolis, fourteen years old (very likely the most valuable animal on the farm; reportedly, there have been offers nearing a half million for him); Reaping Reward, sixteen; and Coldstream, seventeen. Mr. Kenney told me that a large part of the farm's revenue comes from the stud fees earned by these stallions. In 1949, Heliopolis served twenty-two outside mares, at $1,500 each. That year, Reaping Reward served thirty-two outside mares, at $1,000. The fee for Bull Dog was $2,500 when he was at his peak. "And Coldstream," Mr. Kenney said, "well, he's considered a desirable sire, but by nature he's a shy fellow, and he had only thirteen outside mares last year, at five hundred dollars. We sold one of his sons a few years ago for fifty thousand dollars. That was Royal Blood, whose mother was Spotted Beauty. She was a daughter of Man o' War."

Early one morning a couple of days afterward, Mr. Kenney and I were walking across the paddock next to the foaling barn when my attention was caught by something about fifty yards away. "Hold everything, Mr. Kenney!" I said, and took him by the arm. "I think I've got it! Look over there! See that patch just this side of the big tree? The sun's hitting it exactly right and there's enough of a breeze to bend it a little. That's blue grass, all right! Now I can understand the name. I must be getting to be a Kentuckian. I can see the blue grass now."

"You sure are learning fast," he said. "That's onions! One of the most unwelcome things we got, a patch of wild onions. Always sprouting up right in the middle of a nice field of grass."

"Oh," I said. "Hard to get rid of, is that it?"

"Old Kentucky man told me once that there was only one way to get shet of wild onions," Mr. Kenney said. "When I asked him what it was, he said, 'You die and leave 'em, that's all.' "

On my last day in Kentucky, Mr. Kenney, for reasons best known to himself, had to take two mares out of one paddock and lead them to another, and I accompanied him. As we were driving over to their paddock, he stopped at a barn and got a quart bucket of oats, which, he explained, would make it easier for us to get the mares to come over to us. Then he went on to the paddock. There was no need of the oats to lure one animal over. She came ambling across the field while we still sat in the car. The door of the car was open, and the mare came up, stuck her head in, and looked around inside, bold but friendly.

"That's the famous Miss Mommy," Mr. Kenney said. "Good mare.

They named her after Mrs. Shaffer. Children around Coldstream call Mrs. Shaffer Miss Mommy."

We got out, and Mr. Kenney put a leather lead on Miss Mommy and told me to hold her while he took the oats and walked over to lure the second mare. When he came back with her on a lead, I asked him who she was.

"This is Be Faithful," he said. "A pretty costly girl. Mr. Shaffer paid Louis B. Mayer a hundred thousand dollars for her in 1946. She was a great racer. She won about eighty-eight thousand dollars for us at the races the very next year. She's eight years old now. Here, take the oats. You can lead Miss Mommy. Give her some of the oats. Be Faithful has had her share."

I held the lead in my right hand and walked uneasily along with the famed and amiable Miss Mommy. I was on her left, holding the bucket in my left hand and letting Miss Mommy have a few nibbles of oats as we walked. Be Faithful was on my left, and on *her* left was Mr. Kenney. Be Faithful wanted some oats, and she reached over for them. I turned my head toward her and, with my elbow, tried to nudge her away from the oats. At the same time, Miss Mommy decided to take the matter of oats into her own hands. She began trying to jerk the lead out of my hand and, turning, kicked out at Be Faithful with both hind legs. She missed Be Faithful, but she landed on me. The kick struck me precisely where kicks are supposed to strike. Be Faithful started kicking back, and I was between the two of them. Oats and lead flew out of my hands, and I made for a tree on the edge of the field.

Safely behind the tree, I tried to catch my breath. Mr. Kenney had the situation in hand. He had skillfully separated the two mares and grabbed Miss Mommy's lead. "You made that furlong in nine and a fifth seconds!" he hollered over.

The kick didn't hurt, really. It did me no harm physically. And spiritually, I've been thinking, it did me a lot of good. Excellent for the ego. How many other two-dollar horseplayers around East Seventy-second Street will ever be in a position to say that they have been kicked in the pants by Miss Mommy?

BELLEVUE DAYS

One afternoon recently, after visiting friends on Gramercy Park, I took a cab to go to East Seventy-second Street, where I live, and the driver chose to go up First Avenue. We were halted by a light at Twenty-sixth Street, in front of Bellevue Hospital. While we waited, both the driver and I looked at the big, dull buildings and the many yards, and watched the flow of people through the gates.

"Good old Bellevue!" I said.

"My wife's brother was in there once," the driver said before the light changed and we started on our way again. "He had what they call a sacroiliac, a very painful thing in the back. It must be a tough spot to be in, that Bellevue."

"I was in there once, too," I said.

"No kidding?" the driver asked.

"No kidding," I said. "And you're right. It is kind of tough in there sometimes. But just the same, I've got a soft spot in my heart for old Bellevue."

"What was it—accident or something?" the driver asked.

"No," I said. "Heart attack. But I'm practically O.K. now. That was a couple of years ago."

"You got to take it easy if you've had one of those," he said.

"They made me take it easy in Bellevue," I said. "And I want to tell you I met some fine people in there and they all certainly treated me first-rate."

"Now, that's a funny thing," said the driver. "My wife's brother said almost the same words many a time. Said he met some fine people in there, and the treatment he got from everybody was real good. Almost the same words you said."

When I got home that afternoon, it turned out that my wife was still out shopping, so I made myself a cup of tea and sat down to rest for a while, as I often do these days. I had to laugh a little to myself at the idea of having said "Good old Bellevue!" to a stranger. Yet that is the way I feel whenever I chance to pass the place—almost as if it were some school I attended as a youth and could not let slip lightly from my mind. Indeed, it *was* almost that way—like an alma mater.

In the middle of May, 1947, our flat was being painted (for the first time in three years), and the place was a mess. My wife thought it would be a good opportunity to visit her mother, in Wakefield, Rhode Island. As for me, I had some work to do in town, and I also liked to go to the races at Belmont in the afternoon, when my work was through. So she went to the country, and I moved into an inexpensive room in a hotel in East Fortieth Street, near Lexington.

The night of May 22nd (I remember the dates well, because they have been on so many records since then) I had dinner alone—a steak and au gratin potatoes, with a drink before dinner and a bottle of beer with it. After dinner, it then being about ten o'clock, I bought the *Daily Racing Form* at Forty-second Street and Third Avenue, from a blind man, and walked to the hotel. Before I went up to my room on the fourth floor, I stopped at the desk to chat with Louis Schwartz, the night clerk, who was there early. He and I had struck up a friendship, based on the fact that we both were horseplayers. He had noticed me coming in nightly with the *Form* tucked under my arm, and one word had led to another until we found out that we were both "watching" the same horse, as horseplayers say. That is, we were both looking every day for a particular horse's name in the entries, and sometimes bet on him when he did run. The name of the horse we both happened to have singled out was *Deep Texas*. He was a pretty good sort of horse. He never got famous, but it is safe to say that thousands of horseplayers throughout the country were at that time "watching" *Deep Texas*. He won a few times, too.

"Our horse isn't going tomorrow," Louis said as he gave me my room key.

"No, I already looked," I said. "Well, I'll give you a ring if I see anything. I'm going upstairs and look them over."

"Good night," Louis said. "Ring me down here if you see anything you like for tomorrow. I drop four bucks today."

"Tomorrow's another day," I said, using a practically compulsory rejoinder among horseplayers.

No matter how much a man likes his own home, a week or so by himself in a hotel room can be pretty nice, every year or so. I found it pleasant that night. To come into the small but comfortable room, nicely tidied up after I had left it in disarray, was pleasing, and the room's very smallness made things handy and matters manageable. Everything going fine, I thought, as I opened the window, fixed the bed light at the proper angle, and got into bed with the *Form*. For a moment, I considered spending seventy-five cents in calling my wife in Rhode Island, but then I decided that I didn't have seventy-five cents' worth of anything to say to her, except to tell her I was comfortable and ask if she was the same. I dismissed the notion and looked over nearly all the entries for the next day's racing. It seemed to be a most ordinary card, and there was no horse I had any great conviction about, so I let the *Form* drop to the floor, turned out the light, and went to sleep in two shakes of a lamb's tail. Didn't even have to count the shakes.

I awoke about six the next morning, too early for coffee to be sent up, so I figured I'd get shaved and dressed and go over to the Shack at Forty-first and Lexington for some coffee, and read the papers there. I changed from pajamas into underwear and started to shave. In the middle of that job, a pain came into the center of my chest. It was not a startling pain, not a dreadful one at all, just such a pain as anyone might have, but I thought I might lie down for a few minutes.

Some little passing jiggeroo of the system, I told myself. After a while, when it didn't go away, I thought I might call Louis downstairs, for comfort and reassurance if for nothing else. I was glad I knew Louis, and that he was not just any old hotel clerk. I wouldn't have wanted to call any old hotel clerk if this little mishap turned out to be nothing at all, but with my horseplaying friend it would be all right to call anyway. I picked up the phone and waited until Louis answered. He handled the switchboard as well as the desk at that hour.

"Louis," I said, "I didn't see anything good in the entries, so I didn't call last night. But listen, Louis, I think I'm getting sick."

"What's the matter?" he asked.

"Well, I don't know, but could you come up? I'm not kidding, I'm feeling pretty sick," I said.

"You sound scared," he said. "Don't get scared. It'll only take me a couple of minutes. I'll put the elevator guy on the desk here and run the car myself. I'll be right up."

That smart Louis must have had a key with him, because he let himself in without making me come to the door. I said hello to him, and he said, "Geez, you don't look good. I think you better be quiet. There's a doctor lives upstairs. I'll run up and get him. Take it easy, now. I'll be right back." He was back in a very short time, but in that short interval I was thinking I might be making a hullabaloo over nothing. The doctor who came in with Louis was a jaunty fellow, wearing an undershirt, pants, and slippers. Because he was jaunty, I grinned rather foolishly at him, and started to sit up in bed. "Lie down," he said. "Lie still. What's the trouble?" He took my pulse and listened to my chest. He had no stethoscope—just put his head down and listened to my heartbeat. "Keep as quiet as you can," he said to me, and then spoke to Louis. "Call the cops," he said to him. "Don't try to get him into any fancy hospital. Tell the cops to get an ambulance here from Bellevue right away."

Louis went out, and again I foolishly tried to grin at the doctor. He didn't grin back, he was very calm and on-the-level-looking. "You're having a heart attack," he said. "Don't move around at all." He took a vial from his pants' pocket, shook out two pills, and gave them to me, telling me to swallow them. "I'll get you some water," he said. "Lie still. They'll be here and take care of you. Don't get frightened, old boy."

Soon a white-coated interne and two young cops carrying a stretcher came in with Louis. The doctor talked with the interne in the bathroom, and one of the young cops said to me, most sympathetically, "Take it easy, Mac." (He didn't know that "Mac" was right for my nickname; he probably called everyone that.)

"*You* fellows take it easy," I said. "I'm going to be all right."

"Sure, Mac," the cop said.

"Here's your pants and shirt," Louis said to me. "Put them on nice and easy. I got your topcoat and your other things."

The interne told me to lie down on the stretcher, and I did. Before I had got used to the feeling of being carried, I was lifted gently and skillfully into the ambulance. The siren began to whine, and the ambulance swung around the corner of Lexington and headed south.

Although I was lying down in the ambulance and unable to see out, I could sense pleasurably that it was a fine, bright morning. My apprehension of a few minutes before was inexplicably gone, perhaps only momentarily, but gone. I kept thinking how many times I had heard ambulances sounding in the streets of New York and had paid small attention. This time, it was me who was in the ambulance, with its siren whining away at seven o'clock or so of a May morning. This time, I was the one, out of eight million people, who had suddenly been taken sick. A night clerk, a casual doctor (whose name I still don't know), two young cops, an interne, and an ambulance driver were all pitching in to help the sick man. They didn't know who he was, never saw him before, didn't give a damn, particularly. Man alive, but this is a great town, I was thinking as the ambulance slowed down, went through some gates, and stopped at an entrance, where they lifted me out on the stretcher and carried me into Bellevue. I had heard and read about Bellevue all my life, but I had never been in there before.

Inside the hospital, my anxiety returned. It seemed to me, lying on one of those wheeled tables, that they were asking a vast number of questions before anything was done. Name and address, of course, and age, which was fifty-one, and previous illnesses, of which there had been practically none. Dozens of other statistics, too, it seemed. I answered as best I could, and then I was taken to an elevator and up to a ward. The ward, I heard a man say in the elevator, was B–1. The table I was on was wheeled along between the long rows of beds, so close together, and when it reached the bed I was to occupy, down near the end, I started to rise, to climb into bed.

"Hey!" the attendant shouted at me with authority. "Don't you move an inch." A big, strong fellow, he lifted me into the bed in a jiffy. "What time is it?" I asked him.

"The time doesn't make any difference, pal," he said. "It's about twenty-five past seven." That's really pretty good, I thought to myself. Only about an hour since this hit me, and here I am in bed in Bellevue already. Two nurses were by my bed, and they put a screen around it. But before they had done so, I had time to notice men in bathrobes, walking patients, strolling by. Each one looked intently at me for an instant, studying the new man just brought in, the new member of the ward. These passersby did not stop; they merely looked, in a studious way, and then continued on to stand, with great idleness, looking out the big, arched window at the end of the ward, through which I could see the East River. Tugboats were coming prettily down the river, but in a moment the nurses and their screen blocked all that from view.

Soon, two doctors, both young, were with me, doing things with stethoscopes and, in a kindly but swift manner, asking questions. Dozens of times, from the doctors and the nurses, and even once from a passing bathrobed man, I heard the great admonition of our town, "Take it easy, now." The doctors gave me some medicine, and I lay back on the pillow, taking it easy between trying to get squints at the East River, and then I fell asleep.

The great joke among us men in Ward B–1, for all the twenty-six days I was there, was to call the place the Vitamin Ward, on account of B–1 being a famous vitamin. It was a simple joke, but we all liked it, no matter how many times it was pulled. The Vitamin Ward contained mostly heart cases and pulmonary cases, but there were a few strays of other kinds. The capacity of the ward was thirty-four, and beds were seldom empty more than a few hours.

About the first fellow I became acquainted with was a big man—Princeton 1911, it turned out—who looked like an American version of the traditional British sergeant major. He had a whopper of a mustache, and walked around in his pajamas and bathrobe as if he were about to shake up the troops for regimental inspection. Also on the roster of our ward was Alfred the Armenian, a horseplayer on the outside, like me, who was permanently distressed because he had been saving up betting money all winter and then had wound up in Bellevue exactly on the day in April when the New York racing season opened, at Jamaica. And there was Olsen, a thirty-five-year-old baseball fan who seemed unable to keep from catching pneumonia; he'd been in and out of Bellevue for four or five years, pneumonia having caught him five times in that period. And there were a few others who, as the days passed, changed in my mind from units in a parade of washed-out bathrobes and pajamas into individual persons I knew.

Those bathrobes at Bellevue are honeys. They're curiously pink or purplish-gray, and they've been washed a thousand times, and so have the pajamas. Nearly everyone lying in bed and looking at them go by, with people in them, has the commonplace thought that if the president of U. S. Steel and a scratch bum from a doorway were dressed in that Bellevue rig, it would be all even between them. Great levellers, those bathrobes. Most of the time, as I said, there were thirty-four of us in Ward B–1. Not all of us were stony-broke, but some were. Most were. That didn't make a particle of difference. All thirty-four of us were on the side lines of the city for as long as we were in B–1. Before we got there and after we got out again, we had done and would again do different things to get by. One of us would be a dishwasher once more, as Alfred the Armenian had been. Another would push a hack around Brooklyn, the way Milton, who was three beds up from me, did. No matter what it was we had done or would do for a living, for the time it was all even among us. Whatever was going on outside the windows, in the city of New York, we had no part of it. We didn't even have any part in the affairs of our families, if we had any. Some didn't have any. Perhaps that sounds dismal, but it wasn't. There was a kind of serenity to it.

There was a man died in the bed next to me one night, and I think that to him it was like going through a door he didn't want to go through. He came in during the afternoon, and after the doctor talked to him and those who had brought him, I talked to the doctor about my new neighbor. "He's too late," the doctor said. The new man was gaunt and sepulchral. Later in the afternoon, his folks came in to see him. They sat, a woman and a young girl, whom I presumed to be his wife and daughter, in the narrow space between our beds. When families visit in Bellevue, they often have nothing to say. They sit in that space between the beds, and maybe once in a while the wife of the sick man touches his arm and strokes it, but stops quickly because she is a little ashamed, it being so public a place. They speak a few words and then sit silently, and the sons and daughters usually look around at the other people more than they look at their father. There seems to be nothing the family can say, except to answer the sick man, who generally asks only the simplest questions, like "How is Willie?"

The gaunt man's folks left about six o'clock, and after that he lay in bed staring around a lot but not saying anything. Before the night came down and the dimmed ward lights went on, he began to talk. I couldn't understand the words, but I could see his eyes, and they were looking at me, because I was the nearest person to him. Later—it must have been two or three o'clock—he began to holler.

"Hey!" someone in the semidarkness down the ward shouted. "Shut up! We got to sleep. Shut up, pal!" The man didn't hear him, I guess. If he did, he kept on talking anyway. There was enough light for me to see him. He stretched out a bony arm toward me and said, "Hold me, hold me, somebody, I die." He wanted somebody to take his hand and keep him this side of the door. "Hold me, hold me, somebody, I die!" he hollered, loud this time, and he tried to get up. "Shut up," another voice down the ward said.

"Listen," I said to him. "Nobody who can yell as loud as you is going to die."

"Hold me, somebody," he said persistently.

The nurse came and put a screen around him. He died. In the morning, the bed was empty. We had all gone to sleep, despite the scurrying around the bed.

Mattie was a Negro woman attendant, fat and jolly. Not too fat, not too jolly. The day would hardly come up over the river, over there by Newtown Creek, before Mattie would be in to tidy up. First the dawn, then Mattie. They were alike—sure and certain. As she came in every morning, she would look over the ward with a glance to see that all her boys were still there.

"Aren't you ashamed of yourself?" she would ask. "Look the way you got your bed all rumped up. Push over, I'll fix it." And Mattie would fix the bed, straighten it out, make you feel somebody was taking care of you.

There was the time Olsen was gone. He was the pneumonia man

—always getting pneumonia, and then, afterward, what the doctors call sequelae. That means what follows a disease. (A person picks up fragments of medicine while in Bellevue, usually incorrect fragments.) To take care of one of Olsen's sequelae, they were going to perform an operation. He had a good chance of getting out of the hospital for a little while before the operation if he played his cards right. There was a ball game in Brooklyn the night before his operation, and, sure enough, he was able to talk the doctors into giving him a pass to go out for the evening. "I'll be back by twelve o'clock, so tell the man at the gate let me in," he said to them. Before he left, Olsen came around to see me and told me that, according to the afternoon papers, Ralph Branca was going to pitch. The Brooks had a chance, a pretty good chance, he said. I noticed that he called them the Brooks and not the Bums or any other name by which they are referred to on the sports pages.

It was quite a thing for all of us, Olsen's going to the night game over in Brooklyn. First, he had to sign a paper to get his clothes back. They were rumply when he got them. In Bellevue, ordinarily, they take a patient's clothes away when he comes in and steam them, take the lice, if any, out of them, and put them away until the patient is going to leave. But, even so, Olsen looked pretty good in his clothes, better than in his bathrobe. I don't know where he got the money for the night game, but out he went. "So long, boys," he yelled down the ward as he gave his hat a tap. "I think Branca will pin their ears back. See you in the morning."

He wasn't there the next morning. He had overstayed his leave. He was AWOL. Mattie made Olsen's bed up—hopefully, it seemed. Two days passed, and Olsen was still not back. On the third morning, Mattie came in, glanced around, gave a tug to the cover of Olsen's bed, and walked through the ward to the big, arched window at my end. It was a foggy morning, and the air was nearly rain. The dampness in the streets almost got into the ward. Mattie looked out at the river and the fog. "Man, oh, man, this will wash him in," she said. "He can't take this, the lungs he got. This will wash him right back in here." Then she went and gave a couple of more tugs to Olsen's bed. Olsen never came back, at least not while I was there. We talked about him. Most of us figured he must have got to drinking after the game. Branca won it.

One day, in the middle of a bright afternoon, I looked up and Alfred the Armenian was standing by my bed. He said, "My name isn't Alfred. You got a schooling, I think. Well, my name is Mesrop. Alfred is easier, but my name is Mesrop. Do you know who Mesrop was?"

I told him I didn't know who Mesrop was.

"He was a hell of an Armenian," Alfred said. "Do you think that is much to be, a hell of an Armenian?"

"No," I said.

"Well, I think it is," said Alfred. "Do you know what Mesrop did?"

"Can't say as I do," I told him.

"He invented the alphabet, that's what he did," Alfred said.

"No kidding?" I said.

"Made up the whole alphabet," Alfred said. "He was a hell of an Armenian."

Alfred wandered away from my bed and went back to his own, across the ward and two down.

My wife came in to visit a few minutes afterward. She brought some cookies. While we were talking, I looked over and saw that Alfred was sitting in the straight-backed chair placed alongside his bed for the visitors who never came to see him. He had his hands folded on the bed, and his head was on his hands. "I think Alfred is crying," I said to my wife.

"Oh," she said. "I'll give him some cookies." She went over and nudged Alfred and gave him some cookies. I was right. He *was* crying.

He said thanks, ate a cookie, then strode over to me. Right in front of my wife, he said, "She thinks I'm a baby. She gave me some cookies to stop me crying."

"She's nuts," I said.

Alfred lit a cigarette and walked away.

The friends who come to visit a man when he is in a hospital like Bellevue become, for ever afterward, a special group in the man's mind. Even years later, whenever the man runs into one of them, he will identify him with a sudden, swift, unspoken thought: He came to see me at Bellevue. It isn't altogether easy or pleasant to go visiting in Bellevue. It's such a big, sprawling place that getting from the gate to a certain bedside is a task in itself. For us in the beds, our ward became the whole hospital as the weeks passed, for we hardly knew of the existence of the scores of other wards surrounding us, but to the visitor Bellevue was enormous, mystifying, and tortuous. Then, too, as the visitor makes his way through the place in crowded times like the pneumonia season, he is apt to come upon whole corridors lined with beds, upon which lie men who are gravely ill, and it sinks the visitor's heart. However contented we members of B–1 effortlessly were, our visitors always seemed a little depressed. After they had left, we often agreed that it was quite a job cheering them up.

Apparently, there is not a great deal for medical men to do about a heart case—or, to give it the name the cardiacs of the Vitamin Ward always used, "a bum ticker." The basic idea seems to be to keep the patient in bed and quiet. That is not to say that care was lacking in Ward B–1. Sometimes we used to think there was too much of it. It was not uncommon to be gone over by doctors seven or eight times in a day. That came about not wholly through solicitude for patients but largely because Bellevue is a teaching hospital as well as a healing hospital. The medical students of Columbia, Cornell, and N.Y.U. gain practical knowledge to supplement their classroom work by being taken through the wards by their teachers, who are older men, of medical eminence. Thus, the various wards are regarded as provinces of Cornell, N.Y.U., or Columbia. Ward B–1 was a Cornell ward.

At odd times of the day, we bed patients, always looking up and down the ward to watch the goings on of our world, would see a group of white-coated men gather around the nurses' desk, near the door. "Here comes the two-o'clock show," the Princeton 1911 man would say to me. Or perhaps it would be the four-o'clock show or the supper show. He knew, as we all knew, that the white-coated group was a professor of medicine (as well as a practicing notable, of course) and his students, and that they were about to come down the ward, stopping here and there and going over us.

To be sure, the medical lore a patient picks up in Bellevue is about comparable to the military law a soldier masters while he's a prisoner in the guardhouse—fragmentary, sometimes distorted, and often downright incorrect, yet to the soldier or the patient intensely interesting, since it concerns him pretty directly. Often enough, I was the subject of the teacher's brief talks and demonstrations ("the two-o'clock show"). A teacher that I remember was Dr. Cary Eggleston, who is one of the big cardiologists of the country. As he and the students stood around my bed, he would pick up one of my hands, for instance, turn it palm upward, and show it to his pupils. "Liver palm," he would say. That didn't sound any too complimentary, but I understood, as did the rest of us, that whatever was said in those sessions was really none of our business. We were eavesdropping, in a way.

There was some medicine administered during the routine of the day, of course, and what I heard about one particular drug caught my fancy. As a rule, neither nurses nor doctors, or anyone else, will let a patient know too much about the medicine he's getting, but sometimes they can be importuned into telling. A young technician, not a doctor, came in every day for a week or so and gave me capsules. Sometimes he gave me one, another time he would give me four, and a third time two. The range went all the way from one capsule to six. "Just what the hell are those capsules?" I asked him one day. He must have been feeling talky, because he told me. "It's an experimental thing," he said. "But don't let that alarm you. There's no danger."

"That's all right," I said.

"You know, don't you, that what caused your trouble was a clot?" he asked.

"Yes," I said.

"The stuff in the capsules is called dicumerol," he said. "It's not exactly new, but they don't know as much about it as they would like to. They hope it will serve to keep blood from clotting. You notice we take a blood test every day?"

"Certainly I notice," I said.

"That test daily is to show us what the previous day's capsule or capsules of dicumerol have done to your blood. You see, we are trying to find out what level is best in your particular case. We don't really know. We'll help you eventually, we hope, but the bigger idea is to use you as a means of adding just one small thing more to the store of knowledge about hearts."

"I get it," I said.

"Want to know how they came upon this drug?" he asked. He seemed to be a fellow of a nosy turn of mind, as, I would say, befits a fellow in a scientific field.

"How?" I asked.

"On certain farms, an unusual number of cows were losing their calves," he said. "That is, losing them before they were born. They looked into that and found that these cows were eating a certain kind of weed that thinned out their blood so much that it caused them to lose their calves. From that weed, they extracted the agent that was causing the trouble, and that's dicumerol. Properly controlled, it could possibly stop blood from clotting dangerously. And that's what we're trying to learn from you guys, if you don't mind."

"Don't mind a bit," I said.

In time, I stopped getting those capsules, for reasons best known to the doctors, so I didn't see the young technician for more than a week. Then, one day, I spied him across the ward, giving medicine to another bum-ticker man.

"Hey!" I hollered over to him.

"Oh, hello there," he said, and when he was through with the other man, he came over to my bed. "How're you doing?" he asked.

"All right, they say," I replied. "What did you learn from me about dicumerol?"

"Not a goddam thing," he said, and walked away.

We had one Bowery bum in Ward B–1. His name was Dooley, and he didn't weigh more than a hundred and two, give or take a pound. He was a panhandler on the outside. He made no bones about that. He was around sixty-three, and that is the way he had wound up, panhandling. He had terrible arthritis in his legs, and the treatment he was getting required his legs to be in casts. He was in casts from the soles of his feet up to his thighs. Dooley was one of the fellows who didn't have any visitors. He shared other people's visitors. After your visitors had left, Dooley would ask, in a nice way, who they were. Conversation between Dooley and me had to be hollered, because we were so far apart in the ward.

"Hey, Mac!" Dooley hollered to me one morning. "Did I ever tell you how embarrassed I got once?"

"No," I hollered back.

"It was a time I twist my ankle," he said. "Come to think of it, I twist both of them, and I was drunk into the bargain. And on top of that it was the pneumonia season, and they were all jammed up in here. In the corridors, everywhere. They take me in, but they have to throw me out in two days. Give me crutches, though. Brand-new crutches. I never had crutches before. Geez, it was icy outside. I had a hell of a time working the crutches. I start down the avenue toward the Bowery, and up comes an old man and give me something. I wasn't used to handling crutches and taking money at the same time. So I just hang on to what he give me with my right hand and say thanks and go along. 'I got dough,' I say to myself, 'I guess I'll go to the movies.' Well, do you know what happens, Mac?"

"No," I said.

"I get up to that movie house—you know the one, on the west side of the street?"

"I know where you mean," I said.

"I walk up on the crutches to the window where the lady sells the tickets, and I unclutch my hand, and geez, what I have is a cent," Dooley said. "I been thinking all the time the old man give me a dime, and in those days you could get in the movies for a dime. My God, was I embarrassed! I didn't know what to do, so I say 'Excuse me' to the lady and go on down the avenue."

In Ward B–1, we did considerable grousing about the food, like soldiers in the army. The food at Bellevue is skimpy, but it will keep body and soul together, and the way one of the young doctors explained it to me, the primary idea at the hospital is to mend the body and patch it up, and that is more a question of medicine and instruments and apparatus than it is of food. He meant that Bellevue would rather economize on the food and spend more of its narrow budget on medicine and equipment, and when we patients chewed the matter over (in lieu of something better to chew), we tended to agree with him.

One thing there always seemed to be plenty of, though, was eggs. Breakfast for us bed patients usually consisted of a small bowl of porridge, fairly thin; two eggs, usually hard-boiled; a slice or two of bread; and some coffee, kind of weak. The eggs were in comparative abundance for a good reason. Prisoners on penal farms are kept busy raising hens, among other things, and the eggs that derive from the prisoners' forced industry go to public institutions like Bellevue. We all used to squirrel away a few eggs. Each patient, in the narrow space between his bed and the next fellow's, had a metal table with several shelves. For the time a man is in there, his worldly possessions are encompassed by the small space of those shelves: a towel, some soap, toilet articles, a book, maybe a letter or two—and, thanks to amiable thievery, a couple of eggs, against emergency hunger. The hospital doesn't hand out eggs to be hoarded; they are acquired by benign larceny, which is prevalent in Bellevue. At least, it was in Ward B–1.

When the food comes up to the ward, on rolling steam tables, from the kitchens, the walking patients have to help hand it out, because the nurses have too much else to do. Well, shortly after breakfast was over, Olsen (or some other walking patient) would come strolling along, an uncommon look of innocence on his face. He'd saunter up to the bedside, engage in the most immaculate of small talk. Then, out of the corner of his mouth, in the manner of a prisoner talking to a fellow convict in a jail yard, he'd say, "Could you use an egg, Mac?"

"Certainly could, pal," I'd say, also corner-of-the-mouth. And in a jiffy Olsen would dexterously slip a couple of hard-boiled eggs into the folds of my towel, on the shelf of my bedside table. A minute or two later, I'd see him doing the same thing for Dooley, across the way. Olsen could hide more eggs more effectively than Fred Keating, the magician. It was a good feeling, I learned soon, to have a few eggs in reserve in Ward B–1.

Lucky lads, like myself, sometimes got help on the food problem from the outside. There was the matter of the steak. After a few weeks of Bellevue fare, a man actually dreams of steak, which is one item he doesn't get there. One day, when a friend of mine came to visit, I mentioned the steak mirages we all had. My friend keeps a tavern in the Forties, where I had assailed many a sirloin. "Don't eat any supper tomorrow," he said. "I'm coming in."

About six o'clock the next afternoon, I looked down the ward, as I had been doing every minute or two since five o'clock, and I saw my friend heading toward me in a great rush. He was burdened heavily with something ponderously wrapped in towels and napkins. He practically ran up to the bedside, and sweat was glistening on his face and his eyes were popping. He put his burden on the bed, hastily unwrapped it, and there was a steaming steak as big as a banjo, with onions and French fries beautifully girdling it. "Wade into this!" he said, and he whisked a sharp knife and fork out of his pocket, where he had had them, wrapped in a napkin. The smell of steak got into the air, and right away practically everybody in the ward was staring at my bed. "Man alive!" I said. "This is too much for me."

It really was, so I hailed Princeton 1911 and Olsen to join me in the steak, and got the nurse to cut off a couple chunks and take them over to the encased Dooley. It was marvellous eating, we all agreed. "How in the world did you get that steak here piping hot and everything?" I asked my friend as I settled back luxuriously on the pillow.

He laughed. "Well, I guess I might get in bad if anyone found out," he said. "And maybe a cop would get the sack. But you got to maneuver things in this town; you got to get guys to rally around when somebody's in a jam."

"Explain yourself," I said to him. "I don't know what you're talking about."

He grinned at the sight of Princeton 1911, Olsen, Dooley, and myself so well fed, and said, "There's a motorcycle cop comes into the store [the saloon is always "the store" with my friend] for a little slug now and then. Especially on cold days, when it is bitter on one of those motorcycles. He has one slug and lets it go at that. Good cop, not a scrounger. Well, when you told me a steak would come in handy, I wondered at first how the hell I could get it all those twenty blocks and more and still have it hot for you. Then it came to me. I explained the situation to the motorcycle cop, and he said, 'This is official business on behalf of a bona fide taxpayer of the City of New York.' That's what he said. He told me have the steak ready at quarter of six on the dot. And at twenty to six he came and asked where's the steak? It was ready, and the cop said for me to wrap it up well and come on. He had a taxi waiting right outside the door, and what does he do, after I get into the cab with the steak, but jump on his motorcycle and speed off ahead of the cab. In two seconds, we were roaring down the street, with the siren howling. We went through lights fifty miles an hour, like nobody's business, and I bet it didn't take us four minutes to get down here. Regular motorcycle escort. The cop beat it as soon as the cab got to the gate. He stopped a minute and told me not to say anything about what he did. The Commissioner might not approve, he said, but what the hell! How was the steak, anyway?"

"It was goddam good," I said.

"I'll say it was goddam good," said Princeton 1911.

"Me, too," Dooley hollered over.

"You can say that again," said Olsen.

One bird of passage blew into Ward B–1. He came in during the night, while we were all asleep, and he was put in Olsen's bed, because this was the time when Olsen was AWOL. "Bird" is not the right word for him. The poor man looked just like a marmoset, his face was so small and he was so frail. He had the same kind of darting, shoe-button eyes as a marmoset, and he also had the same evident desire to ingratiate himself.

When we looked at this newcomer next morning, the first thing we saw was a pip of a shiner. His right eye was in a setting of black and purple and magenta, which made the eye itself look all the more bright. His right forearm was in a splint. Ordinarily, injured men didn't get into B–1, but this fellow was only an overnight guest, so to speak, and Olsen's bed happened to be empty.

Alfred the Armenian halted at his bed and asked him what was the matter. "Something must have happened to me," the little man said. "I got a kind of a black eye and what they call a fractured noola." One half of this announcement—the black-eye part—was an enormously unnecessary statement, and the other half was mystifying. It was some time before we figured it out. The marmoset man had evidently peeked at the description of his injuries that the doctors had written down on his record, and he had got a little balled up in his anatomical terms. He had a fracture of the ulna, and the word must have looked to him, through his black eye, like "nula," which he pronounced "noola." They sent him out after lunch, and we all promptly forgot about him, except to ask, once in a while during an idle moment, "I wonder whatever became of the noola man?"

The evening and early morning were the best times in Ward B–1. The food in Bellevue is scanty, as I said, so the snack that came around on a rolling table at eight-fifteen at night was a big event. Before Olsen went to the night game and never came back, he was the one who pushed the table around. The nurses do not have time for such chores, and so walking patients, like Olsen, take over. About eight o'clock, nearly three hours after dinner, we would begin thinking, and often talking, about the snack.

"I hope they have cocoa tonight," Dooley would say.

"I think they *will* have cocoa," Milton, the Brooklyn cabdriver, might reply. "They had grapefruit juice now two nights hand-running. I think it will be cocoa."

The snack that Olsen wheeled around usually consisted of a couple of slices of bread and something to drink—sometimes it was grapefruit juice, occasionally plain milk, if some was left over from dinner, and, on big nights, cocoa. I would watch Olsen make his way along the ward to my bed, and all the while my appetite would grow. Finally, the table would be in front of my bed, and Olsen would say, "Cocoa, Mac, or what?"

"Cocoa," I would say.

"How about you, Mr. Darton?" Olsen would ask the Princeton 1911 man, in the bed on my right.

"Don't mind if I do," the Princeton man would say. And in a minute we would all be having our slice of bread and our cocoa, and talking bed to bed. "What a bunch of chumps up there at the Racquet Club," the Princeton man said to me one night. "They think they're living high. Chumps. That's what they are, eh, Mac?"

"What could be better than this?" I said.

"Isn't that river pretty?" he asked, waving a chunk of bread at the arched window. "Look at all those lights." A tug was coming down in the dark, and strung above her were red and green lights, betokening to oncoming vessels what kind of tow she had behind her.

"Real handsome little river," I said. The cocoa was good, and we were all happy for a while.

Heart cases usually stay in the hospital for from six to eight weeks. When my day to go home came around, I found I was to go out as I had come in—on a stretcher. But the stretcher was now a precaution, rather than a necessity. The nurse brought my clothes, to be taken, but not worn, home. Right away, I noticed that they were unwrinkled and did not have that shrunken look that Olsen's had had. "How come my clothes aren't all rumpled up like Olsen's?" I asked her.

"I guess the attendant noticed that you were brought in from a good hotel, and figured he wouldn't bother to delouse them," she said.

"Caste system?" I asked. "Is that creeping in here?"

"No," the nurse said. "The man was merely saving wear and tear on the delousing machine, that's all."

My wife took charge of getting my clothes home, and I got onto the stretcher myself. On the way out, naturally, I was wheeled along between the rows of beds. We B–1 veterans had been talking for a couple of days about my going home. As well as we had known each other, we hadn't said anything about looking each other up sometime on the outside. All of us were grown-up enough to know that such promises are never kept. Dooley hollered goodbye and good luck from his bed, and so did the others, as the stretcher went by. Bellevue fellows are always glad when somebody—anybody—has won out over whatever was the matter with him, and, thanks to what had been done for me (I had done nothing for myself except be obedient), I had won out. While they were hollering goodbye, I knew they were thinking about the day they'd go home, too. Even Dooley, who could look forward only to going back to the Bowery, had told me that he had a couple of pals down there he'd like to say hello to once again.

A DASH OF TABASCO

One evening, eating dinner alone in a restaurant on East Seventy-second Street, I was tossing a drop or two of tabasco on my clams when I fell pray to a habit I picked up a long time ago. I read the label on the bottle, right down to the small print. I have always been a steadfast reader of labels on bottles, even from as far back as when it used to say on ketchup bottles, "Contains one-tenth of one per cent of benzoate of soda as a preservative." The contents of any bottle, as set down by the manufacturer, have always made good reading to me. So I read the label on the tabasco bottle. It said, "Tabasco is the pepper sauce manufactured since 1868 by McIlhenny, New Iberia, La. Tabasco is made of vinegar, red pepper, and salt. A few drops mixed with soup or gravy, with breakfast eggs or glass of milk give a piquant and delicious flavor. No sea food should be eaten without tabasco. There is only one tabasco, McIlhenny's. THIS IS THE GENUINE ARTICLE. Made in U.S.A."

Well, I was in step, all right. I wasn't eating sea food without tabasco. I was putting it on the clams. A man eating dinner alone is apt to think thoughts that are quite idle—trivial, perhaps. I thought to myself how often I'd read that label, and how often the name "New Iberia" had struck me as a resonant sort of name. By the time the soup came, I was saying to myself, "Why don't I go down there and have a look at the Deep South, where I've never been?" Many a time I've heard people say, "One thing leads to another," and now I'm beginning to believe this is one of the great, irrefutable declarations in any language. I went to New Iberia and the Deep South and had a look at it, or them.

The day after reading the label, I telephoned to New Iberia. Tell the truth, I didn't really know if there were still any McIlhennys around. It's a long while since 1868, and it seemed quite possible that only the name had been retained by the makers of the sauce. (As one thing led to another, I was destined to learn that there are indeed McIlhennys around, and Averys and Clarks and Simmonses, and many more—all, in a manner of speaking, centered about the small bottle whose label also says, "Net Measure 2 ozs.")

When I got the tabasco factory on the phone, I asked for Mr. McIlhenny, regardless. A magnolia-tinted voice told me that he was not there at the moment but that I could speak to his assistant, Mrs. Fisher Simmons. I explained to Mrs. Simmons that I was thinking of coming down to see the place. Mrs. Simmons said they have numerous visitors and I would be welcome. She told me that New Iberia, a town of about sixteen thousand population, had a comfortable hotel, the Frederic, where I could stay. "It's about ten miles or so from Avery Island, where we are," Mrs. Simmons said. "But you'll have no trouble getting back and forth to visit."

I took the train, the Crescent, at Pennsylvania Station at 1:45 P.M., railroad time, the next day, which was a Sunday.

I am a city man, proficient to some degree in combat with the perils of Second Avenue and Seventy-second Street but ill-equipped to fend off whatever dangers there may be around the bayous and marshes of Louisiana, especially snakes. I am afraid of snakes anywhere. As marshes began to show up occasionally outside the train window after we were in Louisiana, I mentioned this fear to the porter. He was a slow but thoughtful speaker.

"Them snakes don't want to mess with you any more than you want to mess with them," he said. "They trying mighty hard day and night keep away from you, maybe more than you trying keep away from them."

"I guess that's so," I said.

"Course," he went on, "if a snake do just zackly the wrong thing, and a man do just zackly the wrong thing, and they both do just zackly the wrong thing just zackly the same wrong time, something bound to happen and it do."

From New Orleans, out across the Mississippi, New Iberia is, by rail, a hundred and twenty-six miles west and slightly north; the place was named by homesick Spanish, back in the days when Louisiana belonged to Spain. On my first morning there, in the Hotel Frederic, I phoned for coffee to be brought to my room.

"Light or dark?" the girl said.

"Oh, I thought you'd send the cream on the side and I could mix it myself," I told her.

"I don't mean that," she said. "I mean do you want Northern or Southern coffee?"

Perplexed a little, I asked for whichever was stronger.

"You want the Southern," the girl said.

In remarkably fast time, much faster than is usual up North, there was a knock on the door. I opened it, and there, holding the coffee tray, was a tall, lean, deeply tanned man of middle age, in a white coat and khaki trousers, and shod in moccasins. He had a brief, sharply pointed mustache, and he looked precisely as D'Artagnan would have looked had he been a room waiter in a white coat, khaki trousers, and moccasins. "*Bonjour!*" he said. "Good morning!"

He was the first of many Cajuns I was to meet during my visit. They are, as is well known, descendants of the French Acadians, who, around 1755, were exiled by the British from Nova Scotia and painfully made their way to Louisiana, because Louisiana was at that time a colony of France.

The waiter's accent baffled me at first. I know a few words of Fraser and Squair or Chardenal French, but Cajun is something else again.

When he talked in English, he splashed in a word or two of French here and there.

"*Est* nice weather fo' travellin'," he said, putting down his tray.

I agreed, and he asked politely where I was from. When I said New York, he said, "*Est* nice place, New York? *Est* New York nice place up there?"

It was the first time anybody had ever asked me, simply, whether New York was a nice place, as if never having heard whether it was or not, and I was stuck for an answer. I said I thought it was a nice place.

"*Est bon*, good, you have nice place up there at that New York," he said. "*Merci*, thanks." He left silently on his moccasined feet.

Early that afternoon, after telephoning Mrs. Simmons at Avery Island, I went out there by cab. The driver was Robert Broussard, another Cajun. Everywhere, as we drove along, were French names, on stores, filling stations, and such—names like Delahoussaye, Breaux (there pronounced "Brurr"), Louviere, and, as frequent as any, Teche, which is the name of a big bayou nearby. For years, "bayou" has struck my ears as a gentle, musical, and beckoning word. In New Iberia, I was told it is not a French word, as I had surmised, but Choctaw Indian.

Leaving the outskirts of the community and heading south, we followed a long, straight road with flat fields on the left, interrupted at infrequent intervals by small houses, some of them not much more than shacks; on the right was a narrow stretch of water. Beyond the bayou was a vast stretch of marshy land. "In there, plenty muskrat, plenty mink, plenty nutria," Broussard said. "They trappin' all winter plenty furs round here. Louisiana got pret' near most furs anywhere."

As we neared Avery Island, there were marshlands on our left, too. Our road, indeed, ran right across the marshes. Broussard explained to me that the Bayou Petite Anse, or Little Cove, meanders on three sides of Avery Island—north, west, and south—and the fourth side is cypress swamp. So watery, indeed, that the place has always been called an island, even if technically it may not be one.

Unwittingly, Broussard reminded me that one thing leads to another when he said, "My wife is boss of the bag room at the salt mine on the island." It was the first I had heard of a salt mine there, although I learned later it is one of the famous salt mines of the world;

it is run by the International Salt Company. There's another famous salt mine under part of Detroit, I also learned later.

"Is nice place, salt mine," Broussard said. "Good place to see."

"I'll try to," I told him.

The long, straight road crossed a bridge over the Bayou Petite Anse and ended at a tollgate—the entrance to Avery Island. Tourists are charged a quarter admission. After I stated my business, the gateman waved us past. Immediately, we were in a world of lush and amazingly varied growths—palms, bamboos, palmettos, magnolias, and, most striking of all, majestically large live oaks, their seemingly eternal sturdiness accented by the delicate, mysterious grace of Spanish moss hanging from their strong, twisty limbs. Overhead, at times, great-winged white birds that I recognized as egrets flapped their way. It was hard to believe that an industry lay ahead. Soon we reached a crossroads with the sign

LOUISIANA LAW
STOP

We halted, then turned a bend, crossed a railroad track I was astonished to find there, and came to the tabasco factory.

It isn't a big place at all, as factories go—three stories high in one part, four in another, made of brick painted gray, and covering the area of perhaps an eighth of a city block. To the left, as we approached, was a great cage, about twenty-five or thirty feet high. In it, I could see several score pheasants, the brilliantly colored males strutting happily about, and a lean, tanned man (nearly all Cajuns seem to be lean and tanned), wearing spectacles, who was scattering grain around for the birds. A gentle breeze suddenly brought the scent of tabasco in the making. It was delightful—pungent and spicy, with overtones of vinegar, but of vinegar sort of under control. As I stepped inside, I saw eighty or ninety covered oak casks standing in rows. Two women, each with a wooden paddle, were going from cask to cask, lifting the covers, then stirring the aromatic sauce within. I peered into a cask and saw the rich, bright red of the mixture. The woman stirring it told me that this was one of the last steps in the long process of making the tabasco I'd been shaking on the clams up in New York a couple of nights before.

The factory is unlike most factories, for it has an unhurried, almost sauntering air. Walking toward a stairway that leads to the offices above, I stopped for a moment at a room from which there came the siren fragrance of strong coffee. Two workmen, in khaki, and three girls, one in khaki and the others in fluffy summer dresses, were sitting around a table, each with a demitasse in hand, chatting. The accents of some of them were Cajun. The coffee was in an urn, in a corner close by. Whenever anyone in the factory feels like having coffee, it's there, waiting. There are no specific "coffee breaks," as there are in more bustling operations. I tried a demitasse and it came near lifting the top of my head off. "That's pure coffee, Louisiana roast," one of the men told me. "They roast it right near here in Lafayette. No chicory. Those New Orl'ns people use chicory. Not here."

The office, on the second floor, appeared to be a parlay of McIlhenny and Charles Dickens—quiet, air-conditioned, lacking in the frenzy of efficiency that plagues some Northern offices, and with a high, four-legged, slant-topped desk, bookkeeper-style, against one wall. Mrs. Simmons—gracious, busy, blond, and the grandmother of four children—came forward to greet me. She is a widow. Her grandchildren are the offspring of Fisher Simmons, Jr., the oldest of her three sons. The two others are Edward McIlhenny Simmons and William Matthews Simmons. Later, she candidly told me that she will be fifty-one in July. Mrs. Simmons is the daughter of the late Edward Avery McIlhenny, known always as "Mister Ned," who, after many memorable years as the lord of the island and head of the tabasco company, died in 1949, at the age of seventy-seven. Soon after his death, Walter Stauffer McIlhenny, who is the son of the late John Avery McIlhenny, a brother of Mister Ned, was made president of the company, and Mrs. Simmons became his assistant. Mister Ned had three daughters and no sons.

With easy courtesy, which to my ears was enriched by her accent, Mrs. Simmons asked me if the hotel in town was all right. I said something about its being perfectly comfortable—not the Ritz-Carlton, but perfectly comfortable. "With the right frame of mind, you can make any place you are into a Ritz-Carlton, can't you?" she remarked cheerily. "Besides, isn't the Ritz-Carlton torn down? I don't get up to New York much. Cousin Walter does, though, now and then." She turned and introduced me to her cousin Walter Stauffer McIlhenny, who had been busy at the telephone when I came in. He is a dark-eyed, handsome man of forty-one, over six feet tall and muscular, with a certain dignity about him and a direct gaze. Behind his desk, on the wall, was a banner with the inscription "U.S.M.C. Reserve." Gossiping around the hotel lobby that morning, I had been told that he holds the rank of lieutenant colonel in the Marines, following a distinguished record of service in the Pacific, including two awards of the Navy Cross. He became a major in combat, I'd been told, and was released from active duty as a lieutenant colonel. One of the great marksmen of this country, he is a life member of the National Rifle Association of America and was formerly captain of the Marine Reserve Rifle Team.

Mr. McIlhenny seemed a trifle incredulous when I told him I had come down to visit merely on an impulse inspired by reading the label on a tabasco bottle. "I didn't know that anyone read the label so fully," he said, smiling. "Personally, though, I've always thought it's rather quaint on the Lea & Perrins Worcestershire Sauce label where it says, 'From the Recipe of a Nobleman in the County.'" He went on to tell me that he and various other members of his family, and of the Simmons and Avery families, all related, live on the island, and are all generally referred to as "The Family." Each family has its own place, he said; his is in the old slave quarters, and he'd like me to lunch with him there one day. It was hot outside that afternoon, around ninety, with the humidity running a Louisiana eighty-six or so, and Mr. McIlhenny, no doubt thinking of that, added, "The slave quarters are air-conditioned these days."

Mrs. Simmons then turned me over to a man in his early twenties, Matthew Louviere by name, a medium-sized, good-looking chap who was wearing a linen jacket and dark trousers. Mrs. Simmons said that Matthew knew a great deal about Avery Island, since he had been born and raised there, and that he would be glad to act as my guide.

Matthew and I started out for a look around an island that I did not even then suspect could be so wondrous.

Matthew's manner of speech was that of an exceptionally well-educated young man from somewhere up North, almost professorial in its precision and choice of words. In view of what Mrs. Simmons had said about his having been born and raised on Avery Island, I was surprised that he had not the slightest trace of a Southern accent. "My mother came from up North," he explained when I commented on this. "My father was a Cajun." I was even more surprised to dis-cover later that afternoon that he had never so much as finished high school. Gradually it came out that he had for the most part educated himself, by diligent study at home and at libraries in the region. Moreover, several years in the Army, which included additional schooling and a period in Japan, had given his obviously avid mind an opportunity to pick up matters far beyond the ken of most of the people on the island, which, with equal obviousness, he loved profoundly.

Right from the start, however, it was clear that Matthew was reluctant to talk about himself, and preferred to talk of the island. Riding away from the factory in a company car, we passed the great cage of pheasants. "They are for use on The Family's table when the occasion demands," he said. "Mister Ned greatly admired pheasants, as he did almost every form of animal and bird life. Miz Polly does, too." "Miz Polly" is the name by which Mrs. Simmons is known and by which she is addressed by nearly everybody on the island.

Quite suddenly, the road turned and ahead of us lay a wide opening surrounded by thick woods. I caught my breath. Out in a large pond, on a bamboo platform perhaps three hundred feet long and twenty feet wide, and rising about ten feet above the water, were thousands and thousands of great white egrets—of startling beauty every one—nesting. Thousands and thousands, and the trees that closely bordered the pond, like a jungle, were crammed with more of them. They were snowy egrets, Matthew said, among the loveliest of birds, and this pond was the heart of a sanctuary for them that Mister Ned had created way back in 1895, when he captured eight young egrets on the island. So lovely, indeed, are these birds that man once killed them by the thousands for their plumage; a law protecting them was passed in 1913 largely as a result of the efforts of Mister Ned and the Audubon Society. "In the eighteen-nineties and early nineteen-hundreds, the slaughter of snowy egrets was utterly abominable," said Matthew. "Women at that time coveted the dainty, exquisitely delicate plumes of the egret, and these plumes were called aigrettes when used for millinery purposes. On the bird, these plumes are beautiful, but there were many people, including Mister Ned, who thought they were brutally ugly on a woman's hat. To be sure," he continued, as we left the car and walked to the pond's edge, watching the ceaseless activity around the nests, "Mister Ned was a hunter famous all over the world, and a marvellous man with a rifle. But he shot only creatures used for food—not pure beauties, like egrets."

I told Matthew I was happily flabbergasted at the sight before us. Up in Rhode Island a couple of years ago, I saw twenty-four egrets that had been staying for some time in the marshlands near the sea, and bird people there thought that was a great many. They were of the type called American egrets. I remember looking up the pronunciation in the dictionary, and it says the accent is on the first syllable, "EE-grets." Matthew said "e-GRETS," and I asked him about that.

"Possibly we here accent the last syllable because of the French influence in our speech," he replied. "However, *revenons à nos moutons*—back to our sheep. To get aigrettes, hunters used to shoot the egrets on their nests, because those special plumes grow on the birds—both male and female—only during the nesting season. So, with their parents killed, the young birds in those days starved to death in their nests. It was despicable. The law had not yet been passed when Mister Ned captured these eight birds, and here at the pond he built a cage for them. When they grew old enough to leave, he tore down the cage and bade goodbye to them, fearfully, and sure that he would never again see them. But when the next March arrived—the last days of March—back came these beauties to this very spot, and bringing friends with them. A cage was no longer necessary, and year after year they came and multiplied. Now look!"

I asked if anyone had any idea how many birds made their homes on the pond and around it.

"Understandably, the number can't be computed precisely," said Matthew, "but it is perhaps safe to say that there are between seventeen thousand and possibly twenty thousand on that platform. We have reached that estimate by taking one small square of the platform, counting the birds in the square, then multiplying that number by the number of squares. The result is approximate, of course. The total in the whole sanctuary may easily be over a hundred thousand."

Matthew said there were undoubtedly some American egrets on the platform, such as I had seen in Rhode Island, but that most of the birds were snowies. The American is taller, being more than three feet high, while the snowy is about two feet high. The American has a yellow bill and all-black legs. "The snowy has a black bill, black legs, and yellow feet," Matthew said. "That's why he is often called the bird with the Golden Slippers."

We walked up the road a piece, and came to several large piles of twigs. "Bamboo twigs," Matthew said. "Miz Polly has a couple of men assigned to gather those twigs every day, cutting them off the bamboos and putting them in piles at different points around the pond. The egrets know all about that. When they're making their new nests, after they come here from Central and South America in March, and when they need new material to repair their nests after a storm, they know just where to go—where Miz Polly has had the twigs put."

At that moment it occurred to me that Avery Island, where men spend hours piling up bamboo twigs for visiting egrets, is far, far away, both in miles and mores, from the restaurant on East Seventy-second Street where, ninety-six hours earlier, I'd been shaking some tabasco on some clams.

We got back in the car, and Matthew drove me to a clearing in a small forest of bamboo. "This is called timber bamboo," he said. "It is sold to people all over the country for landscape purposes, such as the building of decorative stockades, and also for other uses. Perhaps you do not know that bamboo is one of the fastest-growing plants in the world?" I didn't know it, of course, and when he showed me a young bamboo, green and erect, about thirty feet tall, and said it was only four weeks since it had come out of the ground as a sprout, I expressed skepticism. "Very well," Matthew said. "Let's choose a shorter and younger bamboo, and check its growth."

It was at that moment 2 P.M. on a Tuesday. We found a younger bamboo (the young bamboos are a tender, subdued green, in contrast to the darker tan of the older ones) and we recorded its height—it came about up to our waists—by making a mark on a full-grown tree a few inches away. (Two days later, at 10 A.M. on Thursday, Matthew and I returned to the bamboo glade and found our young bamboo. It had grown exactly thirty-six inches, or, as we ascertained by doing a little paper work then and there, at the rate of about four-fifths of an inch an hour in the forty-four hours that had elapsed. That's something like nineteen inches a day. Bamboos in Louisiana eventually get up to around forty or fifty, sometimes even sixty, feet.)

As Matthew and I were riding away from the bamboo glade, we encountered a two-wheeled cart, filled with brush and drawn by a placid mule. Its driver was sitting in comfort beneath a large and dusty umbrella. "That's brush for the New Year's bonfire," Matthew said. "We'll come to the bonfire pile in a minute." The driver, a colored man, tipped his hat as we went by and said, "Good evenin'." It was only midafternoon, but down there they say "Good evening" when the noon hour has passed.

Soon we were on a road skirting the foot of an unwooded hill on our right. To our left was a meadow, and in the middle of it was a vast pile of brush, perhaps twenty-five feet high, perhaps forty feet across. "Every New Year's Eve," Matthew told me, "all the people on the island, white and colored, come and stand on that hill and watch the New Year's bonfire, and the children have a wiener roast. During the rest of the year, the brush that's cleared off the land is brought over here and put on that pile. It is a custom that has gone on since plantation days. I used to come as a child, and, like the others, I used to believe that all the bad demons of the old year were burning up in the bonfire, and that in the new year to come there would be no malevolent demons around. Sheer voodooism, of course, but it was pleasant to believe as a child. On Christmas morning, too, I remember, Mister Ned used to sit on the porch of his house, and all the men on the island came visiting. Punch was passed around. Old-timers used to shake hands with Mister Ned, and some made speeches, I remember."

I said such scenes seemed to me to belong to the distant past, maybe more than a hundred years ago.

Matthew, with the almost apologetic reluctance that beset him whenever he spoke of matters unrelated to the island, said, "Do you recall what Henri Bergson said about the past?"

I said I didn't recall it, because I never knew it.

"Henri Bergson said, 'The present contains nothing more than the past.' "

A few turns in the road through the green shadows of some coolish woods and we paused again, for two reasons. One was that, soundlessly and unafraid, two young deer came out of the woods on legs whose grace would shame the finest ballerina, and stood, big-eyed, not twenty-five feet away, watching us. One was male, one was female, and both were of the most tender shades of brown. The other reason was that on our left, by a smallish pond, were some birds that no one could pass unheeding. Among them was a crane, his plumage shading through four or five tones of gray into black, with what seemed a touch of deep blue along his slender neck. Hanging from the back of his head was a pure-white manelike feathering.

"That white part looks like Einstein's hair, doesn't it?" I said.

"It does," said Matthew. "That white on the back of the head is, I believe, called a *mèche* in French, and I believe Napoleon had a *mèche*. That bird is an African demoiselle. Mister Ned imported a family of them."

Sharing the banks of the pond with the demoiselle were two white swans, at least eight pairs of Canada geese, their young waddling around behind them, and a bird that looked fantastically like a gaudily painted hen and had a walk that was chickeny, too. Its neck was purple, its back was green, its legs were yellow, and its bill was red with a yellow tip.

"That is a purple gallinule," Matthew told me. "I often think of him as a swimming chicken. He swims adeptly, even though he hasn't webbed feet, like most swimming birds."

We turned to look at the deer and found them still gazing curiously at our car. A moment later, the female decided to go back into the woods. The male, on the top of whose head were small velvet-covered antlers, or the beginnings of antlers, was bolder, and he was still watching as we drove away.

Just about then a demitasse seemed to be indicated, so we started back toward the tabasco factory, perhaps a mile off. Driving along, Matthew told me that the island is roughly oval in shape, about three miles long and two miles wide, and that it has thirty-eight hundred and forty acres of "high land." There are also hundreds of acres of marshy land that are regarded as part of the island. "The marshland is quite an asset, too, because of all the furs it produces," he said. "I don't know how many pelts each winter, but it's a great many. Muskrat, mostly, but also mink and nutria. Mister Ned was one of the original breeders of nutria. The Fish and Wildlife people here in Louisiana imported some from South America and gave them to him, so that he could experiment with raising them. The nutria is something like an otter. In fact, I believe I am correct in saying that 'nutria' is the Spanish word for 'otter.' The fur is in considerable demand. I think it was around 1930 when Mister Ned first brought them here. He kept them in an enclosed portion of the marsh. Mister Ned was very upset when he discovered one day that the nutria had broken out of the enclosure and scattered all over the marsh. It worked out well, though, because they survived and multiplied in the marsh, and there they remained, to be trapped in great numbers every year."

A person can get used to anything, even hanging, they say, and this time the "Louisiana roast" coffee tasted better than pretty good and had no shock to it. While we were having a second demitasse, Boss Jim Markey, a white-haired man of seventy, came in for coffee and said that he'd like to show me around a little in the factory. Boss has been working there for forty-eight years, and he's now the man responsible for the making of the tabasco.

Boss told me that the factory is not big and employs only sixty-two persons. Even so, it turns out five million bottles of tabasco a year. He said the oak casks containing the beautifully red and memorably pungent mixture represented the last three weeks in the process of making tabasco. "The peppers in those casks were harvested almost three years ago," he went on. "I guess you know we grow all the peppers here on the island. After they're harvested, they're crushed, and a small amount of salt is added to them. Next, we put them in oak barrels with covers that have tiny air holes in them, and spread a thick layer of salt on top of the covers. Then we move the barrels into the aging rooms, where fermentation starts and continues for three years, while the juices and gases from the peppers escape through the air holes and the salt above them. At the end of that time, fermentation ends, and the salt hardens and automatically seals the barrels until we're ready for them. Then we remove the covers, add the vinegar, and for three weeks, in this room here, we stir the mixture. After that, we filter it, and it's ready for bottling, upstairs. That's all there is to it—peppers, vinegar, and salt."

"Just as it tells you on the label," I said.

"Just like on the label," said Boss. "But it takes three years and a little bit more."

As I was leaving the factory a short time later, preparing to go back to the hotel in New Iberia, I came across Mr. McIlhenny, talking to one of the foremen. They were both speaking Cajun French, and when the foreman had left, I asked Mr. McIlhenny if he had any difficulty with the Cajun patois. He smiled and said, "Not in the least." He told me that as a child he had spoken nothing but French at home. Not Cajun, but pure French. His mother, Mrs. Anita Stauffer McIlhenny, a granddaughter of General Zachary Taylor, is of French and German blood. Her family has lived a long time in Louisiana and French is her natural and beloved language. She now lives in Baton Rouge.

"There's a little family story about speaking French that might amuse you," Mr. McIlhenny said. "When I was in the Marines, I got to Melbourne, Australia, and I telephoned to my mother in Baton Rouge. It was wartime, of course, and it was quite a task putting the call through. However, after a day or two the connection was made, and I spoke to my mother, with a military monitor listening in, as was required. To my astonishment, my mother hung up on me. After another long wait, the operator got her on the wire again and told her that her son wished to speak to her from Australia. 'That's not my son,' my mother said. 'My son knows better than to address me in English!' I got on the phone again, and spoke to her in French. Immediately, the military monitor cut us off. He couldn't understand French and therefore couldn't let the conversation go on. After looking around some, I found an officer who knew French well. He monitored the call, and I finally talked with my mother."

The next morning, Matthew and I went back to the pond where the egrets nest. The bamboo platform was still crowded with them. There were also some wading at the edge of the pond, on their long black legs with the golden-slippered feet, fishing for frogs. Matthew pointed to an almost indiscernible wake in the water beneath the platform. I spied an alligator's head. Matthew handed me a pair of binoculars, and through them I could more plainly see the ugly, prehistoric-looking old fellow. "He'd love to have some of those birds," Matthew said. "But only when one dies and falls off the nest, or is pushed off by the other birds, does he get one."

Egrets kept taking off from the nests and flapping away in the sky in the direction of the big bayous, miles from the island. "They go fishing in the bayous," Matthew said. "The males and females take turns sitting on the nests; one stays while the other goes fishing and brings home food. Then the other goes fishing."

At that moment, twenty or thirty egrets soared toward the sky in a group. As we watched them, clouds of smoke rolled over the treetops, momentarily obscuring the birds, and we heard, coming strangely out of the deep woods, the sound of a locomotive. "They're hauling empty cars out to the salt mine to bring back the salt this afternoon," Matthew said. "How'd you like to go see the salt mine?"

I thought it a splendid idea, and so we started for the other end of the island, where the mine is. On the way, I told Matthew that to me the phrase "the salt mines" had always had a sinister sound, because of the many things I'd heard and read about people being exiled to the salt mines of Siberia.

"In reality, it doesn't seem an unpleasant place to work at all," Matthew said. "All year round, the temperature is a steady seventy-two down there, and the ceilings are certainly high enough to permit proper ventilation, with the help of mechanical fans."

At the mine, Lester Jay, a young engineer, took us in hand. He led us to an elevator, on which four-ton carloads of salt are brought up to the surface, and we stepped aboard. There were no lights as the elevator went slowly down the shaft. Mr. Jay's voice came through the pitch-dark. "We're working at around the five-hundred-and-thirty to five-hundred-and-fifty-foot level," he said. "It's been at that level for about fifty years."

We reached the bottom of the shaft, stepped out, and saw in the light of numerous powerful bulbs, strung on poles as tall as telephone poles, the far-reaching streets of a cavernous underground city. Over our heads, in that particular spot, the roof, of solid salt, was about sixty feet high. The tracks of a narrow-gauge railway fanned out into the distance. Small electric locomotives were hauling trains of dump cars, filled with salt that looked like crushed rock. Mr. Jay picked up a handful from a passing car. Most of it was gray, but there were fragments as clear as crystal. "It's very easy to prepare for commercial use, it's so pure," he told me. "It'll run ninety-nine and a half pure sodium chloride." He said that about thirty persons work in the mine, and that most of them live on the island. The remainder are from New Iberia and neighboring communities.

We climbed into a jeep to tour the mine. I noticed now that, as Matthew had said, the temperature was cool, in comfortable contrast to the ninety-two it was five hundred and fifty feet or so above us. In most mines, you aren't allowed to smoke, but in a salt mine you can, because there are no inflammable gases. The walls, the roof, and the huge pillars that support it are all of almost pure salt—no rocks, no dirt, no other element except that possible one-half of one per cent. "This whole deposit is called a salt plug," Mr. Jay said as we set out through the eerie light. "The theory generally held about it is that millions and millions of years ago, perhaps billions, part of the ocean got trapped in here by some geological upheaval. Then, in the Ice Age, fresh water was added by the melting of glaciers. After millions of years more, all the water evaporated and left the salt. That's simplifying it pretty much, but that's a rough idea of the theory most scientists hold to."

At one point in our jeep ride, which took us more than a mile, we turned a bend and came to a vast, lighted cavern, where the ceiling, Mr. Jay said, was more than a hundred feet above us. A large, complicated drilling machine stood against one of the walls of salt, but the crew was working elsewhere. Mr. Jay called my attention to a number of holes that had been drilled in the wall at regular intervals. "They'll blast here this afternoon," he said. "That machine drills four holes at a time, until there are over a hundred of them. Then charges of dynamite are put in the holes and all set off at once. Each blast brings down from a thousand to twelve hundred tons of salt."

When our tour of the enjoyably macabre world beneath the earth's surface had ended and we were again "up top," Mr. Jay explained that the salt from the mine needs only to be crushed and graded to make it ready for industrial use. As for the daintier end product of the mine—the kind of table salt, say, that I had sprinkled on the clams before I shook the tabasco on them—Mr. Jay told me that it is made by an evaporating process, in great tanks that stand not far from the mine shaft. "It's made from the dust that accumulates while crushing salt," he said. "That word 'dust' isn't a good one, because everyone thinks of dust as impure. Really, it is pure, or ninety-nine-and-a-half-per-cent pure, salt dust. Water is added to it and heat applied, and the evaporation carries off that one-half of one per cent impurity."

Now, here is the story of the salt mine as I have pieced it together from what various people on the island told me—Mr. McIlhenny, Mr. Simmons, Matthew, and some others.

One day in 1790, a young man named John Hayes was out deer-hunting on the island, which was then called Petite Anse Island. He stopped at a spring for a drink and found the water briny. He got curious, and he and his family began going to the spring, taking home water, and boiling it off to get the salt. That became a regular thing with them, and with other people of the region, and they went on that way, evaporating water for salt, right up to the War Between the States.

In those days, salt was even more important than it is now, because it was one of the most efficient ways then known to preserve food.

When the war broke out, the Confederate States were hard put to it for salt, because they were blockaded by the forces of the North. Providentially for the Confederates, a great discovery was made at the spring around 1862, shortly after the start of the war. In that year, Daniel Dudley Avery, a Yale graduate and a district judge in Baton Rouge, moved to the island with his wife, the former Sarah Craig Marsh. She was the daughter of John Craig Marsh, who settled on the island about a hundred and fifty years ago and was the first ancestor of "The Family" to live there. The Judge and his wife had a son named John Marsh Avery, who, being too young to go to war, was given the job of getting salt from the spring. He put some men to making the spring deeper and widening it. In doing so, they ran into rock salt about thirteen feet below the surface. This was wonderful news for the South. Shafts were speedily dug to get at the salt, and each Confederate state was assigned one. With prodigious labor, a "plank road" of cypress logs was built from New Iberia through the marshlands to the island. Along the plank road, oxcarts lumbered day and night, carrying the salt away.

"Then, in the War Between the States, the Federals came and defeated us," Mr. McIlhenny told me. "The Federals came in and seized the salt mines. Then, as they had every right to do under the rules of war, they burned and destroyed everything in the region. They flooded the salt mine to make it unworkable. It was a punitive expedition, and that's what you do in a punitive expedition." At that moment, Mr. McIlhenny appeared to me, admirably, in two roles: He was both the proud descendant of Confederate fighters and the former major of Marines serving the whole United States, North and South.

After the war, the salt mine was restored to working condition, but it was not until 1869 that it was operated commercially. It wasn't very successful, largely because of transportation difficulties, and in the eighteen-seventies the mine closed down. In 1880, expanding railway facilities made it feasible to resume operations. Nineteen years later, in 1899, the International Salt Company, then called the Avery Rock Salt Mining Company, leased the mine, and it has been digging there ever since. The island was given its present name at around the beginning of this century.

As we were leaving the salt mine, Matthew said, matter-of-factly, "Perhaps you'd like to see the oil wells, too. There are fifty-three of them." I hadn't known there *were* any oil wells on the island, but I replied that I supposed I might as well, so we drove out to the far rim of the island and there they were. I didn't count them, but there were a large number of oil wells, all right. Somehow, though, by that time they seemed to me to be a mere incidental, and later it occurred to me that any island on which fifty-three oil wells seem incidental is an uncommon island. The oil fields, owned by "The Family" and leased to the Humble Oil & Refining Co., have been in operation for about ten years, Matthew said.

The next morning, Thursday, I again met Matthew on the island. It was a hot yet lovely day, and after we had made our check on the growth of our bamboo, he said he had something altogether unexciting in mind for us—a visit to the old burying ground of "The Family." We ascended a gentle hill, serene and deeply wooded, and came upon a partially cleared grassy circle, about fifty yards in diameter. Neatly bordered with a privet hedge and scented with magnolias, it was indeed a place of peace. There were four magnolia trees growing in the burial ground and five great live-oak trees, all with their pennons of Spanish moss.

Matthew pointed to one granite headstone and said, "There is the man from whom all the possessions you have seen really came." On the headstone was the barely decipherable inscription "John Craig Marsh. Pioneer. Born at Cherry Bank Farm, N.J. July 28, 1789. Died at Baton Rouge, April 26, 1857."

Below this, near the ground, skillfully set into the granite, was a reddish stone, roughly oblong, into which the date 1703 was chiselled, and over it was a bronze plaque that read:

This is the cornerstone from Cherry Bank, at Rahway, N.J., home of John Marsh and his wife, Elizabeth Craig, birthplace of his son, David, his grandson, Moses, his great-grandson, Jonathan Alston, and his son, John Avery Marsh, who lies buried here.

I walked a few steps over the silky grass, and examined another headstone. The inscription on it moved me with its grace and gentility, its old-fashioned reverence for the dead. It read:

Sarah Craig Marsh, wife of Daniel D. Avery. Born New York City, March 30, 1813. Died New Iberia, La., March 29, 1879. Possessed of a vivacity of temperament that no burdens could chill, with a sympathy so tender and steadfast that no appeal seemed able to exhaust it. She was one to whom others turned in trouble with a confidence that was never disappointed. In her life illustrating that love is the fulfillment of the law.

We stayed at the burial ground only a little while and didn't talk very much. The headstone for Mister Ned was the simplest of all I saw. It said only:

Edward Avery McIlhenny. Born March 29, 1872. Died August 8, 1949.

As we were leaving the clearing, we came to an opening in the hedge. Matthew led me through it. Beyond were a number of untended, hardly noticeable mounds. "Here is where the colored folks were buried, from away back in plantation days," Matthew said. Only one had a headstone. It bore no inscription.

Matthew walked over to the grave with the headstone. "This is where Doc Russell is buried," he said. "He was a childhood playmate of Mister Ned's, and worked in the factory for years and years and years. We always called him Doc. I loved him. He taught me how to tell time. He had a great big watch on a great big gold chain and he was very proud of it. I learned how to tell time on that watch."

On my last day on the island, I had lunch with Mr. McIlhenny, Mrs. Simmons, and some others at Mr. McIlhenny's air-conditioned home in the slave quarters, where he has a superb staff to care for him and his frequent guests, who most often are former comrades in the Marines. Crawfish Newburg—the crawfish gathered right over in the swamp nearby—was the main dish. In plantation days, rows and rows of buildings constituted the slave quarters. Two of the buildings, constructed of brick handmade on the island, have survived in fine condition. They are low buildings, and in the century or more they have stood there, sun and rain have given the brick a texture and tint to be acquired by no hastier means. These two houses, overlooking a large pond, Mr. McIlhenny has made into the bedrooms of his home. The two are connected at one end by a newer building, constructed of bricks as like the old bricks as skill can make them, which contains a high-ceilinged, open-beam living room, a kitchen, and quarters for the staff. The three sections of the house face on a patio.

Before lunch, a number of us—Mr. McIlhenny; Mrs. Simmons; her daughter-in-law Lanier Simmons, the wife of Edward McIlhenny Simmons; Matthew; and I—sat around chatting, while a colored boy, Willie, moved quietly about, preparing a buffet table near a picture window. I asked the host to tell what the other guests would doubtless consider the oft-told story of tabasco.

"It *is* an oft-told story," Mr. McIlhenny said, "and oft-told with some inaccuracies. There really isn't any secret formula. It's just peppers, vinegar, and salt. Of course, the proportions are our own and the patience it takes also seems to be our own. So's the name." The McIlhennys are of Scotch origin, he went on. The family went from Scotland to Donegal, in Ireland, whence Ezekiel McIlhenny, the first of the clan to come to America, emigrated in 1745 to Nova Scotia. He moved later to Hagerstown, Maryland, and then to Philadelphia. A grandson, Edmund, was probably the first McIlhenny to venture into the South. That was around 1830.

"Edmund was a banker, and he married the daughter of Judge Daniel Dudley Avery," Mr. McIlhenny said. "Now, there's a lot of stuff frequently mentioned about the island originally being a land grant from the Spanish king, which is romantic and high-sounding, but we prefer to believe it was obtained by purchase by the Marshes and the Averys, a matter of simple buying and selling. In the early days, sugar cane, corn, and cotton were its principal products. Anyway, Edmund had a friend who went to the Mexican War in 1846, and when it was over, he hung around Mexico for a while. From the state of Tabasco, way down near Guatemala, he brought Edmund back some peppers the people there grind up with spoons on their plates and mix with their food.

"Matter of fact, the McIlhennys started growing these peppers merely because they were so beautiful. Had them in their gardens. Then, more or less for fun, they experimented with making a hot sauce from the peppers, for their own use. They gave a few jars to friends, and gradually it came to be known as McIlhenny's Sauce.

"To make a long story short, the family had to get out when the Federals came in during the War Between the States. The Federals—and I repeat that they had every right to do so—destroyed and burned everything around here. When the family came back after the war, they were impoverished. It happened that the peppers were unharmed. And so it came about that the manufacture and the sale of the sauce, which was started in 1868, was really what held the family fortunes, such as they were, together for those bad years. That's about all."

In the reminiscences that followed, it became apparent that Mister Ned was the one who spread the fame and use of tabasco. He was a man of singular energy and interests. He served as a naturalist with an Arctic expedition with Dr. Frederick Cook in 1892, and headed his own Arctic expedition in 1897. He was a friend of Teddy Roosevelt and Jim Corbett, to name a couple of the celebrities he knew. "He was a splendid man with a rifle," Mrs. Simmons said. "Even after he had had a stroke, and was confined to his room, he proved that. He could not leave the room, but one day, when he was seventy-seven and with only a few months to live, he looked out the window and saw a big buck deer eating the buds on one of his favorite camellias. He sent for his rifle, the boy brought it, and ill though he was, Father dropped that buck with a bullet between the eyes at two hundred yards." One of Mister Ned's hobbies, they said, was the breeding of new varieties of camellias, many of which are today sold commercially. His particular pet was a delicately tinted one, which he named Virgin's Blush.

While we talked, the buffet had been made ready. In many homes, there's an awkward moment when lunch is ready and whoever is to serve it tries, furtively, to catch the eye of host or hostess to make known that fact. Not here. Everybody was talking easily, and Willie waited for no gap in the conversation. Instead, he just took his place with his back to the fireplace, set his feet precisely so, put his arms to his sides, and, bowing from the waist, said, "Lunch is served."

Everyone strolled over to help himself at the table. The crawfish looked—and presently proved—delicious. I tossed a dash of tabasco on mine and tried to make a small joke. "No sea food should be eaten without tabasco," I said.

"Quite right!" said Mrs. Simmons. Then Mr. McIlhenny added, "And thank you so much for saying so!"

A ROOM AT THE BARN

Once in a great while, a man all of a sudden finds himself completely happy and content. His stomach feels good; he's breathing fine and easy; there's nothing whatever bothering him in his mind; the sun is shining, perhaps, but it doesn't have to be; a breeze is blowing gently, perhaps, but it doesn't need to be; and nearby there is something or somebody he has a deep fondness for. What he's fond of can be a boat, or a woman, or a horse—anything at all. About eleven o'clock in the morning on Tuesday, April 14th, I was silently grateful to find myself in that pleasant fix. At that hour, I was sitting alone in a warm and comfortable room no more than thirty yards away from the stall in which stood the race horse Native Dancer. I have a deep fondness for Native Dancer.

Because of my feeling about the horse, I had long wanted to know him better—pay him a visit and stay with him for a day or so. That's not an altogether easy thing to do; my idea, in its way, was like having the notion that it would be nice to drop in at the White House for a weekend to see how things go around there. Nevertheless, through the intercession of friends, I had got permission to go and stay awhile with Native Dancer, who was then stabled in Alfred Gwynne Vanderbilt's barn at Belmont Park.

That Tuesday morning, I left my house in Manhattan about seven o'clock and, in a car driven by a friend, went out to the track, at Elmont, Long Island. It was a gray, chill morning, brightening slowly, with a fairly sharp wind nosing about. The gates at Belmont are closely guarded at all hours, and we were stopped there by uniformed attendants, who examined our credentials and then waved us inside, to the stable area of the vast racing plant.

A sign on the road that wound between the dozens of long barns said:

SLOW
PLEASE CONSIDER
THE HORSES

So we went slowly, and here and there, as a group, or "set," of horses hove into view on the way to or from early-morning exercise at the track, we stopped until they had passed. My friend pulled up at Barn 20, where two men were standing near two automobiles and chatting. The license of one car was AG–2; the other's was ND 46–46. "That AG one is Mr. Vanderbilt's, for Alfred Gwynne Vanderbilt," said my companion, who is well versed in such matters. "The one with ND on it belongs to Bill Winfrey, Mr. Vanderbilt's trainer, and the ND, of course, is for Native Dancer. That's them, talking." In a few moments, I was introduced to Mr. Vanderbilt and to Mr. Winfrey. When I said, "Pleased to meet you, Mr. Winfrey," he corrected me. "I'm Bill Winfrey," he said. "Mr. Winfrey is a trainer over at Jamaica. He's my father."

"Make yourself at home," Mr. Vanderbilt said to me cordially. "I got to be going along."

There is a well-made two-story brick dormitory a few yards from Barn 20, for the use of trainers, stable foremen, and some of the help. It contains two offices and twenty-two rooms and four baths; half of it is occupied by the Vanderbilt people, and half by the Woodvale Farm people, whose barn is nearby. Bill Winfrey took me to a ground-floor room he had been using and told me it would be mine during my visit. He and his wife live in an apartment house about ten minutes away from the track.

That morning, the sports pages of the newspapers had announced that if conditions were right, Native Dancer would have a public trial between the fifth and sixth races at the Jamaica track, which is currently holding its spring meeting. (Racing doesn't start at Belmont until May 6th.) Native Dancer had been scheduled to run in the fifth race the previous day, but only two owners had expressed a willingness to put their horses up against him, and the race had been cancelled. Mr. Vanderbilt requested that the public trial be substituted, and the Jamaica authorities had agreed, in order to satisfy the thousands of racegoers who wanted a look at Native Dancer. In the trial, Native Dancer was to take the track with two stablemates from Barn 20, break from the starting gate, as in a regular race, and run six furlongs, or three-quarters of a mile. It would be a make-believe race, without betting, but—or so it was hoped—it would give Native Dancer the feeling of having been in a real race, and this was desirable because, as Bill Winfrey explained while I unpacked, the horse had not raced since October 22nd. "He needs racing to tighten him up for what's ahead of him," he said.

Bill told me that he was going to drive over to Jamaica and see what shape the track was in, and that I could go along if I liked. "It's been raining a lot," he said as we got into ND 46–46, "and the track's still pretty wet. We'll go walk on it—see exactly how it feels." Driving along, he explained that he'd like to run the horse with his forelegs bandaged, and for that reason he didn't want a wet track. "It isn't that anything's the matter with the forelegs," he went on. "But sometimes a horse will rap himself running fairly fast. That is, he will clip the back of a foreleg with one of his hind hoofs and make a cut. Bandages on the forelegs tend to prevent that from happening. But if the track is wet, the bandages naturally get wet and shrink up, and they're apt to squeeze too tight on the tendons, harmfully. Well, we'll look at the track and see."

At Jamaica, we stopped alongside the track at a point opposite the clubhouse and offices, and clambered between the rails onto the track itself. Bill took eight or ten analytical steps on the sandy, loamy, and still wet surface. The wind was now blowing hard. "Oh, this is O.K.," he said happily. "This wind will do the trick more than the sunshine.

They'll harrow this up after every race and the wind will get at it. Then the horses in the early races will toss it up and the wind will get at it some more. So by the time we go on, it'll be all right. So far, O.K.; we'll go ahead and run him."

We climbed back through the rails and drove around the track to the offices, so Bill could notify the officials that he was willing to proceed with the public trial. As we walked through the office corridors, I noticed that horsemen who were gathered there greeted Bill with a cordiality tinged with friendly envy, which I attributed, no doubt correctly, to his being the trainer in whose hands fate had placed Native Dancer. An odd thing, though, was that they never mentioned that name. "How's the big horse?" some would ask, and others, "How's your gray horse doing?" To all of them Bill answered, "First-rate, so far." The touch of envy was certainly understandable. Last year, as a two-year-old, Native Dancer ran in nine races and won them all.

On the way back to Belmont, I asked Bill to tell me a little about himself—where he was born and all that. He said that he was born in Detroit in 1916, but that his family had moved here soon afterward and he'd gone to grammar school at P.S. 108, in Queens. "It's right across from Aqueduct," he said. "You can see its roof from the stands there. Later, for three or four months, I went to high school at John Adams, down the boulevard from Aqueduct. Then, my father being a horseman and all, we went down to Florida, where there was a big fuss about letting me into high school without papers from up in New York, and we didn't have the papers with us. Anyway, that gave me a chance to convince my folks that I wanted race track more than high school, and they let me do it. I went to helping my father. Walking hots and things like that." The phrase "walking hots" denotes one of the lowly and yet one of the necessary jobs at a race track. It means slowly walking a horse around and around, leading him by a shank, for an hour or more, until he cools off from a race or a workout.

When Bill was a little over sixteen, he got a license as a jockey; sixteen is as young as a jockey can be, by law. But his jockeyship was short-lived, Bill said. "When I got my license in Florida, in January, I weighed ninety-one pounds, and by Saratoga, in August, I was a hundred and ten. I was long on weight and short on ability—that's what it amounted to. I just plain wasn't any good as a jockey, but I turned out to be pretty good as an exercise boy, and I went along for a while at that." An exercise boy is a fellow, sometimes a former or a future jockey but not always so, who rides race horses during their practice spins in the early mornings. I asked Bill what qualities he thought made a good exercise boy. He didn't answer right away. He has, I noticed soon after I met him, a mannerism that he indulges in whenever he's thinking something out, big or small. He holds his left hand up to his face, palm outward, and nibbles the second joint of his little finger. He nibbled it now. "Well, after at least ordinary skill at riding, of course, I think it's confidence that makes a good boy," he said finally. "A boy lacks confidence, he's apt to communicate that lack to the horse, I believe, which makes everybody nervous—horse, boy, trainer, everybody. A boy has confidence, he sits there feeling good, and the horse feels good because the boy's confidence imparts itself to the horse, and there you are. Confidence is probably the main thing. Bernie Everson, our boy for the gray horse, has it. Good boy. We trust him."

I then said something that has been said many times about the gray horse—that, conceivably, he might turn out to be one of the great race horses of all time. "He's got a lot yet to prove—got most of it yet to prove," Bill said, and after a pause, he went on, still nibbling and driving one-hand. "Tell the truth, a man my age doesn't deserve a horse like him," he said. "I'm only thirty-seven—not quite that yet. My father, training horses all his life, is sixty-eight, and he never had the luck to handle a horse like him. And I know so many trainers—some seventy, seventy-five years old, training horses fifty years and more, working hard, knowing their business much more than I know it—who never had the luck to get anybody like this gray horse. Tell the truth, a man of thirty-seven doesn't deserve it, that's all. I've had good luck, and all I can do is hope it holds. Still, I don't want to get greedy for luck. I've had more than my share already. For instance, I came on with Mr. Vanderbilt at just the right time. I don't want to get technical with you, but for a long while Mr. Vanderbilt bred his horses according to one system, or method, or whatever you want to call it. Then he changed to another system. I wasn't with him when he changed; my luck was in the fact that I stepped into this job just when the fruits of the new system were ready to be harvested, and that's what's happening. Whether the gray horse would have done as well, or perhaps better, with some other trainer, I don't know. Nobody else knows, either."

I said that training a horse with such a record and such potentialities must give rise to a lot of worry. "I try to worry as little as I can," Bill said. "I think of it like this: Say we take every precaution we can think of against something happening to him; say we feed him as right as we know how; say we have the best men we can get to take care of him, the best to ride him in workouts, the best to ride him in his races—that way we give him every opportunity to do the great things. That's all we can do. From then on, it's out of our hands—turned over to luck, Providence, or whatever. That's all we can do, and we're trying to do it."

By then, we were back at Barn 20, and it was still only about ten o'clock in the morning. "Now let's go in and see him," Bill said.

Bill conducted me into the long barn and to Stall No. 6, where Native Dancer lives. We looked in at him standing cater-cornered across the boxlike stall, in deep straw. Kneeling beneath him and adjusting the comfort-and-protection bandages he wears while resting was a large colored man, who glanced up at us and smiled a greeting. "This is Lester Murray, who takes care of him," Bill said to me, and Murray, while still going on with his work, kneeling calmly beneath the horse's belly, acknowledged the introduction. "I got some small chores to do," Bill went on, "so I'll leave you here with Murray."

I asked Murray how much Native Dancer weighs, and he told me about eleven hundred and twenty-five pounds, or about ninety pounds more than he weighed at the end of his two-year-old year.

"How high is he?" I asked. "How tall, I mean?"

"He'll go a little more than sixteen hands," Murray answered. That means Native Dancer is a fairly big horse—five feet four and more from the ground to the withers, which is that hump on a horse's back just above the shoulder.

"Would you like to have a good look at him, sir?" Murray asked me. "What did Mr. Winfrey say your name was, sir?"

"McNulty," I said.

"I mean your first name, sir."

"John."

"I'll turn him round, Mr. John, so you get a good look at him."

Murray got up and slapped the horse loudly on his massively muscular rump. "Turn round, now, you big bum!" he said to him. It was the rough tone of endearment some men use when they greet a crony.

Obediently, the horse swung around as far as he could, considering that his halter was chained, loosely, to two walls of the stall at one corner.

I believe that Native Dancer is handsome, majestic, fit to be looked at for a long, long while and looked at often, just for the pleasure of seeing a living creature so marvellously contrived by the millions of years that have passed since a horse was a creature about eleven inches high. I thought he looked just wonderful, though I have to confess that once race horses move off the pages of the *Morning Telegraph* they are reasonably unfamiliar to me. He is not a light gray, which is what most people think of when someone mentions a gray horse. He is dark gray—almost black here and there. Iron gray, some might say, but "iron" is too prosaic a word. His face is quite light; sometimes, when seen from a certain angle, it appears to be a silvery mask. On his left side, just below and just behind where his saddlecloth sits during a race, there is a very light-gray design—something like a free-hand map of France. His tail is dark, with a shimmer of gray toward the end. There in the stall, he looked much bigger than he ever looks on the track. He was very calm as Murray knelt down again and went back to work on the bandages.

While Murray worked, he talked to the horse banteringly, in a kind of reassuring monotone with music in it. "Don't you lift up that old leg at me, you big old horse, you," he'd say. "Stand still there now, you big bum, stand still now, while I get this here bandage fixed up pretty and nice, stand still. You got work to do today, horse, and I going to fix you up so you can do it right, like you always do."

A plump black cat strolled along, stood beside me for a minute, and then impudently, superciliously, stepped into the stall. Around her neck was a beautiful collar woven of two strands of leather—one cerise and one white—in a diamond pattern. Cerise and white are the Vanderbilt racing colors. Later, I learned that the harness-maker for the stable outfits all the stable cats with these collars, which he fashions from old browbands once worn by the Vanderbilt racers as part of their full-dress regalia.

Murray finished his bandaging, stood up and stretched, and slapped a happy slap on the horse's rump. "Hello, you old cat!" he said, looking down. "Mr. John, let me tell you something about that old cat. When we was coming back here all the way across the country from Santa Anita, out in California, that old cat—we call her Mom—she come along with us. She had a little box in the car, not far from this horse. Once in a while, he'd lean over and nuzzle her in the back of the neck with his nose. That old cat's not afraid of him, and he don't mind her. Well, Mr. John, that Mom never in her life had anything but black kittens in her whole life. Then we get back here, and in a week that Mom have five kittens. And every single, solitary one of them gray! Gray like him! He's a powerful horse, he is."

Murray came out of the stall and said he was going to feed the gray horse about half an hour early because of the doings that afternoon. Ordinarily, he explained, Native Dancer, along with the twenty-six other horses in the Vanderbilt barn, is fed at eleven in the morning, four in the afternoon, and one in the morning. This is a routine more or less peculiar to the stable. "Feeding him at one o'clock in the morning like that lets him get his food digested up some before his workout time," Murray said. "I'm going to cut him a little short on this feeding. Usual, he gets two quarts of oats at eleven o'clock, but this time I'll give him about a quart and a half. Then, usual, he gets four quarts at four o'clock, and four quarts more at one o'clock. That makes ten quarts altogether. Night watchman give him that one-o'clock stuff." He told me that the gray horse is a "good doer," which means a horse with a fine appetite. He would eat more than ten quarts a day if he could get it. Then, of course, there's his hay. The hayrack in his stall is filled twice a day, and he munches at it when he isn't resting—sort of a between-meals snack, the hay is. Later, Bill Winfrey told me that his hay is mixed clover until about four days before a race, when he's switched to plain timothy. "Timothy doesn't have any of those nice sweet buds in it," he said. "With the clover hay, he's like a child with Tootsie Rolls or something; he stuffs himself with it. The timothy is just straight food, and he's more sensible about that."

Murray got the quart and a half of oats ready, poured it into the feedbox, and then unfastened the halter chains so the horse could turn around and eat, which he did avidly. We both watched while he ground away the oats. Pretty soon, Murray said he was going to get some lunch and let Harold Walker, his second-in-command, carry on.

Walker, another big colored man, came in and took a look at the gray horse eating. "He doing good, like always," he said. Then he and I went into an office at the end of the line of stalls and sat down in two chairs there, leaving the door open. "I set here and I can see every one of them stall doors," Walker said. "That's a rule—got to be somebody here every minute, keep an eye on everything. Tom Drysdale, he the night watchman, he's here all night." There was hardly a sound in that great big place, except us talking and a few barn swallows or sparrows chirping or making a swift flutter of wings as they swooped toward nests in the eaves with bits of loot—wisps of hay, or some oats, or pieces of string they got Lord knows where. There was a television set by our side, but neither one of us thought of turning it on—not interested. It was enough sitting there, looking down past the gray horse, past all the others, smelling the clean, unforgettable smell of grain and hay and liniment and ammonia and faint old aromatic race-horse sweat. "I think I'll just walk down past all those horses and look at them," I said. "Then I guess I'll go to my room for a little rest," I said to Walker.

"That's good," he answered. "Just walk along and see 'em. Them two-year-olds, they'll want to know who you are. But them others, they won't care." I walked along past the stalls and peeked in at First Glance and Young Buck and Whence and Whither and Half Caste and Lap of Luxury and the others. The two-year-olds turned around and stared and the others didn't care. I went back to my room for a while.

Back in the room, that was when the time came that I felt so good that Tuesday morning. Very quiet it was in the room, just as in the barn. I thought how Native Dancer looked, over in his stall, thirty yards or so away. He was tuned so exquisitely he almost thrummed standing still. I wondered how many people knew about the gray horse. Millions, certainly, have heard of him, and thousands, like me, read all they can about him. They know that his sire was Polynesian and his dam Geisha; that's where he gets the gray, from Geisha. They know about the nine races he ran last year and won, and a few of them know to the dot his share of those purses, which was $230,495. Thinking about that figure led me to speculate on how much the gray horse is worth, which, in turn, led me to the conclusion that such speculation is foolish, because there were so many things about him that had no price. So I gave up this train of thought and went back and sat down with Harold Walker again.

It was getting to be time to take the gray horse and the others over to Jamaica for the public trial. Pretty soon, Bill Winfrey came along and outlined his plans for the run. He said that the two horses he would race against the big horse were Beachcomber and First Glance. Beachcomber is a three-year-old gelding who had never raced. "Sometimes he runs pretty fast for a short distance in the morning, though," Bill said. First Glance is a well-known handicap horse who has won some big races. He is six years old—twice as old as Native Dancer. He is cleverly named, being by Discovery out of Bride Elect. "The plan is this," Bill said. "We'll start from the gate, of course. The regular rider, Eric Guerin, will ride the gray horse, Bernie Everson will ride First Glance, and Albert Bao—that's one of our exercise boys—will ride Beachcomber. What I figure to do is have Beachcomber get away from the gate fast and grab a lead on the gray horse and the other. Beachcomber won't go fast very far, and when the gray horse catches him, I'd like to have First Glance kind of take over and give the gray horse a run. That way, there'll be some sort of competition for the gray horse all through the thing. That is, if everything works out as planned, which it may not."

The van that was to take the horses to Jamaica hadn't come yet, so we strolled down to Stall No. 6. As we looked in, Murray was just turning a bucket upside down and climbing onto it, on the off side of the gray horse. Standing on the bucket and talking to the horse, Murray began to braid his mane. "Now I'm going to fix you up pretty, you big bum, before all those people look at you," he was saying. He worked away patiently, the horse hardly moving at all. Every once in a while, he'd wet his fingers in his mouth and then moisten the braid. It took him about half an hour to fix the braid just right.

As Murray finished, the van pulled up outside the barn door. Big yellow van. A ramp was put against the side door of the van, and a heavy mat was laid down on the ramp. Wooden side railings, more than waist-high on a man, were affixed to the ramp. John C. Mergler, the stable foreman, supervised operations, and Winfrey also stood by. Altogether, eight men took places in or near the van, as if they were taking battle stations. A horse could get hurt at a time like this. Native Dancer was the first to go into the van. He went up the ramp willingly, and as he went Murray slapped him goodbye on the rump. The two other horses also went in easily, and the van door was closed and locked. The driver invited me to climb up in front with him, and we started off, taking Native Dancer to the races. Oh, well, to a make-believe race, anyway.

The two other horses didn't quite do their jobs in the public trial. But after it was over, Bill Winfrey said it was all right, things hadn't worked out badly at all.

When Fred L. Capossela, the race announcer, said over the loud-speaker that Native Dancer was coming onto the track, hundreds of horseplayers ran to the trackside from near the mutuel windows, where they had been engaged in the engrossing business of betting on the sixth race. Running out to see him close to, they looked like hundreds of water bugs skating on the surface of a brook. The gray horse and the two others walked up the track, then back around to the three-quarter pole, where the gate was. On a track, the three-quarter pole means a pole on the rail three-quarters of a mile from the finish—not from the start, as a non-racing person might, and often does, think.

What happened was that when the three horses got off, Native Dancer jumped out of the gate ahead of the two others. Beachcomber never did head him. Jockey Guerin had to hold the gray horse tightly in order to let First Glance catch up. That way—Native Dancer on the outside, First Glance inside and a little behind, and Beachcomber straggling—they went past the crowd and past the finish wire.

After we got back to Barn 20 without mishap, Bill and Murray and Walker and Mergler all felt the legs of the gray horse and found them O.K. The other men drifted away then, leaving Murray and me standing by Stall No. 6. "He keyed up," Murray said. "He a little mixed up in his mind, but he all right, Mr. John. He don't know was that a race he was in or wasn't it a race. They had the gate, they had them other two horses, and I guess they had the crowd yelling. Just the same, he don't know. He like a race, but he mixed up about *was* it a race."

Unconsciously, as he talked, Murray was cleaning a fleck of dirt off a bridle strap hanging by the stall door. I was looking down at his overalls. On his left pants leg, between the knee and the ankle, was fastened a row of shiny safety pins. They looked like some odd military decoration. They were, in reality, the badge of the man who "rubs horses." With the safety pins thus arranged, Murray, while on his right knee beneath a horse, could handily reach one to fasten a bandage with. "You know what I think is missing in his mind, what got him mixed up in his mind, Mr. John?" he asked.

"No," I said.

"It all look like a race to him except one thing," Murray said. "They never brought him back to no winner's circle. Mr. John, this horse never been no place else but in that winner's circle. Every single, solitary time he run a race. He don't know what to make out of it, no winner's circle this time. It got him mixed up in his mind."

When I awoke the next morning, it was not yet fully daybreak. I turned on the bed light to look at my watch and saw it was ten minutes to five. Race-trackers go to bed early and get up early. When I went to close the window against the morning chill, I heard three voices.

"Get an extry ring!" one voice said loudly, as if to someone a long distance away.

"What kind of ring for what?" another voice said, far away.

"Extry coffee ring!" the first voice said.

"Oh, coffee bun!" the faraway one hollered back.

"Yuh, yuh, coffee bun—get an extry one!" the first voice said.

Then there was a third voice, this one singing. Five o'clock in the morning, the sun coming up, and the voice singing a blues—"Got nobody to call my own!"

After breakfast, I walked over toward the training track, which is adjacent to the Vanderbilt barn. A couple of stable lads were there beside the rail. On the far side of the track, in the gray morning, two horses were moving. In the grayness and chill, one of the far-off horses was gray, too. Nobody mentioned his name. As the two horses came around the bend and into the stretch, the gray horse became grayer to the eye. The sound of hoofs hit sweetly on the ears. Although it is made by four hoofs, the gallop has a triple beat—"Tump-a-tum! Tump-a-tum! Tump-a-tum!" I watched and listened for a moment and then returned to the stable area.

Even before the big horse came back to the barn after the workout, his imminent approach was felt. It was in the air. "He coming back," I heard Murray say. Some of the men around the barn gathered outside to see if "he" was in sight yet. He was. He came down the road, between the barns, back to his home.

As Native Dancer passed each stall where a Vanderbilt horse was being groomed, work stopped for a few moments. "There he go," one groom said, pausing to watch, holding his currycomb in his right hand. Then he went back to work on his horse, and it was nice to hear him say, "You a good horse, too."

THE JACKPOT

The diary of Mrs. Jane Caffrey, the slim, good-looking wife of James P. Caffrey, of Wakefield, Rhode Island, says, for Saturday, August 28th, 1948: "Took kids to beach in the morning. Very hot. Jim and I went to clambake in afternoon at Willow Dell. Asked a few people to house for late afternoon. Jim won $24,000 jackpot on 'Sing It Again' program. Everybody excited." This would be an extraordinary entry in anybody's diary, and it is especially notable for the seeming calmness with which Mrs. Caffrey recorded the great good fortune of her husband. I would not know of this entry in the diary, or of other things about that historic day in the life of the Caffreys, had I not been a friend of Jim Caffrey's long before the twenty-eighth of August. After he won the jackpot—realizing the ambition of millions of people in the United States—I resolved to reconstruct exactly what took place that evening and then keep close track of everything that happened to Caffrey as a result of his success. This I have tried to do.

The Caffreys are substantial people in Wakefield. Mrs. Caffrey is the daughter of Grafton Kenyon, whose grandfather, William G. Kenyon, founded Kenyon's Department Store in 1856. It is the only department store in Wakefield. Caffrey works in the family store. He is thirty-five and fair-haired, and looks like a photogenic football player. When he was at Providence College, from which he graduated in 1936, he did play some football. The Caffreys, who have two children —a seven-year-old daughter named Carol and a four-year-old son named Kenyon—live in a pleasant twelve-room house of two and a half stories. It is painted white and has a well-kept lawn on three sides.

When the Caffreys drove home from the clambake at the Willow Dell Beach Club, a little before six o'clock that Saturday afternoon, they left their 1946 Pontiac sedan in the driveway back of the house and went inside to prepare for the guests they had invited. In a few minutes the phone rang. Caffrey answered, and a girl who said she was with the Columbia Broadcasting System in New York asked if he was James P. Caffrey, of 20 Kenyon Avenue, Wakefield, Rhode Island. He said he was, and she asked, "Will you be home tonight between eight and nine o'clock to listen to 'Sing It Again,' on C.B.S.?"

"I *can* be home," Caffrey said. He suspected a joke, because the fellows who hang around Al Weibel's newspaper store and Gene Wilcox's garage are great ones for playing jokes involving phone calls. "What's it all about? What's it all about?" Caffrey asked the girl, politely but in the tone that is employed for letting pranksters know that one is not being taken in.

"Well, Mr. Caffrey, your telephone number has been picked as one of those to call during the program tonight," the girl explained. "You may have a chance at the twenty-four-thousand-dollar jackpot. You'll be home, won't you? We have to be sure, so the program can go right along without any 'Don't answers' or 'Busys'. Be sure not to use your phone between eight o'clock and nine o'clock, so the line will be open for us when we call."

"Oh, all right, I'll be home," Caffrey said. He still felt fairly certain it was a gag.

Mrs. Caffrey was upstairs, getting Carol ready for bed. Caffrey went up to tell her about the phone call. He was careful to begin by saying, "You know, this may all be kidding by somebody over at Al's or Gene's place . . ." He pointed out, however, that the phone call unquestionably came from New York. When Carol heard the news, she, naturally, protested, quite energetically, against going to bed at her seven-o'clock bedtime.

"Oh, no, Carol," her mother said, "You heard what Daddy said. It's just a joke, that's all." Still protesting, Carol went to bed. Mrs. Caffrey got Kenyon into his bed, in the room across the hall, and she and her husband went downstairs.

"I've never heard 'Sing It Again.' Have you?" Caffrey said. Mrs. Caffrey didn't remember hearing the program. Their guests, who had also been to the clambake, started to arrive, happily sated with lobsters, clams, sweet corn, and watermelon. The Caffreys got busy with the cocktail shaker. They held back the news for a few minutes, but then they decided to take a chance and tell about it.

"Jim, you'll never have to work another day if you win it," one of the guests said. "Twenty-four thousand smackers!"

"Are you sure you people didn't frame up that call at the bake?" Caffrey asked. "Oh, well! What have I got to loose? I'm going to listen at eight o'clock anyhow."

"We're all going to listen," another guest said. "This is the biggest night in Wakefield since the hurricane. The jackpot! Twenty-four thousand bucks!"

By five minutes after seven, the predicament of the Caffreys was painful. The kidding was all well and good, but, as one of the guests had remarked, without contradiction, twenty-four thousand dollars is twenty-four thousand dollars. It was impossible to think about getting supper, but nobody eats much after the abundance of a Rhode Island clambake anyway. The guests were still arriving. The early arrivals were now phoning friends and asking them over to the Caffreys', and the living room was becoming crowded. "They're going to call Jim from New York and let him have a whack at the jackpot on some program. It's twenty-four thousand dollars! Can you imagine that? Hurry up over! The whole gang's here!"

Curiously, considering the popularity of the "Sing It Again" program, none of the guests could give the Caffreys much of a notion of what it was like.

"I think they ask you to tell the name of a certain tune they play," one of them said.

"No, that's 'Stop the Music,'" another one said.

"Isn't this the program that has the Phantom Voice or something like that?" another guest asked. "I think it is. In fact, I'm sure it is."

"Gosh, I don't know," said Mrs. Caffrey. "Neither does Jim. Now, isn't that just our luck? All the radio programs we listen to, and we never heard this one. Oh, maybe somebody's kidding us, as Jim says. It doesn't matter. We'll all have some fun. What time is it, anyhow? The program's at eight o'clock."

It was ten minutes after seven. What with all the guests, it was a while before Jim and Jane Caffrey could get off to talk to each other privately. Then one Caffrey (neither of them remembers which one it was) managed to say to the other, "Wouldn't it be great, with our anniversary Tuesday and twenty-four thousand dollars?" They decided that it would be a shrewd idea to phone some people and ask if they had any dope on "Sing It Again." After trying a couple of other friends without learning anything, Caffrey called me, at a cabin in a woods ten miles from his house. I was sitting in on a Saturday-night poker game. I couldn't help him, either, because, as I told him, I try not to listen to giveaway programs.

"Is there anybody you can call in New York who might know?" Caffrey asked.

"I'll do what I can," I told him.

I thought of a friend of mine, David Broekman, a composer and conductor of symphonies who sometimes conducts on the radio. I got him on long distance and he said, "Well, they have a riddle, a kind of jingle lyric set to a popular tune, and that is usually easy to guess. When you guess that, why, they let you guess at the Phantom Voice. That's on a recording, and they've been guessing it wrong for eight or ten weeks now, I believe."

"Have you any idea whose voice it is?" I asked.

"Well, the best dope I hear around is that it is either Irving Berlin or Louis B. Mayer. But, to tell the truth, I don't know. I don't listen particularly—just offhand. But you know yourself Irving Berlin's voice is high-pitched, sort of, and he has a New York accent. Mayer's is lower and he almost sounds British. He's from Haverhill, Massachusetts, you know, so there's a little New England accent there. But listen, I'm not sure it's either one of those two. Gee whizz! Don't blame me if it's wrong."

"No, no, thanks, goodbye," I said hurriedly, and perhaps brusquely, because I wanted to give Caffrey this news as soon as I could. Luckily, his line was not busy, and I told him what Broekman had said. I was scared of losing a friend if I was wrong, so I tacked on, "Don't blame me, Jimmy, if it isn't either Berlin or Mayer, but that's the best information I can get."

"No, no, thanks, goodbye," Caffrey said, eerily repeating the very words I had just spoken to Broekman.

At five minutes to eight, when the house was full of guests, all talking at once, the Caffreys made an alarming discovery—the radio and the telephone were pretty far apart. The radio was in the living room and the telephone was out in the hall. It would be difficult, perhaps impossible, in that crowd, to listen for the phone and at the same time pay close attention to the radio. Caffrey ran upstairs, two steps at a clip, and brought down a small radio from his and Mrs. Caffrey's bedroom and plugged it in not far from the telephone. He then sat beside the phone, and Mrs. Caffrey stood in front of the living-room radio. She was too nervous to sit. As eight o'clock approached, the guests began to quiet down.

"Sing It Again" came on the air. Broekman had described it accurately. The master of ceremonies, Dan Seymour, said, after the opening hullabaloo, "Now listen to this voice!" Then the low-pitched Phantom Voice was heard, singing, to the tune of "Pop Goes the Weasel!":

> Twinkle, twinkle, up in the blue,
> And I'm not in the middle.
> Take a ten, divide it by two.
> Pop goes the riddle!

There was dismay on every face in the Caffrey living room. The riddle sounded like complete gibberish. The guests looked at one another blankly, for this abracadabra did not seem to fit either Mayer or Berlin. Then everyone wanted to talk and the radio was nearly drowned out. "Sh-h-h! Sh-h-h!" Mrs. Caffrey said. "Listen to those prizes!"

In the manner of radio, the announcer shouted, "THE TWENTY-FOUR-THOUSAND-DOLLAR JACKPOT!," speaking in capital letters. Two other voices then alternated in the recital of the dazzling list of prizes, each voice, in its turn, mounting in volume and intensity.

"A Cavalier hope chest!" said one voice excitedly.

"A thousand-dollar Bulova wrist watch!" barked the other voice.

"A two-thousand-dollar Columbia diamond ring!"

"An Ansley television receiver!"

"A Vita-Var paint-and-varnish supply for your entire house! Inside and out!"

"And Jencraft Venetian blinds for your entire home!"

"A Westinghouse refrigerator!"

"A Westinghouse range!"

"A Westinghouse Laundromat!"

"A Lennox heating system for your home!"

"A Virginia House dining-room suite and bedroom suite!"

"A Cavalier cedar chest—stocked with five dozen Spring Maid sheets and pillowcases!"

"A Kelvinator Home Freezer—plus a three-year supply of Snow Crop frozen foods for a family of four!"

"A complete steer, dressed and delivered to your home!"

"A General Electric automatic dishwasher!"

"Two thousand dollars' worth of Stark fruit trees!"

"An airplane trip for two persons for two weeks to Elko, Nevada, arranged by V.I.P. Service, New York!"

"A complete set of Amelia Earhart luggage, all in Parisian pink!"

"A Ceil Chapman vacation wardrobe!"

"A men's wardrobe of Eagle Clothes!"

"Your portrait painted in oil, by Fred Wright, of New York City!"

"A Darra-James workshop, complete with motors!"

"Seven thousand five hundred cans of Phillips Delicious Foods!"

"A two-thousand-dollar Trane air-conditioner for your home!"

"A new 1949 Ford custom-built sedan!"

As each item on the list was announced, the Caffreys and their guests laughed almost hysterically.

Finally, the m.c. said that telephone calls would be made to people all over the country. To each person who answered, a special lyric, containing a riddle, would be sung, to a familiar tune. If the contestant solved this riddle, the Phantom Voice record would be played again and the contestant would be asked whose voice it was.

Then an orchestra began to play, and intervals of music were broken by the sound of a buzzer, which meant that a phone call had been put through to one of the listeners, who had presumably been alerted, like the Caffreys. The announcer's end of the conversations could be heard over the radio. There were calls to Centralia, Illinois; Springfield, Massachusetts; Nanticoke, Pennsylvania; Jersey City, New Jersey; San Antonio, Texas; Marion, Indiana; Cleveland, Ohio; Omaha, Nebraska; Geneva, New York; and Gainesville, Georgia. Six people were able to solve the preliminary riddle but were unable to name the owner of the Phantom Voice. Caffrey, sitting at his phone, stared at it, in the hope of hypnotizing it into ringing. Fifty minutes of the hour passed and it still hadn't rung.

Upstairs, Carol was wide-awake. Every once in a while, she shouted down to her mother. First, she wanted a drink of water. When she was told to get it in the bathroom, she said, "No, I mean orange juice." "Please, please, Carol!" her mother shouted. "We'll tell you all about this later!" Carol's brother Kenyon slept through everything. The Caffreys' two dogs—Gretchen, a dachshund, and Whiskey, an aged Scotty—were in a dither. Usually, Whiskey spent his evenings drowsing on the floor. This night, he went about ceaselessly on his slow legs, smelling drinks on the coffee table (that's how he got his name), smelling shoes, and getting in everyone's nervous way.

At seven minutes to nine, the Caffrey phone rang. Everybody fell silent. Caffrey hastily picked up the phone, put his face almost into the mouthpiece, and tremulously said, "Hello?" Guests clustered around him, bending over to listen. "Jim," they heard someone say, "we were wondering if you and Jane would like to come over—"

"Hang up! Hang up!" Caffrey shouted. "Can't talk! Can't talk!" He slammed the phone back onto the cradle. "That was Eddie Martin," he said. "Must be the only guy in South County doesn't know what's going on."

At five minutes to nine, the Caffreys had all but given up. Seymour was talking to someone in Bakersfield, California. That contestant failed, too. The Caffrey phone rang again. This time, it was C.B.S. The switchboard girl asked Caffrey to hold the line, and said she would speak to him every few seconds, to make sure he was still on. Thirty seconds passed.

"Is this Mr. James Caffrey, of 20 Kenyon Avenue, Wakefield, Rhode Island?" Seymour asked over the air.

Caffrey could hear the same thing three ways, the announcer talking to him on the phone and the words coming out of the two radios. "Yes, this is Jim Caffrey," he replied shakily.

"The Riddlers' Quartet has just sung 'Do Ye Ken John Peel?,' Mr.

Caffrey," Seymour said. "Now, Mr. Caffrey, do ye ken these two comic characters they are going to sing about now? Listen, Mr. Caffrey!"

A harmony team sang, to the tune of "John Peel":

> Do ye ken Ken Kling,
> With his horses to play?
> Do ye ken Ken Kling,
> With his big parlay?
> Or if Joe woulda stood in bed that day,
> Then you wouldn't find me in mourning!

Caffrey, trying to think of too many things at once, had no idea what the answer was. But from the living room Jane yelled, "Joe and Asbestos, Jim! Joe and Asbestos!"

"Joe and Asbestos," Caffrey said into the receiver.

"Absolutely correct, Mr. Caffrey!" the announcer shouted. (Joe and Asbestos are two race-track characters created by Ken Kling, who gives tips on horse races in a syndicated comic strip.)

"Mr. Caffrey, you have won a beautiful Cavalier hope chest!" Seymour shouted ecstatically. "Now you have a chance to parlay that hope chest into twenty-four thousand dollars' worth of prizes! Are you ready? Listen to the Phantom Voice!"

Once again, for the eighth time that night, the Caffreys heard "Twinkle, twinkle, up in the blue . . ."

"Can you pop that twenty-four-thousand-dollar riddle, Mr. Caffrey?" Seymour asked.

"I think it is Louis B. Mayer, of Hollywood, California," Caffrey said, with amazingly meticulous diction.

"Will you please repeat that?" Seymour demanded.

"I think it is Louis B. Mayer, of Hollywood, California," Caffrey said again.

"Louis B. Mayer?" Seymour repeated, for millions to hear. "That is absolutely right, Mr. Caffrey, up there in Wakefield, Rhode Island! YOU HAVE WON THE TWENTY-FOUR-THOUSAND-DOLLAR JACKPOT!"

In the happy ruckus that broke loose in the Caffreys' house, someone, historical-minded, looked at his watch. It was 8:57, three minutes before the end of the program.

"Mr. Caffrey, how long have you known the Phantom Voice was Louis B. Mayer?" Seymour asked.

"Oh, a couple of weeks," said Caffrey, and turned and winked at his guests.

"A couple of weeks! And you hung on and we called you!" Seymour said. Then he, too, was apparently overcome by the tenseness of the moment, for he went on confusedly, "Mr. Wakefield, up there in Rhode Island, you were ABSOLUTELY RIGHT!"

Somehow, the Caffreys and their guests managed to listen as Seymour continued, "You were right! 'Twinkle, twinkle, up in the blue'—that meant the stars in Metro-Goldwyn-Mayer's studio! And 'I'm not in the middle'—that meant Louis Mayer was not in the middle. Goldwyn is in the middle and Mayer on the end. Metro-Goldwyn-*Mayer*. And 'Take a ten, divide it by two'—that means five, and there are five letters in 'L-o-u-i-s,' and five letters in 'M-a-y-e-r.' " All this was very interesting information—and news—in the home of the Caffreys, where the twenty-four-thousand-dollar jackpot had just been won.

"And by way of an extra hint, the fifth sign of the zodiac is Leo!" Seymour said. "And Leo is the lion who roars in all the Metro-Goldwyn-Mayer movies!" At 20 Kenyon Avenue, Wakefield, Rhode Island, that precious bit of knowledge was hilarious news indeed.

"Those twenty-four thousand dollars' worth of prizes are on their way!" Seymour concluded. "Clear the tracks to Wakefield, Rhode Island!"

It was nine o'clock. The program ended. The guests at the Caffreys' were screaming with delight, kissing each other, all trying to throw their arms around Caffrey and Mrs. Caffrey. Carol, in her nightdress, ran down the stairs into the turmoil and into the arms of her mother. (Weeks later, Mrs. Caffrey said, "All I can remember is that Carol looked just like an ad for kids' nighties when she ran downstairs!") Caffrey was by now in the middle of the living room, being whirled around by guests.

"Daddy won twenty-four thousand dollars, Carol!" Mrs. Caffrey cried.

"I heard it all! I heard it all! I was hiding behind the banister!" Carol yelled. Her mother told her to go upstairs and put on her bathrobe, then come back down and have some ginger ale.

The phone rang again. It was the Providence *Journal*, wanting to interview Caffrey about the jackpot. What was he going to do with all the things he had won? Caffrey said he didn't know. How about the seventy-five hundred cans of soup, the *Journal* asked. Later on, Caffrey realized that of the twenty-eight prizes in the jackpot, what caught the fancy of most people was the "seventy-five hundred cans of soup." The prize was actually seventy-five hundred cans of food of many kinds, but people had got the idea that it was all soup, and they seemed fascinated and vastly amused by the idea of a family's suddenly coming into possession of seventy-five hundred cans of soup.

As soon as the Providence *Journal* had hung up, the phone rang again. It was a call from a woman in New York, a stranger, whose name Caffrey did not catch. "I'm so glad you won it, especially because I helped you," the woman said. "I listen all the time, and when I like people, I pray for them. I prayed for you." Caffrey thanked her and hung up.

Another call came, from a police matron at Providence Police Headquarters. "I remember you when you were a policeman here," she said. "You used to have nice curly yellow hair, didn't you?" "Maybe I did," said the fussed Caffrey. "Thank you, thank you." He had once been a motorcycle cop in Providence, to help pay his way through college after his father's death.

The phone kept ringing. Caffrey finally managed to break away from the house, by saying that he had to go to the Wakefield Diner and get some more ice from Berry Whiting. The walk gave him a chance to calm himself and to try to realize what had happened to him. He couldn't, quite.

The last of the guests didn't leave until after four, and even then the phone was still ringing every once in a while.

At seven o'clock in the morning on Sunday, August 29th, the day after Caffrey won the jackpot, he drove up to my house in Wakefield, where I was spending the summer. His face was sorrowful and puzzled. We often have coffee together early on summer mornings, and I had expected that if he came to my place that morning, he would practically dance out of his car.

"This is silly, having things happen this way," he said.

"What's the matter with you?" I asked. "You're the luckiest man in the land."

"I've just been burying the dog," he said.

He and his wife had not been able to go to sleep. They had talked about the two-thousand-dollar diamond ring they had won, the two thousand dollars' worth of fruit trees, the television set, the airplane trip to Elko, the custom-built Ford sedan, the thousand-dollar wrist watch, the electric refrigerator, the air-conditioning unit, the Venetian blinds, the complete set of luggage, and the prize they regarded as absurd—having Caffrey's portrait painted in oil. "I got up at six o'clock," Caffrey said, over our coffee. "I thought I'd take a ride down by the beach and try to think this thing out. When I looked out the front window, Whiskey was lying there on the lawn. I knew the minute I saw him he was dead." Whiskey had, of course, been very lively, for him, the night before. "At his age, he was bound to die any day," Caffrey went on. "He was past sixteen years old. Just the same, it does seem ridiculous to have it happen on this morning, of all mornings. I mean on top of the jackpot and all that excitement last night. Maybe the excitement, and having so many people around, was what really killed Whiskey. I had to take him out in the woods and bury him right away. I was afraid the kids might wake up and see him dead. I wouldn't want them to do that."

"He *was* pretty old," I said.

"Yes, that's what I said," Caffrey answered. "But I hate to see him go, just the same. Funny that it should be this morning, isn't it?"

One of the first things Caffrey wanted to talk about that morning was how he could show his gratitude to David Broekman for helping him win the jackpot. So, with Caffrey standing by, I telephoned Broekman, thanked him in Caffrey's behalf, and said that Caffrey wanted him to have some share in the winnings, when they materialized.

"Forget about it," said Broekman. "I'm glad the boy won, and please tell him to let it go at that."

"Well, how about a case of Scotch?" I asked Broekman, at Caffrey's suggestion.

"Don't drink, myself," said Broekman, "but if he feels that way about it, why, a case of Scotch does come in handy around the house."

"Tell him I'll send him three cases," Caffrey prompted.

I told Broekman that, and he laughed and asked me to congratulate the winner for him.

After having our coffee, Caffrey and I went downtown to Al Weibel's store for the Sunday papers. Weibel's is a favorite gathering place in Wakefield, and the minute Caffrey entered, he was surrounded by people. They slapped him on the back and said, over and over again, "A twenty-four-thousand-dollar jackpot! Twenty-four thousand dollars! Some dough for Jimmy Caffrey! Twenty-four-thousand bucks!"

Everybody in the store knew that figure. Everybody seemed to like to say it. Caffrey was obviously trying to be modest about his good fortune, but he was understandably proud of it. "I certainly was lucky," he said repeatedly. All of them had read the story in the Providence *Journal*. The headline was "24,000 IN RADIO PRIZES TAKEN BY FORMER PROVIDENCE POLICEMAN," and the story said, in part:

The winner, James Caffrey of Kenyon Avenue, Wakefield, a former Providence patrolman and now a floor manager at Kenyon's Department Store, Wakefield, was worried by just one thing—where is he going to store 7500 cans of soup, one of the major items in the all-inclusive prize.

Caffrey won the embarrassment of riches that threatens to engulf his house by correctly identifying Louis B. Mayer as the owner of the "phantom voice" after listening to an abstruse riddle on the "Sing It Again" show.

Of particular note any day in view of present high food prices is a "complete" steer, suitably reduced to steaks and roasts, and a three-year supply of frozen foods—with a home-freezer for the storage thereof.

The fellows in Weibel's agreed that the jackpot was certainly one of the biggest things that had ever happened to Wakefield. And when Caffrey read the story, he said, "I forgot all about the steer, and so did Jane. We can't remember all the things on the list, and I forgot all about the steer, for one thing. Wonder what we'll do with *that*."

After Caffrey got the Sunday papers, he went home, and I went along with him. "Daddy, I looked everywhere and nothing's come!" Carol said as we arrived. "I looked all over the house and out on the porch and on the lawn, and nothing's come at all! Not a single thing!"

When Seymour had yelled, "Those twenty-four thousand dollars' worth of prizes are on their way! Clear the tracks to Wakefield, Rhode Island!" Carol had taken him literally, and she was grossly disappointed at not finding the house filled with fruit trees, diamond rings, and other treasures when she came downstairs that morning. Caffrey assured her that the prizes would come, all right. Kenyon, who stood around in the living room looking happily from one to another of us, didn't understand exactly what had happened the night before, but he realized that it was something wonderful and he was enjoying the excitement.

Mrs. Caffrey came in from the kitchen. "The phone began ringing soon after you left, Jim," she said. "I guess we'll hear from everyone in South County about that twenty-four thousand dollars. Don't you think we'd better take the children to the beach and get away from the phone calls?"

That afternoon, the Caffrey family and I went to the beach club. It was the same there as it had been in Weibel's. Mr. and Mrs. Caffrey were the center of interest, and they had to tell the story of the previous night dozens of times. Finally, Caffrey sent Carol to the club office for their bathhouse keys. Half an hour later, when she hadn't returned, he and I went looking for her. We found her surrounded by a crowd of kids and adults, who were asking her about the family's stroke of luck. Carol was giving her version of what had happened, and her playmates were marvelling at the coming of such a high-powered Christmas in late August.

During that day of glory, I noticed that Caffrey, under the stress of frequent congratulations, was forced to adopt a formalized reply to well-wishers, something like the remarks that movie stars have for people who crowd around them. "Thank you, thank you," he would say. "Oh, it won't be quite twenty-four thousand, I'm afraid. That's a radio figure, you know. And don't forget, those tax boys will be after me. Still, I was pretty lucky, I guess."

I spoke to Caffrey about his sounding like a movie actor, and he admitted that he had noticed it himself. "When I was a cop in Providence, they used to assign me to escort visiting movie stars," he said. "And I saw then that they all had little set speeches for when people were around them. Can you imagine me doing the same thing? This is one hell of a country, isn't it, when you can suddenly get a phone call and there's some kind of monkey business on the radio and the next day you're famous or something, and tons of prizes are on the way to your house! Seems a little silly to me."

Now and then, during the rest of the day, Caffrey discussed the prize list with me—which things he and Jane planned to sell, which things they planned to keep. "Of course, it isn't going to be any twenty-four thousand dollars," he said. "I've got sense enough to know that. Practically everybody I talk to turns out to be some sort of tax expert, but so far I haven't been able to get any official dope." Then he decided that if "the stuff," as he had begun to call the prizes, turned out to be worth eighteen thousand dollars, he would have to pay about a 50 per cent tax on it, and that would leave him nine thousand dollars. "Even that isn't bad, is it?" he said.

By Sunday night, the Caffreys were weary of talking to everybody they met about their good luck. Since Kenyon's Department Store is closed on Mondays as well as Sundays, and Caffrey didn't have to work, they decided to go to Block Island for the day, on a cabin cruiser owned by a friend. (The island lies in the Atlantic, twelve miles off Point Judith, a famed promontory not far from Wakefield.)

"When we tied up at the dock on Block Island," Caffrey told me upon their return, "the first guy who came up to me asked about the twenty-four-thousand-dollar jackpot! I guess one of the fellows on the boat must have told this islander about it the minute we touched the pier. And this islander said the very same words, exactly, that I bet a dozen people have said to me in the last couple of days. He said, 'By God, I'm glad to meet somebody at last that won one of those things! It's usually somebody way out West that wins them.'"

Caffrey did not say so, but I noticed that by Tuesday evening the endless repetition of the words "twenty-four-thousand-dollar jackpot" had begun to get on his nerves. He was too mannerly to tell anybody that, yet he winced when he heard the phrase. That was the figure people had in their heads, and if Caffrey was determined not to build castles in the air, his friends seemed equally determined to set him up as a man who suddenly had twenty-four thousand dollars in cold, new cash in his pocket.

The Caffreys celebrated their eighth wedding anniversary, the Tuesday after "the day of the jackpot" (around the Caffrey house, events were being dated that way), by giving another party. It was inevitable that some of the guests should bring boxes of crackers. "You'll need them for all that soup," they said.

"Those seventy-five hundred cans of soup are one thing we're going to get rid of," Caffrey said, by this time stringing along with the people who insisted on lumping all the assorted canned goods together as soup. The Caffreys told the guests their plans for some of the other prizes, too. They would keep the deep freeze, because they did not have one, and the television set, a thing they had never even thought of buying. They could use the electric range, as the one they had was prewar, and they would keep the washing machine. "We think the trip to Nevada ought to be nice," Mrs. Caffrey said. "We've never been out that way, and after the first of the year Jim can probably get away from the store for a couple of weeks and I can make some arrangement about Carol and Kenyon, and Nevada ought to be fun." Caffrey's favorite prize was the car. The Caffreys' 1946 Pontiac sedan was in good shape, but they had been trying for two years to replace it with a station wagon. They figured that they would use the Ford custom sedan as a trade-in for a station wagon and pay the difference out of the proceeds of the sale of the Pontiac.

The luck of the Caffreys was far too big a thing to be overlooked by the alert and enterprising Narragansett *Times*, the weekly newspaper that serves South County. In its issue of September 3rd, the Friday after the day of the jackpot, the *Times* said in an editorial:

What pleased us most about the success of our Mr. Caffrey in winning the $24,000 radio jackpot last Saturday evening was the fact that Mrs. Caffrey had a vital part. Had it not been for her help in giving Jim the answer to the first riddle, he would never have had the chance to name the mystery voice.

The achievement of our Wakefield couple, then, gives us a dramatic example of the value of teamwork—an example which any married couple knows is sound and necessary if domestic felicity is to be the rudder in guiding the matrimonial barque.

We salute the Caffreys, not only in solving the riddle of the mystery voice, but for bringing to Wakefield national publicity by their accomplishments.

This editorial pleased Caffrey, because most people were giving him all the credit for making the right answers and he wanted Mrs. Caffrey to receive her share.

The first of the prizes to arrive was the two-thousand-dollar diamond ring. This came on Tuesday, September 7th. It was the earliest material evidence that the whole episode was not a fantasy. Sheepishly, Caffrey told me that evening that the arrival of the ring was an anticlimax. "You know," he said, "there's been so much hoopla about this that you'd almost imagine there'd be a big blast of trumpets and somebody'd holler out 'THE TWO-THOUSAND-DOLLAR DIAMOND RING!' and a bunch of people in uniforms would run up on the porch and hand us the ring. Maybe it'd be lying on a silk pillow." Actually, the ring, in a registered package, was simply delivered by Sykes, the letter carrier, who said, as he handed it to Caffrey, "Here's some of the loot at last." Sykes, a friendly fellow, had been interested in the "jackpot mail" that Caffrey had been receiving, and he was pleased to be the bearer, at last, of a prize.

Caffrey showed me the mail, which was not voluminous, considering the widespread publicity he had had. It came to thirty-two letters. All those from strangers started out with congratulations and wound up by asking for something. Most of them asked for the two thousand dollars' worth of fruit trees. That was because the Associated Press had sent out a story saying that Caffrey didn't know what to do with them.

Caffrey was puzzled about what to do with the ring, too. Around Wakefield, the solid people do not go in for diamond rings. Besides, Caffrey thought constantly of the tax he would have to pay on his prizes, so he wanted to turn most of his winnings into cash, if possible. He took the ring to W. I. Main, the local jeweller, who "put that thing in his eye," Caffrey said, examined the ring, and announced that the diamond weighed about one and one half carats, and was white, of good brilliance, and without flaws. Main offered the opinion that it might be honestly described, as it had been on the radio, as a "two-thousand-dollar ring." When Caffrey asked how much he could get for it, Main said cautiously that twelve hundred dollars was a possibility. He had no idea where Caffrey could actually sell it for that much, though.

Before the rest of "the stuff" arrived, Caffrey wrote to the manufacturers of the products he did not want to keep and asked if they would send him cash instead, even if it amounted to much less than the retail value of the product, but all the replies said that policy forbade the substitution of cash. In the next few months, consequently, it was a good thing for Caffrey that he was a good friend of Joe Brierley; otherwise, the Caffrey home would have been filled with the prizes that he had won. Brierley is head of a Wakefield company that sells agricultural implements, hardware, and building materials, and he let Caffrey put the bulkier prizes in the firm's warehouse.

Among these were the seventy-five hundred cans, or one hundred and seventy-nine cases, of "soup." As a matter of fact, there were seventy-five hundred and twelve cans, or twelve more than announced, and they took up one entire twenty-by-twenty-foot compartment in the warehouse. The Darra-James home workshop (complete with motors), which came in nine large packing cases, also went into the warehouse, and so did the air-conditioning unit, which was as big as a good-sized clothes closet, and the bedroom suite and the dining-room suite and the heating system.

The two-thousand-dollar ring, the thousand-dollar wrist watch (a lady's watch, embellished with fifteen little rubies and seventeen diamonds), and the other small prizes were easy to take care of. Caffrey carried them in the pockets of his jacket when he was attempting to sell them, and once in a while Mrs. Caffrey would wear the ring for a few hours, just for fun. "Jane wore it to the hairdresser's one day," Caffrey said to me, "and the woman in the next booth said, 'Oh, let me see your stone, will you?' Jane passed it to her, and the woman held it up beside her own ring and then said, 'Look, it's nearly as big as mine!'"

As the stuff piled up, and Caffrey tried to turn it into cash, he became discouraged. He was suddenly in about twenty lines of business, with all of which he was wholly unfamiliar. He was in, to name a few, the diamond-ring business, the Venetian-blind business, the air-conditioning business, the fruit-tree business, the paint-and-varnish business, the food business, and the heating business. Moreover, every prospect was aware of his eagerness to dispose of the prizes, and therefore showed great reluctance to buy. And few of the prospects failed to say, at one point or another, "Well, after all, Jim, you got all these things for nothing, you know."

One businessman of Wakefield offered eight hundred dollars for the two-thousand-dollar ring. "But then he talked to his wife," Caffrey told me. "She said that if she blossomed out with a big diamond ring, people might think business was mighty good with him and that he must be making big profits on everything, and he might lose customers that way. So he didn't buy the ring."

Caffrey made more than twenty trips to Providence, which is thirty miles from Wakefield, to try to dispose of his excess prizes. Having been born in Providence, as well as having been a policeman there, he knew the town well. He said it felt strange to be going around the familiar streets with a thousand-dollar wrist watch in one pocket, a two-thousand-dollar diamond ring in another, invoices for and descriptions of fruit trees and an air-conditioning unit in other pockets, attempting to raise cash.

Calling on some of the more sporty citizens one day, some of the "boys" who keep informed about what goes on at the nearby Narragansett Race Track, Caffrey tried to interest them in the wrist watch. "Little too fancy for us," one of the horsy lads said. "We give the girl friends more conservative stuff than that these days. That's the kind of stuff they used to give them in the old gangster days."

There were times, in late September and October, when Caffrey was abysmally depressed. The difficulty of peddling the prizes was getting him down. "If it weren't for the automobile and the few things we've kept for the house, like the deep freeze and the electric range," he would say sorrowfully, "I'd wish the damned jackpot never happened. And I'm worried more and more every day about taxes."

The automobile had been no problem. He phoned the Somerville, Massachusetts, office of the Ford Motor Company and explained about his interest in a station wagon, and the officials there generously arranged to send both the sedan he had won and a brand-new station wagon to the Ford agency in Wakefield. He could have the station wagon by paying the difference in price. With the accessories he wanted, this difference turned out to be $847. Caffrey sold his Pontiac for $1,500. So, after paying the $847, he had the station wagon and was ahead $653 in cash. The cash was the first he had got out of his winnings, and the station wagon was the rolling apple of his eye. "I spent a couple of hundred out of the six hundred and fifty-three dollars," Caffrey said happily as we took a trial ride in the wagon one day. "I bought three cases of Scotch and sent it to Broekman, at the address you gave me. It certainly doesn't seem much, after what he did for me."

Late in October, the Caffreys made a visit to New York. (By then, I was back living in the city myself and making only occasional visits to Wakefield.) While here, they finally disposed of the thousand-dollar wrist watch. They did so by going to the Fifth Avenue office of the Bulova people and turning it in, in exchange for simpler models. Caffrey was ready to settle for one simple watch for himself and one for his wife, because he had become weary of carrying around the ornate, thousand-dollar watch. The Bulova people, however, had more lavish ideas. "You're entitled to more than those two watches in exchange," an amiable official of the company told him. "Tell you what we'll do. You pick out nine more watches, and we'll send them up to your home in Rhode Island. That all right?" Caffrey told me he couldn't help smiling as he agreed to accept the offer. "So now we've got eleven watches, and only want two," he said.

While in New York, Caffrey thought himself duty-bound to do something about another prize—the privilege, to him embarrassing, of having his portrait painted in oil. He manfully telephoned the specified artist, Fred Wright, and was informed that if he would come into the studio and have his picture taken, the artist would work from that. Caffrey expressed his thanks, and then mumbled something about not having time during his brief stay here. At once, he decided that, having gone this far in life without having his portrait painted, he could get along a few more years, and he dropped the burdensome idea entirely.

The main object of the Caffreys' visit, however, was to call at the V.I.P. Service, the company that was to arrange their trip to Nevada. They were told that the trip must be taken before the end of the year, because the hotel that had offered the prize would be closing December 31st. Neither of the Caffreys recalled any such stipulation, but the V.I.P. official with whom they talked insisted that it had been made. It was impossible for Caffrey to get away from the store for two weeks at that time of year. He and Mrs. Caffrey had been figuring that they would go to Nevada in January, February, or March. The V.I.P. Service was unable to consider any of those months, and the Caffreys left New York resigned to the loss of their trip out West. "We thought, that night we won the jackpot, that the Nevada vacation would be one of the nicest prizes of all," Mrs. Caffrey told me.

The next time I saw Caffrey, early in November, he was more cheerful. In the more than two months since Seymour had shouted, "That is absolutely right, Mr. Caffrey, up there in Wakefield, Rhode Island!" I had watched the jackpot take over his life. When he wasn't obliged to be at the store, he was traipsing around Providence looking for buyers for this or that prize. Depending upon his success or lack of it, he was cheery or gloomy. Not loudly, to be sure, because he is a man who presents a serene exterior. "I got all fixed up about the complete steer," he told me now. This prize had been extended to the "Sing It Again" program, and then to Caffrey, by Newton H. Crumley, a hotelkeeper and entrepreneur of Elko, Nevada. He had written to Caffrey offering to send him a check for the value of the "complete steer" if he preferred that to meat. "Crumley said it would be about two hundred and fifty dollars," Caffrey went on. "I had intended to accept the steaks and roasts, but I changed my mind. I wrote and told Crumley O.K. The check came today, for two hundred and fifty dollars exactly. Here it is."

I asked him how much cash he had realized since the day of the jackpot.

"Let me see," he said. "There was the six hundred and fifty-three dollars in cash I had left after getting the station wagon. Then this two hundred and fifty. That'll make nine hundred and three dollars."

This, I said, seemed disappointing, more than two months after J-Day, as he and I had come to call August 28th.

"I often feel that it is, too," Caffrey said. "Remember how it used to be twenty-four thousand dollars? Well, everybody still thinks of it as twenty-four thousand dollars. Everybody except Jane and me. I'm not ungrateful—honest I'm not. It's taking a long while, but they're giving me everything they said they would, all right. Still, I misunderstood a lot of things, and, believe me, that twenty-four-thousand-dollar figure gets hammered into a man's head until, instead of being thankful for the luck that brought him anything at all, he can't help feeling disappointed when what he won keeps shrinking and shrinking."

I told him I thought I understood. For instance, there was lack of interest everywhere in the seventy-five hundred cans of "soup," largely because the stores had regular channels for buying such things. They shied away from "radio prizes," although the food was of standard quality. It was worth a thousand dollars retail, but the best offer he got was two hundred and fifty dollars. Rather than sell it for that, he gave part of it to his church, to be distributed to the needy, and the rest to the South County Hospital.

Early in December, Caffrey's jackpot business began to move a bit faster. "Sold the hope chest," he said jauntily as we met one afternoon for coffee in the Wakefield Diner. "It retails for sixty-nine dollars and ninety-five cents, I found out in Providence. Just sold it to Freddie Arbolino for thirty-five dollars." Freddie Arbolino owns the Mews, the lone cocktail lounge in sedate Wakefield.

"Sold the Venetian blinds," Caffrey announced to me another day. "Never was able to find out how much *they* were worth, but I sold them for ninety dollars, to a fellow here in town. Jane said we didn't need Venetian blinds at our house. Jane doesn't happen to like Venetian blinds."

By the middle of December, Caffrey had sold the electric refrigerator—retail value, $245.95—to a Narragansett Pier hotel, for $175; the heating system, which was worth $1,000 retail, for $750, to a veteran who was rebuilding a farmhouse; the paint and varnish, to a Wakefield house painter, for $75; the bedroom set, the retail value of which was $239, to a friend in Jerusalem, Rhode Island, for $120; five dozen sheets and pillowcases, to the South County Hospital, for $112.32; and from his "men's wardrobe," three suits similar to some he found selling in Providence for $42.50 each at a sale, to the man who had bought the Pontiac, for $100. (The balance of the wardrobe, a forty-dollar topcoat, he kept for himself.)

"The complete set of luggage, all in Parisian pink, was sold today," Caffrey said jovially a few days later. "It was worth four hundred and fifty-seven dollars, they said in Providence, but I let it go for a hundred and fifty, to a fellow in Lexington, Massachusetts."

"How did you get in touch with him?" I asked.

"Well, when salesmen come into the store to show me goods, and ask about the jackpot, I tell them what I've got to sell, and they keep their eyes open for me while they're traveling around. One of the salesmen made this Lexington deal on the luggage for me."

Bill Beck, the football coach at Rhode Island State College, in Kingston, six miles from Wakefield, bought the home-workshop-complete-with-motors. The retail value was $369, and Caffrey got $250.

"You can see I'm beginning to get some cash out of this thing," Caffrey remarked to me in mid-December. "But I've got all those taxes ahead of me. I still don't know how much they're going to be, but the dope seems to be that they'll come to about one-third of what I realize from selling the stuff."

The Caffreys got some fun out of the things they decided to keep. The television set (retail value $375) worked fine, at times. Caffrey had to pay $128 to have it installed, however. The deep freeze and the washing machine were great things, the Caffreys agreed. Their frozen-food prize, through an arrangement made with the donor, was to be sent in four shipments, at intervals set by Caffrey. The first shipment was thirty-six dozen packages. The freezer would not hold all of them, and Caffrey rented a deep-freeze locker at South County Lockers, at a dollar a month, to keep the overflow. They expected the dishwasher any day, and naturally they would keep that.

"The electric range is perfect, Jane says," Caffrey told me in late December.

"Well, take it all in all, things didn't turn out too badly on this jackpot affair," I ventured.

"You mean the great twenty-four-thousand-dollar jackpot? Remember when we used to call it that?"

"Yes, but you never really believed it would be that much," I reminded him. "You said the very day after winning it that it wouldn't be—when we were down at the beach."

On February 7th, almost five and a half months after Caffrey had hit the jackpot, I asked him if he had ever sat down and figured out the whole thing; that is, what he had received, its approximate value, what he had realized on the prizes he had sold, and so on.

"To tell you the truth, I did just that today," he said. "What I figured was this. The things we kept were worth thirty-two hundred and nine dollars, retail value. So far, I've taken in twenty-seven hundred and sixty in cash for the things I've sold. I still have the ring, and I'm dickering with a man who may give me seven hundred and fifty dollars for it. The air-conditioning unit is still over in the warehouse, along with the rest of the big stuff I haven't sold or we're not using at the house. I have one prospect who will give me four hundred and fifty dollars for it. Then, there are the well-known fruit trees. They're keeping those down in Louisiana, Missouri, until spring, and they'll send them up here then, they said. Maybe I'll get eight hundred dollars for them, at the ratio I've been selling things at. So, figure it all out—what I've kept, what I've sold, what I'm likely to sell yet—and it adds up to eighty-six hundred and sixty-nine dollars. Take off one third of that for taxes, and you take off twenty-eight hundred and eighty-nine dollars. O.K. That drops the total down to fifty-seven hundred and eighty. Boy! What a hell of a drop from the twenty-four-thousand-dollar jackpot! But what am I kicking about? The television was swell last night. The station wagon is a honey, and the two kids love it as much as Jane and I do. What am I kicking about?"

"You're not kicking," I told Caffrey. "You're just acting like a human being."

IT'S A MORNING CITY, TOO

Almost everybody thinks of this as a night city. That's the reputation it has everywhere and probably true enough. But late in life I have come to like it, at least our neighborhood, as a morning city, which is something people hardly ever say it is.

The reason for this goes back to my not being able to sleep in the morning, an uncommon affliction. Quite a while ago I fell into the practice of taking a walk first thing in the morning around the neighborhood, because once the papers were skimmed through after the elevator man brought them up at ten past six, why, the house got lonesome with nobody awake but me. This walking around at seven o'clock or a trifle later got to be a habit, and now I don't see how I can break myself of this habit, showing that a person can get used to anything, practically.

Take one morning recently. It was snowing and slushy when I

started out. The same as always in our neighborhood and, most likely, all over the city, nearly everybody says hello first thing in the morning. Later in the day, there are too many people around, rushing about doing this and that, to say hello to. It would be silly. Besides, first thing in the morning the things that irritate people all day have not piled up yet and those who are out, working or getting ready to work, haven't got rasped up yet by all the nervousness that accumulates from so many millions of men, women, and children all bunched up in one city. Anyway, whatever it is, the doormen along the street say hello or good-morning, as a rule, and are inclined to stop a minute and talk, the newsstand man in our neighborhood, on the East Side, around the Seventies, he is Maxie, who weighs a hundred and fourteen pounds and can work twenty hours at a stretch without blinking an eye, has time to say hello or tell a gag or two, fellows fixing the fruit and vegetables out on the stands in front of the stores on Second Avenue have time to say hello, the policeman is apt to nod some kind of good morning, and there's a feeling all around in the air as if the whole town, beginning with our neighborhood, was saying, "Let's go, boys, a new day is starting in this town, let's go." It is fine to see anything big getting started, and here, every morning, when a man is walking around, is the biggest city in the world getting started.

They're full of talk in the morning early. It must be admitted so am I. Except, of course, on hangover mornings, but nobody is talking about them.

After our own elevator man's hello this morning I'm talking about, he remarked about how Walter Winchell really did give out a good one when he said on the radio "Olympic View on the grass" a few weeks ago.

"I'm a dope," the elevator man said. "I kept watching for that horse, but Winchell said on the grass. You know, running on the turf course they got some race tracks. So I'm too much of a dope to realize when it's mud like it was there at that track, why, that's practically the same as turf. Oh, no, me, the wise guy, I remember Winchell said on the grass, on the grass. So I don't do anything. You see what Olympic View paid?"

"I think he paid something like thirty dollars for two," I said.

"Not something like thirty dollars, it was thirty dollars on the dot," the elevator man said. "But me, the dope, I'm looking out the window."

As I was passing by another tall apartment house between ours and Second Avenue, Martin, the doorman, said good morning, and stood a minute looking the street over to start the day. He's a sturdy man, white-haired and stocky, and once he played Gaelic football in the All-Ireland finals. He comes from the County Cork, and playing in the finals is comparable to playing in the World Series. "It's a soft kind of a morning," Martin remarked, and went on, "I mean that's what they used to say in Ireland if it was raining, they'd say it was a soft morning. Not that they'd have snow and slush like this, but I was thinking of the County Cork and Ireland this morning for no reason at all. Isn't it odd how sometimes a morning comes along and you wake up thinking of old times and no reason for it at all?"

"That's true," I said.

"There was a farmer in the old country and one of the men who worked for him by the day used never get to work on time and every morning when the man arrived at the farm he would say to the farmer, 'A fine morning!' And the farmer would look sharp at him, for by then it would be almost six o'clock and the farmer would say, very sharp and sarcastic, 'It *was* a fine morning!' "

"Well, it *was* a fine morning," I said as I moved along.

"It *was* a fine morning," Martin said and laughed.

Maxie's newsstand in snowy wintertime always looks very homelike and appealing to me. It is like riding through the winter on a train at night and seeing an isolated farmhouse with the living room warmly lighted up and you'd almost want to jump off the train and go and live in that farmhouse lighted in the darkness all around it.

The newsstand is far from isolated, being right spang on a busy corner. With the snow and slush all around the newsstand, Maxie sits back in there and peers out, taking care of the customers who come up one after another. He has an oilstove in there and a small radio in there and a chair with a cushion on it to sit on. The within of the stand always has an air of coziness about it, and warmth, too, amid the surrounding cold, and there's even a kind of serenity in there, no matter how much hurly-burly goes on everywhere in the street and along the sidewalks. It really is like the farmhouse you see from the train window.

"I been up hours," Maxie said this particular morning when I got there to stop a minute on the walk. "This weather got things tied up and I got to come down from way up round Pelham Bay. Took me hours. Anyways, I'm here."

I said he always was, and just then a big, tall man, elderly and strong, came along, bought a *Daily News*, and while I stood there stomping my feet against the cold, the man slipped around to the side of the newsstand where the door is. He was there a couple of minutes and then he came around front and said so long to Maxie and went down Second Avenue.

"See what he did, a very nice guy?" Maxie asked.

"No, what?" I asked.

"He wanted to give me a drink for a cold morning like this," Maxie said. "I only took a little bit, so it wouldn't offend him. He meant well on account of a cold morning like this, your feet wet, perhaps it would be good for you a little drink."

"Probably would at that," I said.

"I never drink only a little bit," Maxie said. "I'm afraid to drink too much—a whole lot, I mean."

"Why's that?"

"I'm afraid I might go besserick," Maxie said.

"Go what?" I asked Maxie, thinking maybe that was a Yiddish word. Maxie teaches me from time to time a handy Yiddish word, always interesting.

"I might go besserick," he said. "You know like you read in the papers every once in a while in some neighborhood some nut goes besserick, runs wild around the neighborhood. Goes besserick, they call it." Maxie was grinning.

"Oh, yes," I said, although the notion of little Maxie, a hundred and fourteen pounds and as agreeable a person as you'd meet in a whole morning's walk, going berserk was unthinkable.

"I only took a little sip I wouldn't offend the man," Maxie said, and I continued my walk.

It wasn't two blocks up the avenue, along came a great big friendly Slovak man I know, whose name is Dayler. That's a shortening of a hard-to-pronounce Slovak name. He stopped and we greeted each other.

"Where have you been?" I asked. "I haven't seen you around lately, haven't seen you for months. Maybe we get around different times of day from each other. Where you been, Dayler?"

"North Pole," he said.

"What's that?" I asked.

"North Pole," he said. "I been the North Pole. Going back North Pole May 15th."

"Holy Pete!" I said. "You kidding?"

"No, no, I been North Pole, only couple miles from North Pole anyway, might's well say North Pole it's round there someplace, North Pole," Dayler said.

"I remember when that used to be a big headline, where somebody been to the North Pole," I said.

"About three thousand guys up there," Dayler said. "No secret. About three thousand guys up there, making airfield. I going back North Pole May 15th."

"Well, well," was the best I could do.

"See you at Stevie's," Dayler said as we left each other.

"I want to hear about up there," I said.

"Not much to say," he answered, back over his shoulder. "Three thousand guys up there, maybe more. Cold only, that's all to say, cold."

It was only about seven-thirty then, and nothing happened the next few blocks. Except suddenly, from a tenement window, out came the sound of a ten-cent tin whistle. Very gay tune, "The Irish Washerwoman." The tune went all over the block, and an even-money bet that some people trying to sleep were cursing it out to themselves. At any rate, it wasn't any radio or television, it was somebody got up, decided to play "The Irish Washerwoman" on a ten-cent whistle at 7:30 A.M., and immediately did so. The next few blocks, even after I was out of earshot of the ten-cent whistle, I myself was whistling happy fragments of "The Irish Washerwoman."

It is a dirty, untidy street in the morning, Second Avenue is, before the Department of Sanitation trucks come by. Everybody's used to it, though, and me, too. There was even a bedspring lying on the sidewalk along there somewhere, a bedspring, full length, somebody had no further use for and threw out the window during the night. Bedsprings thrown away drive Sanitation men daffy, because they won't, naturally, fit in that conveyer and through the aperture where the trash goes into the truck. The men have to strap them on the top to tote them away. Part of the work of the day that was just starting, getting that bedspring out of the way on Manhattan Island. The town could get clogged up with bedsprings and God knows what if people weren't around doing something about it first thing in the morning.

It is always a marvel to me how all these thousands of little, two-by-four stores get by. This morning, like every other morning except Sundays, there they were, opening up for the day, putting remnants of cloth on stands outside, putting pots and pans outside for display in the hope of selling them, putting out, in one place, small machines on a stand, machines designed for making noodles at home. That place with the noodle thing, it has a sign in the window about "Magyar." It says "Magyar Uzydet," something like that, and one other morning, an amiable policeman I asked told me it meant Hungarian spoken. Another man said it meant Hungarian store. All these small stores look courageous starting each day, and they must make a buck here, a buck there, and keep going one way or another. In another window, a delicatessen, a sign said, "Italian Heroes Sold Here." It looks funny, but of course it means those enormous sandwiches made by cutting a half loaf of that Zeppelin-shaped bread horizontally and stuffing in between with salami, pimento, cheese—everything. Years ago, even the Italians I knew jokingly called them Guinea Heroes, because, an Italian friend once explained to me, "They save your life." Nowadays, everybody being more sensitive than they used to be, the sign says "Italian" so as not to get anybody sore. They're valuable sandwiches at times, those Italian Heroes.

Another thing about early mornings, there isn't so much carbon monoxide around. So without trying to be a physical-culture nut or anything like that a person walking twenty or thirty blocks at that time is bound to get at least a lungful of air that might have happily blown in from the country recently. A couple thousand automobiles haven't given out with the carbon monoxide yet.

So this morning I was feeling pretty good when I got back down the avenue and went into Stevie's for a cup of coffee before going back home. Stevie's is our best neighborhood gathering place, a bar and restaurant that says "Dine and Dance" on the canopy outside. It is largely a family-style, the core of the business being people of

Slovak extraction, and there are dance nights, with a four-piece orchestra, Friday, Saturday, and Sunday nights.

Stevie's, too, is pleasant in the morning. The young fellows from the big super A & P come in for a quick coffee, a stray hangover lolls in once in a while, a regular or two comes in for a beginning shot, because that's how he begins his day and helps get Manhattan going, and even that early the radio is on.

This morning, young Jerry was filling in behind the bar. His father, Stevie, owns the place, and Jerry spent his childhood back around Bratislava, which is the Slovak part, you might say, of Czechoslovakia. Now he's at N.Y.U. and he's going to be a doctor.

So this morning, the way nobody can explain, the subject of the human liver came up, somebody mentioned it in front of the bar, and Jerry, very quietly and earnestly, gave a little talk on what he has learned so far, in pre-med school, about the human kidney. Interesting, and informative. Everybody listened.

After the coffee, and hearing odds and ends of comment on what was in the *Daily News* this morning, I left for home, just down the block. As I passed Martin, now busy whistling for cabs for the tenants, he said, "It *was* a fine morning!" and laughed.

Our own elevator man said, on the way up to the apartment, "I suppose the next time Olympic View runs, everybody'll be on him and he won't pay hardly anything, four bucks even probably."

"Could be," I said. "Could be."

IV

THE BELL-RINGERS

I think I have found a key to the spirit and manners of the people of Manhattan. I got it while trying to stop people from ringing my doorbell. I live in a ground-floor apartment and I am a man who likes to sleep at odd times during the day. I get drowsy spells and lie down.

By a kind of folk custom, the ground-floor bell is the one people ring, especially if they can't find the superintendent or don't want to bother with him, and they kept my bell ringing all day off and on. People with packages, with messages (none of them for me), with boxes of rhododendrons or nostalgias, with duns and whatnot. So I put a note on the bell. It said:

DON'T RING THIS BELL

The bell went on ringing. I decided the note was abrupt, and changed it to read:

PLEASE DON'T RING THIS BELL

It seemed to me that the bell rang more often than before. I kept trying, though. The third note read:

FOR GOD'S SAKE DON'T RING THIS BELL

They kept ringing the bell. In a moment of self-pity, I went back to Note No. 1, but I added a codicil:

DON'T RING THIS BELL
(MAN WORKS ALL NIGHT)

From that time on they haven't bothered me. I sleep like a top through the most fruitful hours of the day. I don't do any work at night, of course, and never have.

The other day I saw a policeman who was hauling a misbehaving taxpayer to the callbox neatly stave off an incipient riot by employing my bell-ringer technique. "Supposin' you was me, with a job and a wife and all?" he said to the sullen crowd around him, and the crowd nodded approval of the arrest.

What I'm getting at is that you can persuade New Yorkers to do almost anything if you appeal to them in the right way, and especially if you put it on the basis of Put-Yourself-in-My-Place. They're suckers for that.

A LETTER OF AMPLIFICATION

New York City
October 16, 1946

The Editors, *The New Yorker*,
Sirs:

Alva Johnston's Profile of John F. Royal was exceptionally interesting to me because there was an episode in my life in which Mr. Royal played a benign part. Now, nineteen years or so later, I think that my most painful recollection of this thoroughly painful episode is of a quartet of printers loudly singing, at nine-thirty in the morning, "I Want a Girl Just Like the Girl That Married Dear Old Dad," in a suite in the Statler Hotel in Cleveland, while their four wives applauded and I sat in an adjoining room with my head in my hands, as the saying goes. My head was in my hands because all eight, the singers and the applauders, were living richly in the Statler Hotel, I was supposed to foot the bill, and I had no money. That is, I had a dollar and sixty-five cents, along with a terribly guilty conscience, and every barbershop chord that surged down the hall nearly killed me.

At that time, Mr. Royal was running the big Keith theatre in Cleveland, as Mr. Johnston related. A series of newspaper-sponsored contests for quartets had been held in all parts of the country, and now the semifinals were being run off in big cities like Cleveland, after which the finals would be held in New York. Something like the Golden Gloves, only for quartet singing.

In Columbus, Ohio, where I was employed on the Columbus *Citizen*, a quartet composed of printers had won the local contest—won it fair and square, although, since they were printers, it might sound as if they had some newspaper pull. As promised by the *Citizen*, the winning quartet, with wives, had been sent to Cleveland for four days, all expenses paid, and I had been chosen to manage the party. The four singers were earnest, determined, and industrious. No matter where we were—on the train to Cleveland, for example—they were apt to put their heads together at any minute and burst out into one of their three top numbers. One was the "I Want a Girl" song, another was the one that starts "If I had my way, dear, forever there'd be," and the third was what they regarded as a classic knockout, "Fly Away, Kentucky Babe." In all truth, I liked the four fellows, but they seemed only a fair quartet and I had no confidence that they would pull through the regional semifinals in Cleveland. (Fact is, I was right.)

The office had given me five hundred dollars to pay for the tour to Cleveland, and it was quite a sum. The Columbus *Citizen* was a nice paper to work on, but a person was not paid extravagantly for working there, and expense money had rarely, if ever, before been handed out in that quantity. Still, there were expenses for nine persons (including me) to be paid.

All right. In spite of the endless Kentucky Babes and Girls That Married Dear Old Dad, we got to Cleveland in fair shape and marched into the Statler Hotel. In those days, a man could walk into a hotel and hire a room and think nothing of it. In fact, a man could walk in and hire five adjoining rooms, as I did, and think nothing of it, as long as he had something like five hundred dollars in his pocket.

Now we skip a little, to where I got sick of the company of the quartet and wives at about six o'clock the first evening and went out looking for some fun in Cleveland. It was my intention to have twenty-five or thirty dollars' worth of fun, figuring that it was coming to me. But what I ran into was a dice game, a bad dice game.

The next morning, I looked through my pants and my coat, and found only a dollar sixty-five. That was all. Ten minutes after this discovery, I heard that day's first burst of "I Want a Girl." I didn't have any five-hundred-dollar friends. And the sin of the dice game was far too big to confess to the office back in Columbus.

The phone rang. It was the leader of the quartet, a fellow named Roy. "Is it all right to eat in the room?" he asked. "And is it all right if we can get hold of a little something to drink, will you pay us back?"

"Oh, certainly, certainly," I said. "All expenses paid, you know."

I heard the waiters' wagons, presumably loaded with food, rumbling down the hall a half hour later, a half hour that had been loud with "Kentucky Babe" and "If I had my way." I had never got so sick of a quartet in my life, or worried so about one. Desperately, I began sending telegrams to relatives. The general content of them was "If you cannot send me five hundred dollars, I go to jail. Will explain later, but please send money soonest possible." I would send for a bellboy after writing every telegram and dispatch it by him. My head was still in my hands at noon. No answer from any of the wires. Lunch came rolling down the hall, on three or four wagons. Once I had to drop in on the singers to see them about some detail. "This is certainly the life" was the essence of their comment. "Go ahead, boys, have some fun," I said, with what I hoped sounded like enthusiasm. Then I went back to my room and sat on the edge of the bed, staring. I had only eighty cents left by then because of tipping the bellboys. The singing began again, to my agony.

That night, in the Keith theatre, my quartet lost out. The printers gave their three songs all they had, but it wasn't enough and they wound up fifth among the seven quartets competing. That was the second night after our arrival, but, in accordance with the promises made, my singers still had two days of free gaiety in Cleveland coming to them. Fortunately, I prevailed on them to have the gaiety in the Statler, and didn't have to take them out to some place where cash would have been needed. They kept eating and drinking in their rooms, and I kept dying the death of a dog in my room.

The singing, eating, and jollity were still in progress on the fourth afternoon when, a few hours before train time, I finally went to the Keith theatre and asked to speak to Mr. Royal, whom I had never seen. His secretary let me in, and Mr. Royal looked up and asked me my business. I told him my name and my occupation and that I was there with one of the quartets. "Sir," I said, "I have foolishly spent the five hundred dollars they gave me to pay our expenses and I do not know what to do. The bill is something awful."

"Where?" Mr. Royal asked calmly. I told him at the Statler. He hesitated only a moment and then said, "Look, the nut—the weekly expense of this theatre, that is—comes to seventeen thousand dollars. [I think that was the figure.] Perhaps, for this one week, it can be seventeen thousand five hundred. Have them send the bill over. I'll pay it, give you the receipt, and you can take it back to the paper, and I'll make up the difference between what the bill comes to and five hundred dollars, so you can settle with your office."

That is what Mr. Royal did. Whatever the actual bookkeeping of the transaction, I have, in my mind, owed him five hundred dollars for nineteen years. The chances are I will never pay him, even though I often intend to.

Sincerely,
John McNulty

YELLOW-BALL-IN-THE-SIDE

For years now, the Brunswick-Balke-Collender people and other outfits that manufacture pool tables have been conducting a campaign to take the sense of shadiness out of pool playing. They send Charlie Peterson and other gentlemanly top-notch pool players around the country to prep schools and colleges and to pasteurized pool halls in key cities in an effort to remove from the public mind the notion that there is something sinful about shooting pool.

Pool is a nice game, and it would be nicer if they did manage to wring the sin out of it, so this campaign is probably praiseworthy enough. But as far as I am concerned, the Brunswick-Balke-Collender people and the rest of them might as well give up. Long as I live, when I'm playing pool, I am going to feel that I am not putting in my time in the most wholesome of ways. I wouldn't feel a hundred per cent pure while playing pool if I were playing in the cellar of the Vatican.

This feeling goes back a long way. When I was only six years old and getting acquainted with numbers in school, the sign painted on the window of the ground-floor poolroom in our neighborhood said, "POOL—2½ CENTS A CUE."

This puzzled me very much, because I couldn't figure out how the half cent could be paid. For a while, I tried to dope out this problem for myself, without asking anybody, but I was unable to do so. So one day I asked my mother about it. My mother was a widow who ran a little candy store at the corner of Lawrence and Elm Streets in a small New England town, and we lived in back of the store—my mother, my younger brother, and I.

"Mama, are there any half cents?" I asked her in the store. "How do you pay for anything that's a half a cent?"

"You know there aren't any half cents," my mother said. "You've waited-on in the store enough to know that. Is it something in school? Why do you ask me about such a silly thing?"

"It says on the window of the poolroom—it says, 'Two and a half cents a cue,'" I explained. "How do they pay that—Joe Shine and those men that go in there?"

In an instant, I could see that I had asked something wrong, something that alarmed my mother.

"You just let Joe Shine and those men go in there, and you never mind what it says on that old poolroom window," my mother said. The way she said it made me aware for the first time that there was something pretty bad about going into the poolroom.

It was a long time before I got the half-cent thing straightened out, because our conversation was shunted off right then and there, and I don't remember when or how, finally, I discovered that one person doesn't play pool by himself, and as long as there were two, it would be two times two and a half cents, or a nickel.

It was also a long time—something like ten or eleven years after that—before I was able to go into the poolroom. All those years, it was an unspoken ambition of mine to be able to go in there. It was illegal to have minors in poolrooms, but the man who ran the poolroom, an Armenian named Alfred Avakian, put a kind of rubbery interpretation on the word "minor." To him, the question of who was a minor and who wasn't hinged largely on pants. Males in short pants were minors; males in long pants tended to be of legal poolroom age. To be sure, a boy couldn't prance into the poolroom the very first day he changed from wearing short pants to wearing long pants. For admission to the poolroom, the pants had to have a little age on them. In those days, kids wore knee pants until they were fifteen or sixteen, depending on their physique, and a boy was usually pretty near seventeen before he could go into the poolroom with any confidence that he would be permitted to stay there and to play.

When I slipped furtively into the poolroom a few times during my early long-pants days, I was put out by Alfred. There came a day, however, when I got by with it, and there came a time when I was able to play a tidy little game of pool. Never got to be a "shark," like a select few of the fellows who had been in my class in Caesar's *Gallic Wars*, but I got to be better than fair. Thinking of it now, I believe I was more than a little swell-headed about my pool. I must have been.

One day, I was sitting in the tiny parlor in back of the store reading a book called *Shorthand Tom*. This book was about a young fellow who made great strides in the fields of business, adventure, and romance by reason of his superb skill at writing shorthand. There was one part where Shorthand Tom helped to capture a gang who had contraband on a ship, but I don't recall how writing shorthand worked into that part of the story. Anyway, I was both reading and toying with the notion of studying only shorthand—dismissing all other subjects as extraneous and skipping college—when my mother came in and asked me to do an errand. I was often lolling in the living quarters back of the store while my mother was working quite hard in the front part, and my mother was indulgent about that.

"This is the first of the month," my mother said, "so I want to pay Dixie Sullivan the insurance money."

"Ma, let me finish this, will you, Ma?" I said, meaning the life of Shorthand Tom.

"Oh, there's no hurry, John," my mother said. "It's early, and Dixie Sullivan's will be open all afternoon, until six o'clock."

"I'm almost finished, Ma," I said.

"All right," she said. "Then I'll give you the money and the bill, and you can go downstreet and pay it. I could wait until the tenth, the way some of them do, but I always pay right on the first of the month, and then nobody can say I'm slow pay."

"All right, Ma. Soon as I'm finished, I'll go," I said.

"See, it says on the bill, 'Payment due when bill is presented, or tenth of month at latest,'" my mother said, and I glanced at the bill she showed me. It was for ten dollars, a quarterly insurance payment.

My mother was always good to me, but she was extra good that day. After she had given me Dixie Sullivan's insurance bill and ten dollars with which to pay it, she gave me a quarter for myself. I had said that I'd like to go to the Premier, the movie house, while I was downstreet.

"Why don't you have a nice glass of Moxie before you start?" she said. "It's a hot day, and it's good for you."

My mother opened a bottle of Moxie from the store's supply, poured me a glass, and said, "Good for the nerves, eh, John?" She laughed. "Isn't that what they say about Moxie?"

On my way down past the Common to Dixie Sullivan's office, on Essex Street, I met Danny McCafe. Danny, who was my age, is the only fellow I ever met who had the name McCafe, which was pronounced as if it were spelled McKayfe.

"What do you say we go to the Majestic?" Danny asked me. The Majestic was absolutely the fanciest poolroom in town. The men who racked up the balls there wore white coats, and there were two billiard tables, as well as about twelve pool tables.

"I was going to the movies, after I do an errand," I said.

"We could shoot a little yellow-ball," Danny said. "How about a nice little game of yellow-ball-in-the-side? Got any money?"

"Oh, I got some money," I said. "Only, I was going to the Premeer. But I'll shoot you a game."

So we went to the Majestic. I had it in for Danny McCafe a little. He beat me around Alfred Avakian's quite often, but I was improving fast, and I hadn't played him for some time.

We played the first game for a dime, and I beat him. Yellow-ball is a game where whoever knocks the one-ball, which is yellow, into the right-hand side pocket wins the game. The right-hand side of a pool table is the side on your right when you're standing at the end of the table that has the manufacturer's nameplate on it—in this case, at the Majestic, Brunswick-Balke-Collender.

I beat Danny McCafe two games for a dime, and I beat him two more games, all in a row, for a quarter each, and I don't think to this day that he was giving me a come-on and lying down on me. Playing for a quarter was not common with us, but in the Majestic we tended to play for more than we played for in Alfred Avakian's crummy joint.

We worked up, finally, to playing for a dollar a game, and I remember that by that time about five people were watching us. I felt pretty big, even when I was losing. In the end, I lost the ten dollars insurance money.

"Now I *got* to do that errand!" I said chokingly to McCafe while I was paying him my last dollar. "Jeez, it's nearly six o'clock."

I didn't wait for Danny to go out of the Majestic with me. I almost ran out, in a hurry to be alone. I was appalled by what I had done. More than that, I was terrified about how to get out of it.

It must have been nearly seven o'clock when I finally went into the public library, which was open until eight, and went to a corner, between the bookshelves, where there was a table and nobody around. In big letters I painfully wrote on the bill, "Rec'd Paym't, Dixie Sullivan."

That's what I gave my mother when I got back to the store. I gave it to her quick, before she asked for it. I worried that night about whether I should have waited until she asked for the receipted bill. Awake, worrying, I remembered all the other times I had paid that kind of bill, and it seemed, in my memory, that each time I had stuck the receipt in my pocket someplace, and when I had come back to the store, my mother had had to ask for it and I had had to fish in all my pockets before I found it. Did she notice that I had come right into the store and handed it to her, without her asking? I wondered about that for a long time that night.

In the conscience-tortured days after that, I looked ahead with the greatest fear to the eleventh of the month. That was because I remembered the "tenth of month at latest" that was on Dixie Sullivan's bill. I feared that he would get in touch with my mother precisely on the eleventh and that something terrible would happen.

Nothing did, on the eleventh.

Nor were my theft and forgery laid bare on the twelfth, the thirteenth, or on any of the days that immediately followed them. Then there was a period of relief from anguish when I reasoned that I had until the first of the next month before another bill would come in. Dixie Sullivan, I figured, was being lenient with my mother and would wait until then to remind her of the unpaid insurance premium. I also had a hopeful feeling, during this period, that a miracle would happen—that somehow I would get ten dollars and pay Dixie Sullivan, and nobody would ever know about the disastrous afternoon of pool. The rest of my life, because of those days, I have read in newspapers about trapped embezzlers and I have known in my heart that they, too, waited day after day for the miracle that never happened.

The last night of the month, hope of the miracle had thinned and I hardly slept. The next day, my mother, who wasn't laughing or joking, as she so often was, told me I would have to mind the store for a while, because she had to go downstreet. I knew.

She came back in a half hour. The minute she walked in, she said, "John, put the sign on the door. Please, please, hurry."

"The sign" was a little piece of cardboard that said, "Back in Five Minutes. Please Wait." It was used most rarely. I was shaking when I put it on the door.

"Come on, John," my mother said, and I followed her to the back of the store and into the parlor. She made me sit down next to her on the couch and she took my two hands. We were all alone. "Dixie Sullivan told me about the bill," she said. "Something kept me from telling him about the receipt, John."

"I did it," I said. And I told her how I had lost the money playing pool and had signed Dixie Sullivan's name to the receipt. I could not pull my hands out of my mother's hands.

It has taken me many years to know fully about those few minutes that followed, and the heart and attitude of my mother. It has taken me many years to realize that there was no word of chastisement from my mother, who is dead now, but only a hope of protecting me.

"So Dixie Sullivan doesn't know," my mother said. "John, John, John! Nobody knows. Whatever you do, John, don't tell a single soul about this. It's terrible, John, but it's all right. I'll pay Dixie Sullivan. Don't tell anybody, whatever you do. Don't even tell your Uncle Will."

All this goes to show why the pool-table people are wasting their time and money trying to convince me that I shouldn't feel sinful about playing pool. Not that it isn't an interesting game.

WHAT GRANDMOTHER CARTY TOLD US

When I read a story about the tenth Duke of Argyll in a recent issue of a magazine, I got to wondering, as I do whenever any Duke of Argyll is mentioned, whether my Grandmother Carty was making up stuff, passing along a legend, or imparting a well-known fragment of history when she used to talk to me about the Duke of Argyll years and years ago.

That was when I was a small boy, and spent a lot of time with Grandmother Carty, because my mother was too busy running a small candy-and-newspaper store at Lawrence and Elm Streets, Lawrence, Massachusetts, to spend much time with me and my brother Willie. What Grandmother Carty told me about one of the Dukes of Argyll has always stuck in my head. Also, it has made me think of all Dukes of Argyll as mighty nice fellows, and whenever a Duke of Argyll pops up in the news or in fiction, I can't help saying to myself, "God bless the Duke of Argyll!" It's a benignly haunting phrase that Grandmother told to us two kids.

She said that centuries ago there was a Duke of Argyll who was sorry for Scottish country people with itchy backs. She never made it clear to Willie and me why Scottish country people's backs were any more itchy than any other country people's backs, or, for that matter, any city people's backs. Grandmother Carty came from Ireland to Massachusetts, and, come to think of it, there was another phrase she passed on to Willie and me that I have never forgotten. She came across the ocean in a ship whose steerage fare was extremely low, and she said the immigrants like herself had to bring along at least part of their food for the voyage. She said that at the embarking place, wherever it was, a man hollered, over and over again, "All aboard that's going aboard! Carry your bread in your BOO-ZUM!" Meaning, I guess, carry a couple loaves of bread inside your shirt if you were a man, or inside your shirtwaist if you were a woman. Rhythmic, surging phrases like that, once I hear them, never seem to leave me, and I don't mind that even today, when I hear "All aboard!," why, I sing out inside my head ". . . that's going aboard! Carry your bread in your BOO-ZUM!"

Well, forget about bread in the bosom and let me get back to the Duke and the peasants with itchy backs. Grandmother Carty said the Duke of Argyll she was talking about had a truly fine concern for those people. So, she said, the Duke caused to be put up along the highways of the rural regions a series of stone posts, about as high as a person's shoulders, an average person's shoulders. They were not as close together as, say, Burma-Shave signs nowadays but perhaps two or three miles apart. When an itchy back got too itchy to bear, Grandmother told us kids, the afflicted Scot could go over to the next stone post he came to, lean against it, and rub the itchiness out of his back with a species of physical delight. At the same time, said Grandmother Carty, the grateful Scot would cry aloud, "God bless the Duke of Argyll!"

What is this that Grandmother told us? Is it a well-known legend, or did it happen, or what? Whatever it is, I say to myself, "God bless the Duke of Argyll!" whenever I come across the name. Seems to me the name's always showing up. Sometimes Grandmother Carty's words lead me to attribute even more to the Duke of Argyll than he merits, crediting him for odd, unrelated favors to mankind, regardless. For a long while, I thought that it was on the Duke of Argyll's estate that Rudolf Hess landed that time, even if more accurate minds, uninfluenced by any Grandmother Carty, knew it was on the grounds of the Duke of Hamilton that Ol' Hess plopped down. Wasn't some Duke of Argyll trying to dig up a treasure ship from the bottom of the ocean someplace? God bless him if he was. And what I wish is that somebody would go over to the library and get me straightened out about what Grandmother Carty told us. I could go and do this myself, but I never will, because I don't want to know badly enough to take all that trouble, and that's the God's truth.

"COME QUICK. INDIANS!"

Once I was a movie piano player in the days when films were silent. This was in Andover, Massachusetts, seat of the famed Phillips Academy. The movie house was down Main Street from the Academy, the region known as "the foot of the hill." The theatre was owned by a man named Sam Resnik.

I admit at once that I was a singularly bad piano player. I still am, although I have turned to other trades in the intervening years. But I did get twenty-four dollars a week from Resnik for playing piano for only about seven or eight hours a day, six days a week, and that was not hay. It was not piano-playing either, it was specialized noise. Two of us made a team. One was Nick Baudo, who was the operator. Nowadays they call them projectionists. I was the other member of the team, the piano player.

Nicky and I were good friends and we liked working together. We both lived over in Lawrence, four miles from Andover, about eighteen minutes on the streetcar on account of the stops and all. We'd meet on Essex Street in Lawrence about twelve o'clock, get on the Andover trolley car and go over to work. When we got to Andover, the first thing we would do in Andover Square would be go to Lowe's drugstore and have a chocolate milk shake, each of us. Money meant nothing to us. We were, as they say now, in the chips. I'd get a pack of Sweet Caps on the way out of Lowe's and I recall now how swanky a way I behaved just buying the cigarettes, because I was not engaged in any ordinary trade. I was a piano player.

Then it would be time for us to go down the hill, at right angles to Main Street, to the railroad station and get the cans of film for that day. We had to do that on Monday, Wednesday, and Friday. Each show ran two days—two afternoons and nights—Monday and Tuesday, Wednesday and Thursday, and Friday and Saturday.

When Nick picked up the cans of films at the railroad station, I remember now, I often said to him, "What have we got today, Nick?" and sometimes he would reply, "Sunbonnets and cows." That was a kind of code expression between us. It meant we had Mary Miles Minter. Miss Minter was one of the most popular stars in the Andover Theatre, as she was all over the country.

Sam Resnik would greet us as we got to the movie house. He was a little lame and he would come laboriously down the three or four steps from the theatre to the street and say: "Hello, boys, you got the stuff?"

"Hello, Mr. Resnik," Nicky and I would say in chorus. "We got it."

Of course, he knew we had the films. Nicky was obviously carrying them, the round silvery cans, but Resnik's question and our answer was just an exchange of words. Sam Resnik was not a voluble man, and it was hard for him to make conversation. He was a square shooter and Nicky and I both liked him.

One by one, or in the case of boys from the Academy, by fours and fives, the customers would start to go in. Nicky and I would stand in front, smoking. I remember how proud I was, loafing in front of the place and hearing, just often enough to make my spirits soar, someone say, nodding toward me, "That's the piano player." I'd look at Nicky then, and he'd look at me, good man that he was, and I fear I felt a little superior to my friend, because nobody ever said, "That's the operator."

It would get to be toward half past one. Nicky and I would go into the theatre and he would climb up the iron ladder to the operating room. On a good afternoon, by that time, there would be perhaps three hundred people seated. That was pretty good, when it is figured at fifteen cents for kids and twenty cents for grown-up people. Academy boys were estimated as grown-up people.

They had no popcorn machines or anything else, just a movie show, that's all. I'd take a last drag on the Sweet Caporal outside, the lights would be all on inside as I stepped in, and I would walk down the aisle in a kind of mild swagger. They'd clap. The applause was not for me. It was because they knew by my going to the piano the show was about to start. I took the applause as if it were for me, although in my head I knew better. It made me feel I was quite a guy. I was only nineteen or so.

The piano was an upright. It cost $268, and it came from Knuepfer & Dimmock, in Lawrence. I know because my mother had bought the same one, at two dollars a month, and that is where I had learned, if learning it could be called, to bang on the thing. It was down in a pit, but the pit had no depth. Mr. Resnik was not a stingy man, but he had to make all he could out of the theatre. So he squeezed in all the seats possible. The piano, in this pit, had its keyboard about a foot above the floor of the auditorium. So I sat on the floor. Mr. Resnik, long before, had had Nicky saw the legs off a kitchen chair and put it on the floor in front of the piano, and he bought a cushion for it. So, in a manner of speaking, I sat on the floor. On busy days, there was a spectator on either side of me, usually a kid, because only kids would want to sit that close to the screen and look directly up. Looking directly up is what I had to do all the time. Didn't bother me.

I'd adjust the cushion on the sawed-off kitchen chair and sit down. Overture.

That overture was a honey. Always march time. Frequently, in deference to the scholastic mob from Phillips Academy, I would give them a college march tune which to this day I still hear once in a while on the newsreels.

Behind me, during the overture, I would hear the scuffling of feet getting into anticipatory position, and the additional patrons coming in. Nicky, up in the booth, had control of the light on the piano. Once in a while he would flick it on and off, prankishly, in a kind of hello, or as if to say, "Here we go again."

The show would open with a travelogue, about some strange land far from Andover. One reel. For that I played noncommittal music, neither a waltz nor a polka, nor anything. Favorite one was "Wedding of the Winds." Kind of cozy.

Now the big feature!

(Memory may trick me at this point, and I do not want to do any injustice to Miss Minter, who was good. Yet there were pictures like this feature. I couldn't make them up.)

I had practically only one lead-in to the feature. It was "Chinese Lullaby" from *East is West*, starring Fay Bainter. That was good for the opening because it began in the middle of the piano with seven crashing chords, a pause, and then the same seven chords an octave higher. (For some reason, in silent-movie days, anything played hell-angone up on the piano was Chinese.)

After the two sets of chords came an arpeggio, and then I would swing into the simple melody, carried with the left hand. All the while, on the screen so immediately above me, the titles were being shown. Behind me, the shuffling of feet was growing less and less audible. The people were settling down.

On the screen, the interior of a cabin. A trapper is saying goodbye to his wife. He has a buckskin jacket and pants, and a Daniel Boone hat, a rifle under his arm. On the floor is a child, apparently eight months old, playing and showing, in a close-up, a set of Birdseye frozen curls.

Nice quiet music then. Until the dog shows up. He comes gallumping in, and I have to shift to "Has Anybody Here Seen Rover?" That was a piece that had a whistle part in it. When I came to the whistle part, the Academy boys behind me would whistle. Good dog music, that "Rover" number.

At this juncture, the plot sets in in earnest. I sail into some more homemade waltzes. They all sound suspiciously like nothing, except that they are all in three-quarter time.

The trapper, rather abruptly, has left the cabin. We look back in there and see it still contains the wife, the baby, and the dog. The *heimgemacht* waltzes continue. Maybe once in a while *Tales From the Vienna Woods* sneaks in, since I see a tree.

QUICK! flash of skulking Indians. I shift remarkably quickly into what was known as "Hurry No. 63." I had a book of short bursts of music, for movie piano players, which contained numbered "hurries," or excitement music, as well as "lentos," or gentle stuff, and so on. My favorite hurry was No. 63. That was a thing played alternately with the left and right hand, agitato, as they'd call it at Carnegie Hall. At almost the same time I would work in some Indian music. That consisted mostly of banging a chord of A natural and E natural over and over with the left hand and playing any old thing with the right.

The Indians move near the cabin. I keep rolling on A flat with both hands. We're inside the cabin again. The wife is at her tasks. Waltz. Baby and dog are playing together. It is a lovely scene. Quick version of "Anybody Here Seen Rover?" mixed up with "Rock-a-bye Baby in the Treetop," both fast versions.

Back to the Indians. I have to shift fast here. The Indian music almost gets mixed up with the waltz, "Hurry No. 63," "Rover," and "Rock-a-bye," but somehow I manage it.

This is an exciting part, and to top it all, the light on the piano begins to blink. Nicky is keyed up too. I glance back over my shoulder and see, through the square hole in the operating room, the dark Italian eye of my pal. It is a laughing eye and it is a friendly eye, which spurs me on to new endeavor. I give the piano complete hell.

The Indians start shooting arrows. Not plain arrows. Arrows with lighted paper or something like it on them. The theory is that the cabin is so highly inflammable that the touch of one piece of lighted paper against it would turn it into a holocaust. It does, indeed, for one arrow, with lighted paper, hits the cabin in a close-up.

That calls for fire music. Easy. Just hit A flat high up and roll it. A flat rolled is fire music, I don't care what you say.

The Missus, as she might be called for handiness, glances through the window and sees the flames. Sees the Indians, too. I play tragic music. Very low. Very somber. Minor chords.

Quick shift again. The trapper's lady runs back to the baby, picks her up, clasps her in her arms. Seconds of soft music for close-up of mother and child.

To make everything clear, there is a close-up of the father, Boonehat himself, taking an animal out of one of his traps. That proves, in case anyone has forgotten, that he isn't home.

The interior of the cabin again. She's decided what to do. She finds, right in front of our very eyes, paper and pencil. She scribbles a note.

The note comes up big in a close-up. It says: "Come quick. INDIANS!"

She pins the note on the collar of the faithful dog, while I give them "Rover" fast again. She opens the door, the dog runs out, an Indian shoots at him, the blackguard, but misses. The cabin is flaming.

I am in an awful jam here, trying to figure out whether to play dog music, fire music, Indian music or mother music, and I wind up with a parlay of the whole outfit.

The dog, note on his collar, is shown running through the woods. I give him the full, twelve-dollar treatment of "Anybody Here Seen Rover?"

Next shot, stockade. Gate swinging wide open as dog enters. Complete pause on piano. Too dramatic for music.

Now I play a bugle call on the piano. That's while the commandant, who happens to be hanging around at the gate waiting for dogs to come in with notes on their collars, reads the tidy escriture.

Flash back to the cabin to prove the Indians haven't quit their nasty work. On the piano, "Under the Double Eagle." Horses and soldiers coming out through the stockade gate. "Loud and Fast" on the piano.

Indians almost upon the cabin, which is viciously aflame. I roll on A flat again, for fire. Indian stuff mixed in. Very exciting. Nicky blinks the light. I have no time to look back at him. I get louder and louder. "Under the Double Eagle" practically roars while the soldiers gallop up and the cowardly Indians, what are left of them, skulk away.

The trapper's wife, babe in arms with untouched curls, greets the soldiers. By chance, the trapper has come home at the same time. Big reunion all around.

I play "When You Come to the End of a Perfect Day" and Nicky and I go out and have a milk shake before the night show.

DO ANY THE DOCTORS KNOW ABOUT THIS, I WONDER?

Two sets of remarks came out one morning not so long ago in separate places in our neighborhood—in the lobby and in the delicatessen—and it was odd that they boiled down to the same thing, which is that horses can be good for people, at least in certain cases. Betting on horses, that is.

First, I was going down in the elevator for a walk around early, and Walter, the elevator man, said, about the fifteenth floor, "I was to Charles Town, just got back a few hours ago. I did real good."

Charles Town is a little race track in West Virginia, running that time of year, before they started up in New York. I knew well enough Walter is a horseplayer, but I was still surprised, because Charles Town is quite a distance.

"That's quite a trip just to see a few races," I said to him. I was thinking that it was indeed, especially because Walter is sorely troubled with arthritis that has bent his legs, and it must be that walking around is no picnic for him. He is, nevertheless, a cheerful man. He works the elevator nights, ordinarily, and he's a bachelor, lives in a furnished room up around Ninety-sixth and Broadway somewhere.

"I got it all worked out so it's a nice trip," he answered. "And this time I did real good. I beat the day for forty-five dollars, that's a nice sum of money."

There were few calls that early in the morning for the elevator, so I stood with Walter in the lobby a few minutes, and he told me about the trip to Charles Town. He was feeling fine about it, happy and a winner, standing there on his bent legs and having a big laugh every time he thought back over the victorious day he'd had.

"I got it worked out where I leave here, over near Times Square, on a bus quarter past one in the morning," he said. "I get a kind of a snooze coasting along in the bus and then we get into Washington seven o'clock, around seven o'clock or so. I got my pay, you know we get paid that night, and this time I took a chance, took the room-rent money along with me, instead like usual when I hold out the rent money for the room and give it to one of the other guys here on the elevator to hold for me in case I don't do good.

"Well, anyway, about quarter to eleven I get a train in Washington that goes right to the race track, that's in Charles Town, I mean, and meanwhile I had a couple hours I could sit in the station nice and cozy with the *Racing Form*, and look them over real good, nobody to bother me. That way by the time I get to the track I got them down real good in my mind, just exactly what I'm going to do, naturally subject to change is there a muddy track or scratches and all change the situation.

"Well, to make a long story short, I catch three winners altogether and out I walk, get the train to Washington, and have a nice dinner after I bought the paper and turn to read the charts they got in there about the races I just seen. It's a funny thing—now maybe you know about it. I seen all those races, but as long as I'm a winner, I bet I looked at those three winners I had in the charts at least five times during dinner, and the price they paid and all, and every time I look at those winners, it's like I was winning all over again, just looking at the charts. It's a great feeling. I had lamb chops, hash brown, ice cream and chocolate sauce on it, and two big cups of coffee, get me all set to go on the bus, and off we go again to dear old Manhattan and the dear old elevator—how do you like that—the dear old elevator? I count up, and like I told you, never mind expenses and all, the dinner was two dollars and thirty-five cents and I gave the guy two bits, the whole expenses I know exactly, which is twenty-two dollars and sixty cents, you know I don't do any drinking, but I had a few hot dogs at the track, like after each winner. It's a funny thing, if I'm losing I don't want to spare even hot-dog money, the twenty cents might break into an even two bucks in the end. What I mean is there's no way of betting a dollar eighty at a track, and if worst came to worst like it does sometimes, a man might find himself standing there with them going to the post and he got only a dollar eighty if he had went ahead and bought a hot dog. Well, I started to say, expenses and all, I walk in here an hour ago, off the bus and back at the old elevator, and I'm forty-five dollars ahead on the nose—exactly forty-five dollars more in my kick than when I leave the elevator to take the bus quarter past one the other morning. This was a fine trip this time."

I agreed with Walter that it must have been all right, but at the same time, noticing him, as he talked, shifting his weight from one bum leg to the other leg just as bum, I couldn't help going into all this a little further. "It's a lot of trudging around," I said. "I mean if you should happen to lose, on top of all that bus riding and, not to be a kill-joy, the room rent gone, too. Don't your legs hurt, Walter, here to West Virginia and back and not much real sleep?"

Walter, the winner, grinned and patiently said, "All of them, I mean the other elevator men and people up around where I room, all of them look at me like they're thinking that, or sometimes they ask me, but they don't understand I got it all worked out."

"Oh, I realize you enjoy it, Walter. I realize that," I said.

"It's kind of more than enjoying it," Walter said, this time not grinning. "Lemme explain. So I got bum legs, right? So I'm not married, right? So nobody's depending on me, right? O.K. Not a goddam thing in the world to do about the lousy, twisted-up legs. All right, I'm broke most of the time. I skimp on the eats, O.K. But lemme explain. A long while ago, I find out if I get all wrapped up in horses, make trips to Charles Town—I'm going to Lincoln Downs in Rhode Island with this forty-five bucks my next day off—well, if I make trips around to the races all wrapped up in horses, go out to Jamaica when they open up here, keep right on top of the horses reading every night during the night what happened that day wherever they're running, why, would you believe it, that makes my bum legs very, very unimportant. Maybe you don't understand what I mean?"

"A little, I do. A little," I said.

"Put it another way," said Walter. "I'm worrying so much about some horse's bum legs I'm thinking of betting on, I don't worry any more about my *own* legs. I don't stand around moaning, 'Oh, my poor legs! Oh, my poor legs!' Tell the truth, I don't know what I'd do without horses. This was a swell trip, no kidding."

The elevator bell rang, and Walter got in to go up to the twelfth, as it said on the indicator, and I left for a little walk.

My wife was away visiting that day, and so I thought I'd drop in the delicatessen and get a couple of those small cans of asparagus tips and heat them up at lunchtime on toast, a cinch to do.

When I went into the delicatessen, there was Irving, who had been out of the place for about three weeks, at home sick. He had a bad spell with his heart about three weeks before, or at any rate he thought his heart was going back on him one day and had to go home—scared more than anything, I suspect. Irving is a quiet, almost timid man in his early forties, with soft-mannered ways about him, and he doesn't seem to have much confidence. That is, he has an air that he expects things might go bad any minute. He has that air all the time, although it would seem that a quiet, decent man like him could rightfully expect that everything would be O.K. He wouldn't harm a fly.

I told him I was glad to see him back and asked how he was feeling. He said he was O.K., but he was going to take it easier from now on. It was a quiet time in the delicatessen, so Mat, the other man in there, dropped whatever he was doing and the three of us started schmoosing for a few minutes.

"No matter what you say," I told Irving, "you're looking fine. You look like a million bucks."

Irving looked at me through his glasses in an unbelieving way. It was like some kid in school that's discouraged and thinks he can't do anything right and the teacher all of a sudden tells him he got a B-plus and the kid can't believe it. "No kidding, do I look good?" he asked me, unconfident and serious.

"Sure you look good, din't you hear the man say you look good?" broke in Mat. He is almost the very opposite of Irving. He is full of confidence and bing-bang all day long, doing this and that, kidding the customers in a nice way, with the opposite air to Irving, meaning that Mat always acts that everything, no matter what it is, is going to turn out good enough, to say the least.

Irving brightened up a little bit, and he got gabby. Gabby for him, anyway. "Here's what I can't figure out," he said. "The minute I quit betting horses, I got sick. My heart went bad. Would you believe that?"

I know Irving is not a horseplayer like Walter, that I'd just been talking with. Irving only used to bet a couple of dollars maybe two or three times a week on some horse that's whispered around the neighborhood. Our neighborhood is a great neighborhood for horse-whispering.

"In a way, I can too figure it out," Irving went on. "Like when I put a couple bucks on a horse, say eleven o'clock in the morning—why, all afternoon I worry about the horse, did he win, din't he win, did he pay a bundle if he win, did he lose by a nose, did he walk away with it. Worrying and hoping altogether mixed up. Course, I'm working all the time, pretty busy, but after a while you get so you do the work around a delicatessen like a machine, and inside your head you got room for worrying. I thought maybe it was wrong to bet on horses so much, even six or eight bucks a week maybe, so I cut it out. Anyway, I had seven losers in a row and I cut it out. Would you believe it, no sooner I cut it out than I get sick? I got worrying about my heart instead worrying about did I win, did I lose, how did the horse come out. Instead, I keep hearing my heart jump if I lift up two or three cases Del Monte peaches or cans tomatoes or something, and first thing I know, the heart goes bad on me worrying. I got half a mind start betting horses again, supposing I do have seven losers. Better than a bum heart."

Mat slapped Irving on the back. "Do any the doctors know about this, I wonder?" Mat said, and roared laughing. "Do any the doctors know horses is good for people?"

THE TELEVISION HELPS, BUT NOT VERY MUCH

When I got into the cab to go down from Seventy-second and Second to Forty-fourth and Fifth, it seemed stuffy, so I gave the handle a twist and let the window down a little.

"That's all right," the driver said. "I'll take and close this here one up, if it's all right with you."

"Oh, sure," I said.

"If they're both open, it makes a draft on the back of my neck," he explained, nicely. "I ought to be home, I got a cold."

"That's about all you can do for these colds," I said.

"Go to bed is the best thing," he said. "Only with me, maybe I'm better off milling around in the hack. Too lonesome home. I lost my wife."

"Oh," I said. "Was it recently it happened? I mean when did she die?"

"Pretty near a year ago at that," he said.

We were moving along Seventy-second, getting near Fifth. Traffic was slow even before we hit Fifth.

Some of them are gabby, the hack drivers. This one wasn't, even though it turned out we talked all the way. It didn't seem to be gab. It seemed natural talk, almost as if we had known each other a long while.

"I got myself a television," he said. "For company like. The television helps, but not very much, at that."

"No kids or anything?" I asked.

"No, we didn't," he said. "We didn't have any children at all. No in-laws, even. See, we come from another city here. More than twenty years here. We made out all right. It ain't the best job in the world, but we battle along all right together, twenty years. Long time."

"Yes," I said.

"Like I say about the television, I can get interested, all right, like a fight or even sometimes those cowboy movies they put on. Just the same, sooner or later the television got to wind up, don't it? I mean, it comes to the end of whatever the show is or wrassling or whatever it is."

"I know what you mean. The thing goes off," I said.

"Yeah, the thing winds up and there I am again," he said. "I'm alone again and I maybe go to the icebox and get a beer, but it's lonesome. Do you think it wouldn't be so bad if I had kids somewheres? Even if they were grown-up somewheres?"

"I don't know," I said. "I don't have any children."

"They say it's different if you have kids," he said. "Even if you lose your wife. That's what they say."

"Some people say that," I said. "I don't know. Did she die suddenly?"

"She was sick about two weeks, that's all," he said. "But the more I think about it, she must have been sick a long while. The doctor said she must have been. She didn't like to have doctors. Matter of fact, it was me got him finally. And I had to go to him and say to him, look, I said to him, she's going to be sore at you coming in. I said, she's against you before she even lays an eye on you, I says, so please don't mind if she acts sore. Later on, after it's all over, he tells me it was too late, the thing that was the matter with her it was too late to do anything."

"That was tough," I said.

"Thing is I keep worrying," he said. "Was it my fault maybe I wasn't more bossy and make her get a doctor? What do you think? I worry about it all the time. Like that's why I didn't stay home with this damn cold. I'd be around the house thinking maybe we'd be together just the same as always, me coming home and having supper and help with the dishes and we both sit down and have a couple beers, listen to the radio, if I made her get a doctor and never mind how much beefing, squawking she do about it. What do you think?"

"Oh, I don't know," I said. "That's a tough one to answer." It wasn't that I wanted to give the driver a short answer, but there I was, thrown into the middle of a man's life, and I didn't know the man.

"You're telling me it's a tough one!" he said. "Just the same, I got the notion you're kind of sensible, and after all, what harm is there? Like I tell you, I got no in-laws, no kids, I had an idea I'd talk it over with somebody. Them guys around the garage, what the hell, they're dumber than me, even. What do they know? Know what I mean?"

"Yes," I said.

"Like, the truth of the matter, I could get married again right away," he said. "Those guys all said don't be a sucker—don't be a sucker, they said."

"About what?" I asked.

"Well, might as well out with it," he said. "There's this girl I could get married with. Do you think I look forty-eight?"

"I don't know," I said. "I hardly looked at you much. Just got in the cab, hardly looked at anything except that it was a cab."

"I guess I look forty-eight all right," he said. "Well, this girl is thirty-one. She has a little baby. I met her at a guy's house; he had me there eating Christmas. Didn't want me eating in a coffeepot first Christmas I had no wife, he said."

"She divorced or what, the girl with the baby?" I asked.

"No," he said. "Thing is she was a Wac—you know, in the war they had women they called them Wacs. She was in Chicago and she married this fellow, and it's only three months after and he dies on her. So in a little while she had the baby, and that's the way it is. She's a very nice woman, only seventeen years younger. I mean seventeen years younger than me. I told you I'm forty-eight, didn't I? Well, this girl, or maybe I should say woman, she's thirty-one and got the baby and thirty-one from forty-eight, that's seventeen, see what I mean?"

"Yes," I said.

"The guys at the garage say that's too much difference, and with the kid and all," he said. "What they don't understand is I like the kid, see what I mean? I bought the kid a couple toys, and you should see how this girl appreciated it I bought toys for the kid. Don't think for a minute this is any kind of a fly-around dame. She's nice. She lives with her mother now, and she works when she can get work."

"I bet she's all right," I said.

"You can say that again," he said. "Just between ourselves, she proposed to me, you might say. Know what I mean? Honest to God, it ain't this sex stuff, that ain't the main thing at all, no matter what the guys in the garage say; they're always harping about that angle. What I mean is—well, I would like to have her around, kid and all. I like the kid. He ain't very big yet, but he could look at the television, too. Like I say, it helps keep me from getting so goddam lonesome but it don't take care of things altogether, know what I mean? Will you tell me one thing? I mean, I want you give me your opinion—it's pretty near Forty-fourth Street after we get this light."

"O.K., what is it?" I said.

"Never mind the guys in the garage—do *you* think it'd be all right if we got married? You think it would work out?"

"You're coming at me rather suddenly with this," I said, sparring for time.

"I know," he said. "I don't say I'll do what you tell me, but just the same, you got an idea now how things are, don't you?"

"Well, I think I understand," I said.

"O.K., then, what do you think?"

"All right, you asked me," I said, and drew a deep breath. "I say go ahead and get married. That's what I say, sight unseen."

"Right!" he said, speaking almost loud for the first time in our rolling acquaintance. "That settles it. I guess I only needed somebody, anybody, say go ahead. Like give me a little shove, you might say. I'm going to do it. It's too goddam lonesome. And I like the kid, no fooling. This is Forty-fourth. Do you want this corner or the downtown side?"

"This corner's all right," I said, and got out and hollered back, "Good luck!"

"O.K., doc," he said. He was smiling, and now I guess he'll go ahead and get married. Probably never see him again. I didn't even look at his name beside the picture in the frame, but I hope they make out all right.

AN OLD COLLEGE CHUM

The cab I took at Seventy-second and Second was driven by a lean, easy-smiling man of about my own age, which is getting along up there. Although he was not forcibly gabby, as so many hackies and quite a few passengers are, we did start talking. Perhaps I started the talk, making some remark about the Giants, because I'd been watching them on television alone in the house a few minutes before. I'd had nobody to make remarks to about some of the more startling plays, and it is almost impossible for me to watch a ball game, on television or in real life, without making remarks to somebody. There's no "perhaps" about it, I *did* start the talking, going over west on Seventy-second.

When we got down to Park and Fifty-fourth or Fifty-fifth, somewhere in there, a red light pulled us up, over near the island that's in the middle of Park, and there was a traffic policeman on duty there.

It was drizzling some, and he had on his heavy black raincoat and his black rain hat. We were the front car in the stopped line of traffic, and so not far from the cop.

He was a fairly grim-faced cop, but when he glanced over and saw the man driving my cab he gave a big grin. "Hi!" he hollered to my cabby, as the crosstown traffic drifted by easy for a moment.

"Hi!" the hackie answered, leaning relaxed out the left-hand window. "How you doing?"

"O.K.," the cop answered. "How you making out these days?"

"Not too bad, not too bad," the cabby answered, and then the light went green, the cop waved us all on, and we started down Park again.

I could see the hackie looking at my reflection in the rear-vision mirror. I got the idea he was expecting me to say something.

"Friendly kind of cop," I said.

The driver laughed. He had an unobtrusive, easy laugh. "He's an old college chum of mine," he said.

I hadn't heard the expression "an old college chum" for years and years. It's an old-timey expression, but then, as I said, the driver and I seemed to be about the same age, neither one of us a kid.

"College?" I said.

"Well, that's a kind of a gag," the driver said. "I mean we graduated from the Police Academy together. Way back in 1923. Never forgot each other."

That stopped me for a few seconds, not wanting to be nosy. But I could see the hackie was still watching me in the rear-vision mirror, so I asked him how come he wasn't on the cops, too, or did he go on and retire or what?

"No," he said. "I almost got on the cops but I didn't." He quit smiling and laughing. He seemed to be figuring whether to go on or not, far as I could tell in the mirror, and then he half turned around as we stopped at another red light.

"You went into something else, huh?" I asked.

"I had to go into something else," he said. "But I wanted to go on the cops, like him. I lost out on going on the cops. It's a funny thing, what happened. I think of it every time I see him, and I guess he thinks about it, too. One day we talked about it, one dopey day, Labor Day I guess it was, hardly any traffic and I was riding empty. No use making any bones about it, it doesn't make any difference any more anyway. What happened was they found out I had a petty-larceny rap. A black mark on me. That ended me with them."

The way he talked, the hackie seemed neither resentful nor regretful either, merely thinking about it, brought to mind by the cop hollering "Hi!" The light changed, and we went on.

"I was only a kid and I was delivering groceries," the hackie said. "I went in a house with groceries, and there was nobody in the kitchen and I saw a watch on a table and I took it. Might as well say the truth, I stole it. It doesn't make any difference any more.

"I don't understand what small things a guy remembers when he gets to be our age," the driver said. "I remember it was what they call a 'gold-filled watch.' Course, I know that means the case was gold-filled, what I mean, only part gold. Why I remember is after they caught me and the time came they read out the charge on petty larceny, the guy read out 'gold-filled watch' and I remember thinking then, kind of daffy, about a watch filled inside with gold instead of works.

"Well, that had nothing to do with it, it's only that I never forget about the gold-filled part. What the hell, I was only a kid when I did it.

"Thing was, when I took the examinations for the cops, I didn't put it down about the petty-larceny rap. I was a man then, and honest to God I forgot all about the watch thing that happened when I was only a kid.

"That was it. Maybe if I had put it down, they would have overlooked the whole thing. But they found out on their own hook, they look you up matter of routine, and they found out about the watch. From then on, it was no go with me. I made a good mark, too. I got an eighty-eight and two-tenths, it was. That cop you saw on Park, he got the highest in the class, or pretty near it, he got a ninety-two and something."

It seemed to be my turn to speak, so I said, "And he's still on traffic, with a ninety-two and on the cops all this time since 1923?"

"That's the way it works out," the driver said. "Still on traffic, him, and still pushing a hack, me. That's what we were talking about that Labor Day or whenever it was we talked.

"Still and all, we aren't so bad off, either one of us, that's what we said that Labor Day or whenever it was. Funny thing, after all these years he seemed more sorer than I was after all these years about them holding that watch against me and not letting me get on the cops the way I wanted to get on. He said a couple of times it could have happened to any kid. Kids don't have to be bad to do a thing like that all of a sudden, take a watch from a kitchen table delivering groceries.

"You don't have to believe me. It doesn't make any difference whether you do or not. But honest to God, that watch was the only thing wrong I ever did in my whole life. No, I don't mean that, I did plenty things wrong, I mean that was the only thing illegal, stealing, I ever did in my whole life before the watch or since the watch. That cop up there'd tell you the same thing, never was in a jam, I mean a criminal jam you might say."

We were getting near where we were going in the cab, and the hackie stopped talking for a minute or so. I could see him grinning again in the rear-vision mirror.

"Oh, what the hell, it work out all right after all," he said, before we stopped at the curb, on West Forty-first. "That's what we said that Labor Day or whenever it was. He asked me did I still wished I had got on the cops and I told him sometimes I did, and what does he say but he sometimes see me go by and wished he was a hackie. Turns out I got a wife and family, two good kids, both boys growing up and I make out all right, and he got a wife and family, he got two girls and one boy and he says he's doing O.K. It work out all right when all is said and done."

TELL HIM WHAT HAPPEN, JOE, SEE WILL HE BELIEVE YOU

Three Italian boys were standing together down at the far end of the bar this sunny noontime when I went in our best neighborhood gin mill for a beer. It was very hot.

I knew two of the boys—neighborhood guys, they were—and the third one, slim, and in his twenties, I didn't know. He was a stranger, but he had something of the same look of the two fellows I did know. I couldn't quite make out what they were doing while I stood nearby and had my beer. There were three of them, as I said, but they had four glasses in front of them, all beers. One of the boys would take the fourth glass and from it he would pour a little sip of beer into each of the three other glasses, and then the three of them would lift up their glasses and drink a tiny bit of beer like a toast. I couldn't figure it out, especially because it didn't seem like some kind of gag; all three of them were sad-looking to a certain extent.

Usually, if I happened to bump into those two of the three that I knew in there in the saloon, why, we'd right away begin gabbing about the Giants, or the Yankees, or the horses, or something like that. But while this pouring beer little by little out of nobody's glass, as you might call the fourth glass, went on, there wasn't any gab at all, outside of my two friends nodding hello. Eventually, though, they finished the beer, fourth glass and all. The one they call Vinny, his name is Vincenzo, beckoned me to move over and join them, and he must have noticed me looking at the fourth empty glass as if I was wondering what the hell was going on, which I was.

"We're drinking the old man's beer," Vinny said. "You was away from the neighborhood a couple days, wasn't you? I guess you didn't hear we had our old man die on us?"

"No, I didn't hear that," I said. "I'm sorry."

"We just come from the funeral," Vinny said. "This here is Al, my other brother, you never met him."

Al was the third man, the one I didn't know, of course. We shook hands and I said something again about being sorry for his father dying. He said "Thank you," and asked me if I would have a beer, as they were signalling Johnny, the bartender, for another round, no extra glass this time.

"We were making out the old man was here with us," Vinny said. "So we had Johnny pour an extra glass of beer and we all drank some of it, you seen us. I figured you were wondering what was it all about. It was like having him here with us. He liked a glass of beer, the old man did."

We all took a little swig of the fresh glasses of beer Johnny poured out, and Vinny said, to me as well as to his two brothers (the third one's name is Joe), "He sure was here with us all right, wasn't he, Joe?"

"I can't help thinking he was," Joe said. "Especially after you think what happen, he sure was. Don't you think so, Al?"

"I know he was," Al said.

"Al comes from Haverhill, up in Massachusetts," Vinny said to me. "He come down for the funeral. We just come from the funeral, it's all over. Al got to go back to Haverhill. That's where he lives, Haverhill."

There was something else in the air. I didn't know what it was, the next minute or two, because nobody was saying anything.

"Tell him what happen, Joe, see will he believe you," Vinny said suddenly. We waited for Joe.

"The old man was a shoemaker," Joe said. "Well, we're driving to the church in my car, this is only a couple hours ago. So when I'm going fast, like on Second Avenue, I keep hearing something go tap, tap, tap on a wheel somewheres. I don't say anything, because I think I'm going nuts maybe. Tap, tap, tap on the automobile wheel, and it's like when I'm a kid listening to the old man going tap, tap, tap on a shoe when he's working. The old man was a shoemaker, like I told you.

"Anyway, I get to the church, I mean we all get to the church, all in my car, Vinny and Al and me, and we have the old man's funeral. So after a while it's over and you won't believe what happen. What happen is after it's over and I go look at the tires and the wheels, and Vinny I think it was, maybe it was Al, ask me what's the matter. I told them I thought I heard some kind of a noise like a tap, tap, tap, like, on our way to the church with the old man like him tapping shoes. Al or maybe it was Vinny says by Jeez he heard it, too, on the way to the church. So I was relieved when I heard them say that, because I wasn't too sure did I really hear that noise or was I getting cuckoo.

"Well, I got around to look at the far-off wheel on the back, the last wheel I looked at, and what do you think was stuck into the tire? It was a tap, I mean like the bottom lift off of the heel of a shoe. It was stuck in the tire. The old man was a shoemaker, and here it was, a bottom lift off of the heel of a shoe, like God knows how many thousands of things like that the old man in his life tapped onto shoes. That's what was stuck into the tire and it should have punctured the tire and it never did."

"The old man sure was with us all right," Vinny said when Joe had finished. "No kidding about that, the shoemaker piece of leather stuck in the tire and all!"

Then he turned to me and asked, "Do you believe it, what happened?"

I said of course I did.

"Well, Al got to get back to Haverhill—eh, Al?" Joe said.

"Yes, I got to get going," Al said. "I bet they won't believe me in Haverhill when I tell them what happen. The old man being right with us, I mean, tap, tap, tap all the way to the church."

THE CAP

Here's what my wife told me one time. She said that when she was eight or nine years old, she was living on the family place in the country, in Rhode Island. It was not an ornate place, it had no flash to it, but it was kind of solid and hereditary—fields, and meadows, and a large house, and a stable, and men working around.

She told me she would be in love with one or another of the young men who had been hired by the gardener, Tom Blanchard, to help him. The one she told me about was Norman Morton.

"Why did you fall in love with him?" I asked my wife idly, but not too goddam idly, because even if it was twenty-two or twenty-three years ago, I tended to get a little sore at this Norman Morton.

"Well," she said, "he would come by, pushing a lawnmower, and he would rumple my hair or he would say, 'Good morning, Miss Mary,' and I would get excited because he had noticed me."

"Oh, yes," I said. "Go ahead, tell me about him."

Then my wife said that it was all secret, the way she was in love with Norman Morton. She said that when she was eating her breakfast, it felt fine to think that they didn't know anything about what was in her mind. By "they" she meant her family. They thought she was simply a little girl having cereal, and all the time she was looking at the clock on the wall and thinking it would be only one hour and twenty minutes, maybe one hour and twenty-five minutes, before she would be on the bench under the weeping willow and *he* would come by, pushing the lawnmower, and maybe say, "Good morning, Miss Mary."

There were fine weeks while she was in love with Norman. It would last her all day, the memory of him pushing the lawnmower, and everything he said to Blanchard seemed to have a lasting brightness to it, all secret and cherished as she lay waiting to go to sleep at night. Maybe it would have been the simplest sort of remark, as my wife thinks of it now. He might have said, "Don't you think we ought to use the clippers on the hedge, Tom?" It seemed to her, though, that this question about the hedge took on a special significance. Sure they ought to use the clippers on the hedge, and nobody but Norman would have thought of that, my wife felt then (when she was eight or nine).

One day, leaving after the morning's work to go back to the village, Norman forgot his cap, and left it where he had thrown it in the heat of the August morning. It was on the lawn. She watched him go, and when she was sure he was away down the road toward the village, she got the cap, ran over to the stable, and trudged up the stairs and put it in the loft. Norman's cap.

It was only a couple days later that she overheard something about him. She wasn't supposed to hear it. She eavesdropped. She heard he was "in trouble with a girl." Norman must have been nineteen or so then.

He didn't show up that morning. She sat on the bench for a long while, but he didn't show up. And then another man came to help Blanchard—an old man, about twenty-five years old maybe. When she saw the new man, she ran over to the stable. She went up in the loft.

Do you know where she had put the cap? Well, she had put it

where Socksie, the cat, had had her kittens, in back of a big old chest that had books and stuff in it.

She took out the cap, and she said a prayer. She held the cap that was Norman's and she said, all by herself, "Please, God, get Norman out of trouble with the girl and have him come back. I will be a good girl if You will do that for me."

Reverently she put the cap back behind the chest, and she made up her mind to do something. "Every morning I will come over and hold Norman's cap and pray for him to get out of trouble with the girl so he will come back," she said to herself.

Every morning she did that. After breakfast, while people she didn't care about busied themselves around the place, taking care of the horses or once in a while mowing the lawn, she would get the cap and say the prayer.

A few weeks passed. She said to herself, "I will keep praying." Then, one morning, she went out on the back porch and found a baby robin that had fallen out of a nest. She climbed up the rainspout and put the scrawny, bony bird back in the nest, and sat in a chair, watching to see if the mother robin would appreciate what she had done. The mother robin never came back.

Norman never came back, either. Ten o'clock that morning, she suddenly had a thought. She thought, I haven't said my prayer. She walked slowly over to the stable. It was a duty. She didn't want to do it, but she had sworn to herself she would say this prayer every day. She went up and took the cap out, and it was all of a sudden only a cap. She said the prayer but her heart wasn't in it. It was a job now. She threw the cap in back of the chest. That was the end of that.

VENITE ADOREMUS

The smallest, smallest of happenings, perhaps wholly unimportant, is sometimes what a person remembers the most about all the Christmases that have been granted him, and that's how it is with me. I remember one small happening on a Christmas Eve long ago, and it started still longer ago, when I took piano lessons as a boy.

The way my mother got the piano from Knuepfer & Dimmock was by paying fifty cents a week for Heaven knows how many weeks. The piano cost $268, but that doesn't mean it was exactly 536 weeks before it was paid for. Some weeks, when there had been an exceptionally good week in the candy-and-newspaper store my mother ran, she would send me to Knuepfer's with a dollar, or perhaps a dollar and a half, to pay, because my mother never liked to owe money, even in the form of installments, and she wanted to have the piano paid for as soon as possible.

Perhaps buying the piano, in the first place, was not a good idea. Yet, as I think now so many years later and with my mother long gone, the idea was in keeping with her deep desire to get everything good for me and my younger brother that a widow running a little candy store could possibly get. No realization of the fact ever came to me at the time. I took it for granted when I got a bicycle, a luxury; I took it for granted I'd get what I wanted from Ma if I pestered her long enough. In other words, I was spoiled.

I hadn't asked for the piano. My mother thought it would be nice to have one for me, and in those days, too, more people used to have pianos in their homes than do now.

Reluctantly, over the early years, I learned to play it, after a fashion. I had to practice an hour a day, and my grandmother would sit by the piano chair and count "*One*-two-three, *one*-two-three" (if it was a waltz) while I practiced and asked every few minutes if the hour wasn't up yet.

Some years, not many, went by and I began to get some fun out of the piano because I could play—still after a fashion—popular stuff like San An-tony, An-tony-oh. And some more years passed and I was in my late teens and, one way or another, I got a job in "that place."

"That place" was Boehm's Café, pronounced "Baym's." My job there was playing the piano every night, except Sunday, from seven o'clock until eleven o'clock, which was closing time for such places in Massachusetts in those days.

I guess I shouldn't have been there in Boehm's at all. For one thing, I was only eighteen or nineteen, and the law said nobody under twenty-one years of age could be allowed in places where liquor was sold. This was Massachusetts, and to be a habitué of Boehm's, or even an occasional visitor, was to be a rather high-flying person, someone with a touch of the roisterer and reveller about him. Not that anything bacchanalian actually went on there. Just the same, it was a severe shock to my uncles and aunts, of whom there were many, that Mary T., my mother, would let John do such a thing as play piano in a grogshop, a gin mill, or—in plain, blunt words—a saloon. Merely because they sold planked steaks, lobsters broiled alive, and other such Lucullan stuff did not make Boehm's Café any more suitable a place for a youth to be in, especially night after night, as I was.

I was spoiled, though. My mother couldn't do a thing with me, as the saying went. My brother Willie, it seems to me now, never did anything wrong, never anything to make my mother, or the uncles and aunts, get to worrying about him being on the road to ruin. As for me, they thought that was the only road that ever caught my eye or lured my footsteps.

I guess my mother protested about my working in what she called "that place." She even hesitated about saying "Boehm's Café." It was "that place" whenever she spoke of it.

I loved the place wildly. I loved the show-off opportunities it gave, the chance to bang out "Chinatown, My Chinatown" with a lot of fancy stuff up on the high keys, in pseudo-Chinese manner between choruses. And, truth to tell, I loved the beers that moneyed listeners at the tables sent up for me when I played "request numbers"; I loved being around the smallish town in the daytime and playing the dashing, partly wicked role of "the piano player at Boehm's." The money was good, too: twenty-four dollars a week.

My brother Willie was home with my mother every night. I was in Boehm's, and the beers on top of the upright piano there were numerous. Sometimes a guest, mad with money, sent up champagne to "the professor," who, in truth, knew nothing about music. I really didn't. I didn't play good, but I played loud. I had a few jokes I could use from the piano. One was referring to myself as "Boehm's three-piece orchestra—coat, vest, and pants." Yak-yak! . . .

My folks never got over it, though, never got over their feeling that I, John, was the disgrace of the family. They were all proud, the men as well as the women, that they didn't drink at all, and that wasn't true of me. Not in "that place." Likely, many a prayer was sent up for me by the uncles and aunts. Perhaps by my mother too, but I'm not too sure. She hated Boehm's, she hated my being there, I knew, but she thought an awful lot of her son John, no matter what he did. The other John, my father, a tall, six-foot bricklayer, had been killed in a fall from a building when I was two years old and Brother Willie was two months. From that baby day of mine, from the day Big John was killed, well, Little John, which was me, became "himself" in the house. It is that way, and will be forever, with folks who come from Ireland; the oldest male in the house is "himself," even if himself is toddling on the floor.

And "himself," little or big, got the best of everything there was to be got around the house. Nobody ever put it into words, but it was assumed that that was the way things would be. The house, in our case, meant a comfortable, though small, tenement which formed the back part of the candy store. That's where "himself" (me) was spoiled.

Like when there would be mashed potatoes on the table for supper, which was in the evening and which now we'd call dinner. The mashed potatoes would be in a big mound on a dish in the middle of the table. As soon as they were put on the table, hot from the tiny kitchen, my mother—or my grandmother, who lived with us in that small cozy place—would put a big chunk of butter on the top, in a little crater she made, like a volcano crater, on top of the mound of potatoes. The butter would melt as we four sat down at the table, melt into a golden puddle of deliciousness.

Well, my mother, with the big spoon in her hand, would break the edge of the volcano crater, and the melted butter would run down over one part of the mashed potatoes. That was the best part. And, without fail, never doing otherwise, my mother would take up great big spoonfuls of that part and put them on my plate. My brother's eyes would watch all this and, quiet child, quiet young man that he always was, he'd say nothing. The best part of the potatoes was for "himself," and "himself" was me. I took that for granted too. Spoiled. And from being spoiled, what was more natural than that I became, as the years went on, what they called "wild." Not delinquent, as they would say now, but wild. The guy who, at eighteen or nineteen, was night after night playing the piano in Boehm's, and sometimes not coming home at all.

This makes me wonder now, when I think about it, if I loved my mother for all this—a strange thing to wonder, since it is well known that everyone in the whole world loves his mother. Memory fails to tell me that I ever showed it. Memory says I took her for granted and took all the things she did for me for granted, and so, I suppose, I loved her. Maybe I was too busy being wild to show her that I did. So help me, I don't know. To the uncles and aunts—and since my father was dead the uncles and aunts felt a sort of extra ownership in me—I was the bad boy of the family. Echoes of what they said among themselves seemed to have reached me at times. "Mary T. working so hard in the store, and he never lifts a hand to help her," some of them said. "Isn't it too bad she ever had him take piano lessons at all? Think of it! Mary T. paid Professor Hamer one dollar an hour for lessons for him. And there he is, every night in Boehm's and everybody buying him things to drink. Poor Mary T.!"

Oh, the tenement back of the store was nice, but I liked the nights in Boehm's better. Seems to me now that I felt the delightful evilness of being there, although at the time I don't suppose I ever formulated that thought.

Rarely it was, but once in a while it was, that my mother tried, feebly I guess, to get me not to go to Boehm's any more, not to work there any more, not to play the piano there. She never saw the inside of Boehm's.

"Uncle Mike said he was in there one time, at that place," I can hear her saying, as she did once. "John, he says it's a terrible place for you. He thinks I oughtn't to let you go there at all."

I don't recall an answer to that, unless it was something like a simple, snorted, "Oh, Ma! You don't understand at all. You don't know what it's all about." Perhaps something like that.

Anyway, I paid no attention to her. It was Boehm's every night for me (except Sundays) and for my pal, Georgie Morrison. He was a real sporty guy, which is what I was trying to be. He even made six bucks a week more than I did. He got thirty dollars, in a town where other kids and young men were getting sixteen dollars and eighteen dollars working all day in the textile mills.

Georgie and I cooked up things. On a busy night in Boehm's they'd save a table for Georgie, a table near the piano. And Georgie would ask for a special number on the piano, like "Down in Jungletown." I'd play it, bad and loud, and Georgie would take a quarter from his pocket, throw it through the air so it would hit the piano with a clinking sound, and I'd pick it up off the floor and holler "Thank you!" to him, as if he were just a customer, not a pal I'd give the quarter back to later on. That maneuver would start other people throwing money to me—if not quarters, then nickels and dimes. All that besides the beers, and—as time went on—the whiskeys. It was evil and it was fun, and all the while I knew that my mother and Uncle Mike and all those other ones, they simply didn't understand, that's all. Supposing I was the bad boy? What about it? Willie was home, wasn't he?

There were places for Georgie Morrison and me to go to after eleven o'clock when I was through playing at Boehm's. Crap games, for one thing, in the back rooms upstairs in one of the four or five hotels in town. The leading crapshooter in town would be there, and—so help me I remember it now—his real name was Julius Caesar. Not a nickname, his real name. In the summer, there were camps "at the Lake," to go to on the late fast trolley, camps where I'd play "Chinatown" again, through the night, with more beers and whiskeys on the piano, and a crowd singing, in four-part harmony if they could, songs like "When Uncle Joe Plays a Rag on His Old Banjo." Being the bad boy wasn't bad business, the way I must have figured it.

There was a Christmas, though, when there was the smallest happening—so small that I don't see how I remember it at all, yet I do remember it. Does everybody have some small thing he remembers at Christmas, something infinitely unimportant that happened when he was a kid, or in his teens?

Christmas Eve was big in Boehm's Café. Crowded, and lots of people asking for request numbers from the "three-piece orchestra." Georgie Morrison was there this Christmas Eve, and some of the biggest sports in town, with their girls and, in far less number, some with their wives, those who had modernist wives who would go to Boehm's with them.

The beers and whiskeys must have been coming fast. I got to the point where I was trying to whack out classical numbers on the piano, notably a tough thing called "Salut à Pesth." Mostly played in octaves, only tried by me when the whiskeys were in the saddle, so to speak.

Maybe it was the drinks, maybe it was a vestigial bit of my conscience. Suddenly I thought I oughtn't to be there that night. I thought I ought to go home. For a little while, anyway.

Whatever did it, I left the piano (it was an upright that had an attachment, controlled by an extra pedal, that could make it sound like a banjo—great for "Uncle Joe") and I went to Ozzie Boehm, the boss, and asked him if I could go out for half an hour or so. It was about half past nine, and on Christmas Eve the place could stay open until midnight. It was a different crowd, that night, than Boehm's usually had, because most, in fact practically all, of the family men were home, and a great many of the customers that night were people who lived alone.

Ozzie turned me down at first. "This is Christmas Eve!" he snapped at me. "The place is packed!"

"Yes, Ozzie, that's why I want to go out for a few minutes," I said. "Christmas Eve."

"Oh, all right!" Ozzie said, grudgingly. "Be sure to be back, though. Soon, too."

I telephoned for a cab. There weren't but two or three cabs in town, and they were more funeral cars than cabs. That is, they were the autos and drivers that were hired for taking people to funerals. Nighttimes, they were cabs. The cab came and took me to the candy store. The store part was closed, for Christmas Eve, but I banged on the door. It was ten o'clock.

My mother came to the door and opened it and I said, "Hello, Ma! Merry Christmas!"

She was surprised and delighted. "Merry Christmas, John!" she said, and hugged me, and I remember I wished the smell of the beer and whiskey wasn't so plain. "What happened, John? It's only ten o'clock. Oh, I'm so glad you're home, Christmas Eve and all. I thought you'd be at that place. And maybe you wouldn't come home at all! Uncle Mike's here too, and Aunt Delia!"

In the brief seconds that passed as my mother and I walked through the store part, from the door to the two steps leading up to where we lived in the back, a quick warm feeling came over me about how nice the whole place was. And, perhaps, how dear it was to me, if that is the word. To this day, I recall that feeling. The place I had just left, Boehm's Café, was full of jollity and loudness and enviable hell-raising, it's true, and I'd been enjoying it, sure enough. Yet the store part, even in its semidarkness before we got back to our home part, seemed so neat, so well kept, so respectable in its smallness and quiet.

Then, too, when we got up the two steps and I saw everyone there—Uncle Mike, and Aunt Delia, and my brother Willie, and Cousin George, and some others—it seemed more like Christmas ought to be. The tree was there, and on the table under the lamp were cookies from the store, and some English walnuts in a bowl, and a big pot of tea, and cups. Gaiety in the air, too, but a comparatively quiet gaiety, everyone nice to one another and no drinking needed to make them so.

"Look! Look!" my mother said to them, in a most unnecessary announcement, "John's here!"

Everybody said Merry Christmas to one another, all over again.

"Play something, John, won't you?" my mother said, as a lull set in.

"Sure, Ma," I said. I sat down and pushed the loud pedal down, by instinct. I banged out Uncle Joe and his old banjo. My mother wasn't sitting down, but standing looking at me.

"It'd be nice if you played something for Christmas, wouldn't it, John?" she said. She was a little bit of a woman, with a smiling face most of the time.

"Oh, sure, Ma," I said.

I waited a minute and I played a couple easy chords. "Yes, yes, John, that's it," my mother said. "Why don't we all sing?"

They did, and it was fine and a little solemn, and not at all like it had been for me a half hour before. They sang the Latin hymn for Christmas:

Venite adoremus
Venite adoremus
Venite adoremus
Daw-aw-mee-num.

I didn't feel like playing any more of the other stuff. "I got to get back, Ma," I said.

My mother stopped smiling. "Oh, I thought you were coming home with us this one night anyway," she said.

"I told them I'd be right back," I said. "I told Leary the cabman to wait for me down at the corner. I told them I'd be right back."

"I'll go to the door with you," my mother said. Some more Merry Christmases to one another and I sang out an extra one, "Merry Christmas, Willie!" to my brother. My mother and I walked down the two steps into the store and then to the front door. She unlocked it and turned around and hugged me. I could hear her humming a little, and saying words happily and sadly at the same time, while she held me. "*Venite adoremus!*" she was singing softly.

"I hate to see you go back to that place, John," my mother said, yet not reprovingly. "I thought when you came in so unexpected you were home for good. Tonight, anyway, I mean—Christmas Eve.

"But it's all right, John," she said after the door was open, and she held my arm a little tightly. "It's what you want to do. I don't understand it, but it's what is in your heart. John, I often think about it, that I gave you your heart, do you realize, and I don't know what's in it. But it's all right, no matter what they say."

I looked down at my mother, who was quite little, and she seemed to look to be four or five things at once—puzzled, pleased, and proud of me no matter what I was doing. I started out the door and looked down the street. Leary's automobile was there all right.

"I got to go back, Ma," I said. My mother was smiling then and, curiously, she sang a tiny bit, making a marvellously jolly tune out of it. "*Vay-nee-tay ah-do-raymus!*" she was singing. She made the hymn sound gay, in a way.

I left, got in the cab, and went back to Boehm's. All the way back, I was wondering whether it really was what I wanted to do, as my mother had said, or whether it wasn't.

Now isn't that happening the smallest, smallest thing a person could possibly remember about Christmas? Nevertheless, it is what I *do* remember every year on Christmas Eve, without fail, and on Christmas Day too, even if I'm just passing by a church and I hear from inside:

Venite adoremus
Venite adoremus
Venite adoremus
Dominum.

V

DEAR JOHNNY:

I don't know exactly how to begin this and the way I figure it you don't know exactly how to begin living. That far, we're both in the same fix.

It's six o'clock in the morning and you are in your play pen in the living room of our apartment. I'm having coffee and watching you, my first baby, while you are at play that begins your day. Occasionally you show, without knowing any words, that the little moves I make are interesting. The same goes for you. You make some interesting moves.

This is the best hour of the day for the two of us, I think. Your mother is not yet awake; she has not yet taken you over for the day as she most properly does each day, and you are full of rest, lively with curiosity, nobbly with notions about what the morning's all about. So am I, for that matter. There are many years between us, but they do not matter. You are my son, and I love you; once in a while I get the idea you think I am all right, although I can never be certain about this, because you do not know words yet and can talk only with your eyes and with the hands you don't steer any too well yet. I found out that a kind of slapping you do on my hands when I hold them out to you in the play pen is a means of expressing approval. At least, in my mature conceit, I take it for approval.

That play pen you have, that's something. So far, it is practically your world, a single play pen. It comes to me that while you have only the one play pen, I have dozens of them, and none of them is the couch I'm sitting on right now, watching you. One play pen of mine is Tim Costello's Bar and Grill, 699 Third Avenue, New York; another is Madison Square Garden, and another is Belmont Park Racetrack, and another is *The New Yorker* magazine office, and another is the Players Club on Gramercy Park, and another is the home of Duane and Helen Decker at 12 Gramercy Park, near the club, and another is Joe and Rosie's Restaurant on Third between Forty-sixth and Forty-seventh, and another is up in Rhode Island around the Willow Dell Beach Club, a family place where your mother is more at home than I am. Your mother came from Rhode Island, and so, in a manner of speaking, you came from Rhode Island. You came from all the places that your mother and I came from—that is to say, the generations behind us. She has Rhode Island mostly, and I have Ireland altogether behind me, and what in the world does that make you, Johnny? A kind of Gaelic clambake, I guess, but that could be pretty good. Chances are that you will be a lucky mick, because I have been a lucky mick, never really met any bad people, had a lot of fun, owe the world a lot for how nice it has been to me, and that's about the way it all sums up.

Who are you, Johnny? You are a stranger in our house and at the same time you are somebody that Faith and I know well.

You are part Irish, Johnny. That is both a blessing and a burden. The bog and the wet wind and the poverty that are so far behind you have something to do with the kind of man you are going to be. You will probably be able to stand the wet wind and the coldness, but you will be hurt by sadness. I was. Not bad. But hurt.

You will be hurt by the sadness. The way people try to convey their liking, and try to belittle the hardships they have. If you give them half a chance, then it will come through, and the worst of all is the smiling sadness. Granted that I am not very clear at this point, Johnny, I hope it will get clear as we go on, as you get to be a little man I can take to the Yankee Stadium and meet Joe Stevens, as you get to be a little creature who will sit by me near the FM and hear music, a small lad who is my love and all, my little son Johnny. That's you.

SMILING, DEVELOPMENT OF

We have a new baby, my wife and I; the cellophane is hardly off him yet. And like most people in our fix, we have to have Doctor Spock's book around the house. It costs only thirty-five cents, and we have two copies. One copy is mine, and one is my wife's.

When anything happens in Johnny's room—noises, that is—we both start running. My wife runs for Johnny and I run for the book. She's playing this thing by instinct and I'm playing it by the book. I don't know which of us is wise, but between us Johnny should make out O.K. Hope so, anyway.

A couple of times the noises in the night were gruesome. One night I jumped up and ran for the book, and Faith, my wife, ran toward Johnny. It was two in the morning. I flicked on the light and turned to the index of the book. I was looking for "Strangling," because that is what he sounded as if he were doing.

No "Strangling" in the index. Nearest to that was "Strangers, baby's attitude toward." I was not interested in that at the moment. I ran to Johnny's room. "She," as I often refer to my wife, had the light on by then. Johnny was looking up at the two of us, and he was smiling. He was about two months old, and I had never seen him smile before. I said, "I guess the guy is all right." Then I went back to the living room and got the book, and, as long as my wife had gone back to bed, I thought I would read a few things here and there. I turned to the index. To where "Strangling" would have been if there had been any "Strangling." What I was thinking was that Johnny had not strangled this time, but maybe he would start to strangle some night and I'd better be ready. Still no entry under "Strangling."

But right on the opposite page of the index, page 498, there was an entry that caught my eye. It said, "Smiling, development of."

Oh, boy. He had just smiled! It was so marvellous a simple happening that I had not even dared to speak of it to my wife. He had smiled at me.

The index said the smiling stuff was on page 141. I turned to that. It said there: "He smiles early, because he is a social being. Somewhere around two months of age your baby will smile at you one day when you are talking and smiling to him. It's an exciting moment for you. But think what it means about his development. He knows little at this age, he can't use his hands, or even turn his head from side to side. And yet he already knows that he's a sociable being, that it's nice to have loving people around, that he feels like responding to them. And if he's treated with plenty of affection and not too much interference, he'll go on being friendly and reasonable just because it is his nature."

While the dim morning lay outside the window in Manhattan, where I live, I read that twice. Gee whizz! It had happened to other people before. Otherwise, Dr. Benjamin Spock would not have had it in *The Pocket Book of Baby and Child Care*. A few minutes before, my Johnny had smiled at me, and there it was, exactly right, under "Smiling, development of."

No fooling, I had foolishly thought that what had happened to me —Johnny's smiling up at me—was the first time anything like that had happened in the history of the world.

I put the book down, turned out the light, and went back in to sneak a look at Johnny. He was sound asleep, with his hands, which look as if Benvenuto Cellini had made them, spread out in the crib. He sleeps on his belly.

THE SEARCH FOR THE WONDERFUL CARD

Sometimes I watch my nine-month-old Johnny for a long time while he is playing cards. That a nine-month-old boy should be playing cards perhaps requires some explanation, which I'll try to give.

There are hours, which I like the best, when his mother has gone out, and I sit on the couch and he is in the play pen in front of it, me watching him and, once in a while, him taking a gander at me.

He has a few toys, bought in stores, but he does not appear too fond of them. What he does like is a rolled-oats box, empty, with splotches of red and blue color on its outside. One day I threw that into the pen, for the pure fun of it, and he passed up all the store-bought toys in favor of the rolled-oats box. Many a time I watched him roll that box around, and slap it like a drum, and try to pick the red color off it, and have a fine time all around. Occasionally, he'd look up at me on the couch and grin, a grin that was hopeful that I, too, appreciated such a thing as that box. Matter of fact, after a while, I did appreciate it, and I could see how senseless those things from the store were. I began to like the rolled-oats box, too.

Another day, we ran out of stuff to play with, and even the box was not enough for the moment. So I looked around the living room for something to give him. He was looking up, asking without words.

I found a pack of cards lying on a table, so I opened the box, took out the deck, and handed them down to him in the play pen. Naturally, they were spread every which way all over the floor of the pen in a minute or two. He liked them; I could see that. The backs were red, and the fronts had all the things that packs of cards have: splotches of red and blue, for kings and queens; some cards with a whole lot of red figures (the ten of diamonds, for example, with ten red diamonds); some cards with a lot of black figures on them (the ten of spades, for instance); and others with a lot of white space and two red things in the middle of them. That would be the deuce of hearts, or the deuce of diamonds.

He, Johnny, took a fancy to the cards at once. Where he tended to try to smash the other things in the pen, or make a try at smashing them, I noticed a certain gentleness, a certain respectful handling of these many separate pieces of cardboard. He liked them O.K. That first day he simply spread them around, and spread them around, and spread them around, in a manner to which I could see no pattern, and I doubt if he had any pattern in mind, either.

That is how the card-playing began. Now, during the course of a day, Johnny plays cards probably two hours and a half altogether, and he seems at those times most intensely occupied and at the same time most serenely so.

He wakes up ahead of us in the morning, of course. I have taken to going in at night, into his room, after he has gone to sleep in his crib, and putting the pack of cards in a corner of the crib, in a neat pile, but not in the box, of course.

Each morning, when I heard him begin a bit of a yammer for something to eat, I would go in and see that he had already been awake a while and playing cards. They were all over the crib, all of them—or nearly all—bent just a trifle, where he had picked them up a bit clumsily but not savagely.

Now—because I timed him one morning when I woke up before he did, sneaked in and saw him asleep, and secretly watched for him to awake—I know he plays cards all by himself and without a sound for almost an hour after he wakes up. I have watched him from out in the hall and have checked up on him.

He also plays late in the afternoon. Then I often sit on the couch watching him in the play pen.

It must be understood, at this point, that Johnny and I have been sitting around with each other so much that we understand each other pretty well. I believe, though, that he knows more about me than I do about him. He gives me that impression sometimes.

I almost can get the idea of his game. I believe it is something he made up. I believe it could be called "Looking for the Wonderful Card of All Wonderful Cards."

He plays it this way: he gets the cards all around the play pen, some face up, some face down. He lies on his front, his head up and at least one hand free while the other helps in the creeping that is a necessary part of the game.

Then, with a most solemn deliberateness, he will pick up a card, any card. He will hold it up as a scientist might hold a test tube, and with the same quiet intensity, examine the back of the card, then the front. No, that is not the Wonderful Card of All Wonderful Cards. So he will drop it and creep around and, with what seems to me to be aimlessness, pick up another card. He will hold that up, turn it around from face to back or vice versa, with the solemn scrutiny of before. Alas! Not the Wonderful Card!

Another creep, another card picked up, another poring over the virtues his blue eyes find in that particular piece of pasteboard. And always, he has to lay it down again, because his search, his *search, search, search,* has not brought him to the card he desires.

Occasionally he looks up at me and smiles. He is not losing patience, that betokens. After the smile, he goes back to the game again. What I noticed especially, during the many games of cards I saw him play, is that he winds up nearly always with the King of Diamonds. That is, he hangs onto that one the longest in his scrutiny. And sometimes, if it is face up, he spots it two or three times in a game. At game's end he is most often holding that card.

Watching the game with Johnny, I, too, began to realize that the King of Diamonds is quite a handsome card. Oh, well do I know that aces are usually more powerful, and that any card can be useful under certain circumstances! But looking at the cards cold turkey, so to speak, the King of Diamonds is really a knockout of a card. Plenty of red on it. The King, with his two heads, but not beside each other, has beautiful designs on his royal robes. The diamonds in the corners stand out manfully. It is one brilliant-looking card all around!

The King of Hearts may be practically the same thing; but not to Johnny. That King is head on, and not in profile, I realize. I don't think Johnny realizes that. Certainly not! It would be silly to say that. Just the same, the King of Diamonds has it all over the King of Hearts, any way you look at it. The kid is right.

He, the King of Diamonds, comes close to the Wonderful Card of All Wonderful Cards, although he is not *quite* it. The search must go on. Johnny has set himself to it, to find the Wonderful Card.

JOHNNY HAS A GIRL

Johnny is nineteen months old now, and we have more and more fun together as time goes on. He begins and ends my day, although there are some hours left after he has gone to sleep at half past six; lately I find those hours are only routine hours, fairly dull most of the time.

I can't help getting up early: as I said before, somebody must have put a jinx on me years ago to keep me from sleeping in the morning. Most people hate to get up in the morning, but the jinx on me makes it impossible for me to sleep after five-thirty or so. In a city like New York such early-morning hours are lonesome. They were for me, until Johnny. Nowadays, he wakes up between ten minutes of six and ten minutes past six, and for an hour and a half or so I sit in his room with him while I drink my coffee, and he sits in his crib, gabbing those syllables that have the rhythm and cadence of sentences but do not have any orthodox words in them. That's a fine hour and a half, with me and my friend Johnny palavering together.

And after he has had his bath and supper at night, there's a little while—sometimes only fifteen minutes, before he gets sleepy—when we gab again, with him in the crib and me in the chair beside it. I can do things he can't do that arouse admiration in him, and he can do things I cannot do which arouse admiration in me, and that seems to me to be a good, fifty-fifty deal. I can make the stuffed dog act as if he's walking and barking, running him along the crib railing; Johnny can make musical sounds in a silvery smallness of voice that I, with my gravel throat, cannot even approach. That's about all there is to the few minutes before he goes to sleep, but it seems to be a lot to me, and I wouldn't miss it for anything. I hope Johnny wouldn't, either, and I have the feeling he wouldn't, even if he apparently doesn't give the matter much thought.

Now, that is how he begins and ends my day. The parts of his day, the times in between, are filled in for us by Josephine, who is on loan to us from heaven for the express purpose of taking care of Johnny while we're working.

One evening I asked Josephine the usual question: "What's he been doing today?" I asked her. (With me nowadays, "he" is Johnny, always —no other name needed.)

"Johnny has a girl," Josephine said, and smiled and went on doing whatever it was she was doing, opening a can of that baby food, I think it was.

"He what?" I asked.

"He has a girl," Josephine said. "He chases her in the park. Same one every day. They're cute."

"Boy, is he starting early!" I said. "Chases her, huh?"

"Every day," Josephine said. "When he catches her, she gives up."

"That I've got to see," I said.

The next day I went with Josephine and Johnny to the park.

First off, walking alongside the baby carriage with Josephine pushing it and Johnny in it, I was pleased to see him getting along with people so well. A doorman in the next block, whom I didn't know, stopped the carriage a moment as Johnny grinned at him, and the doorman and Johnny shook hands. "Hello, Johnny," the doorman said.

"Seems they do that all the time," Josephine said.

I didn't know that Johnny knew any people outside of Josephine,

Faith, and me. We went along to the park, and without saying anything aloud, I was glad to know my Johnny knew the doorman. He's got to know a lot of people and get along with them before he's through, I was thinking, and it's nice to see him make a good start.

The playground—the one for little bits of kids—is just to the left of the park entrance. There were forty or fifty children in there, most of them a little bigger than Johnny. When we three got there, Josephine unharnessed Johnny from the carriage, gave him the rattly toy with a long handle that he pushes, and turned him loose, so to speak. He dropped the toy and off he went. He walks funny when he's full of pep, a kind of high-stepping walk, something like one of those five-gaited horses they have in the horse shows.

"Where's the girl, Josephine?" I asked.

"He'll find her. I don't see her, but Johnny'll find her if she's here," Josephine assured me.

Sure enough, he did, right in front of my eyes.

"There he goes!" Josephine said, her warm, big smile one third for me, one third for Johnny, one third for herself.

Oh, but she was a pretty little girl! She had yellow hair, and a blue jacket, and blue leggings buttoned all the way down the side with what must have been twenty buttons. She was across the playground, standing still, and a youngish woman, whom I took to be her mother, was sitting right behind her on a bench.

High-stepping Johnny weaved miraculously through the crowd of playing children, making a beeline (of a young, inexperienced bee) for the little girl in blue, almost exactly his own size.

She saw him and, with a perilous pivot, turned and began to run. Johnny speeded up, with even a higher step and both arms held high, in that jeopardized balance he has when he's excited. The girl ran deftly, but Johnny fell down. No harm. He was on his feet in a moment and staggered in a circle until his eye caught the little lady in blue once more. By chance, it must have been, because no mind nineteen months old could have figured it out. He cut expertly across the playground, and so, in her roundabout run, they came face to face. I moved up near them.

It would be nice to report they smiled, but they didn't. Both stood still and stared. She gave up, as Josephine had said, but there was no smile. Johnny stared at her, and she stared at him, both standing still. He reached out and patted her cheek, and she knocked his hand away. He patted her cheek again, just the same way he pats the stuffed dog sometimes when he holds it in the crib. She didn't knock his hand away.

Johnny turned around. Then he looked over his shoulder and started back to where we had left the carriage. There was a tiny hesitation, and the girl in blue followed him.

It seemed to me that these two saw only each other in all the swirl of the playground. "Across a crowded room," I suddenly thought, remembering the line from "Some Enchanted Evening."

Over at the carriage, Johnny picked up the toy he pushes and, clumsily, gave the handle of it to the little girl. Together they played with the toy, and I thought: For them, there is nobody else in the playground, nobody else in the world.

IF IT LOOKS GOOD, IT'S MINE

Although Johnny has been on this earth only two years and a month or two, I fear he has already worked himself out a dangerous philosophy. I'm only conjecturing, of course, but I fear this philosophy may be summed up as follows: "If it looks good, it's mine."

This is a shocking principle to go through life on, because in the first place, I don't think it will work, and in the second place, if it just happened to work in Johnny's case, then it would make Johnny an awful heel. It is not my intention or my hope to have him turn out an awful heel. If everything works out well as the years go on, I would like him to have a normal, decent amount of possessions; not necessarily be rich, but happy with what he has of his own, without depriving anybody else of anything. Right now, at the age of two or so, he is not motivated by any such modest notion.

What I'm driving at in a windbag kind of way is that I get scared when I watch his behavior in the playground. He has no sense of property whatsoever; if it looks good to him, whatever he sees is his, and he goes after it like Rocky Marciano going after somebody in the ring.

To be sure, I have read all about these growing traits in the baby books; but just the same, reading about something in a baby book and then seeing it with your own eyes are not the same things. Besides, I have an additional set of ideas to go with those set forth so usefully and learnedly in the baby books. They tell about all the stages a baby goes through. I say a father, such as me and a few million other gents, goes through a set of stages, too. Maybe there are books about that, but I haven't run into them yet.

Take this morning, over there in the playground. It was a lovely Manhattan morning on East Seventy-second Street, and so we walked the five blocks to the park. Planning to walk, instead of taking the usual bus, we travelled light, which meant we took only one small twenty-five-cent automobile and a small red sand shovel.

Once in the playground I confess I try to act like an old hand at being a father. I try to be nonchalant. I turn Johnny loose, then take a seat on a bench, by myself or possibly near some stranger there on the same job as I'm on. Truth is, I seldom have my eyes off Johnny for a minute.

He set forth with the two-bit auto and the shovel, and he seemed to pause to reconnoiter for no longer than a minute. He spied an unguarded dump truck with nobody near it, a dump truck worth maybe a dollar and a half, lying in the sand pile. In ten seconds he had the dump truck, while still hanging onto his own auto. He saw an unguarded plastic cup, with the letters A B C D E on one side of it. He had that ten seconds later, and with the plastic cup had filled the dump truck twenty seconds later. Now, mind you, the sand was the property of the City of New York, where I am a microscopic taxpayer, so that was O.K. But the dump truck and the cup were the property of babies unknown.

Not to Johnny they weren't, as far as I could tell. They looked good, so they were his. That's what scares me: my son has no sense of property. A few minutes later, the babies unknown I just mentioned were no longer babies unknown. They came yowling up to claim the truck and the cup, and Johnny fought them off in as vicious a manner as ever made my blood run cold. He was about to bat the truck owner on the head with his own auto when I leaped to my feet and got there in the nick of time. Johnny then turned on me for a moment, until, by superior strength, I got the truck away from him, with a brief verbal admonishment, and gave it back to the owner, who scampered away. To my amazement, the cup owner suddenly lost interest in her cup although she had been hollering for it a moment before, and she scampered happily away, leaving Johnny still possessing the cup he did not own. Also leaving me puzzled.

At this point, I will go back to the idea that we fathers (new ones and first-timers, I mean) have to go through stages just the same as the babies. The affair of the dump truck and the plastic cup illustrates this, because I leaped up from my bench and intervened to prevent my son from inflicting injury upon a fellow baby. The man sitting next to me on the bench enlightened me on this point a few minutes after the incident, which he witnessed. He smiled like a savant, and friendly, too, when I walked back to the bench and sat down.

"I know you meant well," he said to me, "but it's hopeless, doing what you did. I've been through it."

I was grateful to him for speaking to me in that comradely style. I grinned back. "I just didn't want to see Johnny murder that other child," I said. "That wasn't his truck. It belonged to the other boy, and the cup belonged to the other child, the little girl."

"I know," the man said. "But you'd go nuts if you tried to keep these things straightened out. They got to work it out for themselves. After a while you'll come to the stage where you'll sit back and let them battle it out—unless, of course, it looks to you like dead-certain bloodshed."

"I guess so," I said, rather weakly. "I guess that's the way it is. It says something like that in the book."

While I was talking, I had not been watching Johnny. So I was again astonished when he was suddenly standing in front of me. He had one, two, three, four trucks, ranging in value, in my estimate, from one dollar to three dollars. In his own words, which are not yet rich enough in syntax to permit being printed, he told me he wanted to go home, and I could see he wanted to go home in full possession of four trucks that were not his. They looked good to him, so they *were* his. That's what I mean.

The other man on the bench and I, after a lot of yowling, got things back to where they belonged, and Johnny and I went home.

But come to think of it, we didn't have any longer the twenty-five-cent auto or the shovel we left the house with. We didn't have them because, I must deduce, some other little boy must have nabbed them from Johnny while my back was turned. And I think that's a good way to keep my back in a playground—turned.

THERE'S NOTHING THE OLD MAN CAN'T DO, SAYS HE

Johnny does not actually say that there is nothing his father cannot do; he merely assumes that his father can do anything whatsoever, and this, in an inward way, is both pleasing and embarrassing to me. I am his father, and Johnny is at this time two years and three months old.

The realization that Johnny so grotesquely—and to me happily—overrates me came all of a sudden a few days after we bought the television set. For a long while, Faith and I fought off buying a television. For one thing, we didn't want any more electrically operated booby traps for babies around the house; for another thing, we were afraid Johnny might get so unceasingly interested in the television shows that the poor lad might never learn to read, and both of us would regard that as a misfortune.

But along came the World Series and we began reconsidering. The final argument we put to each other, Faith and I, was: "After all, the boy is going to grow up in a world of television and jet planes and so on, and what kind of folderol is it on our part to try and block the little fellow, any more than we'd tear out the electricity in the apartment and put in a batch of oil lamps?" Besides, discreet inquiry had brought us assurances that the danger to Johnny electrically in having a television around would be either infinitesimal or nonexistent. We upped and bought a television set.

Well, it wasn't in the house forty-eight hours before Johnny was an ardent fan of "Howdy Doody," a puppet show that in our part of the country comes on at five-thirty in the afternoon. He saw the show once, and the next day he was asking for it, especially for the clown in it. I have fun trying to figure Johnny out all the time, and I figured he took the greatest fancy to the clown because for a long while, when Johnny was just a kid of a year and a half or so, his favorite plaything was a small clown dressed in almost the identical manner to the clown in "Howdy Doody."

However, the clown and how my son instantly came to like him best aren't the point I'm trying to get to, which is Johnny's belief that his father can do anything, anything at all. That came out the third morning after television in our house. At seven o'clock I turned on a program, a very good program, called "Today" with Dave Garroway. I like it, but Johnny watched it a few minutes and then said, "Papa get Howdy Doody!" It was a command.

(Here I digress to apologize. I am a lifelong hater of baby talk in print. It can't be done. Our own child, for example, tends to leave out all definite and indefinite articles at this stage of the game, and also seems to have an inordinate fondness for the participial forms of verbs. Because of these quirks of his, it is difficult to put down accurately the way he says things. It is also perilously near tiresome; but from now on, willy-nilly, I am forced to risk it.)

In reply to Johnny's demand for "Howdy Doody" at, say, seven-ten in the morning, when the show doesn't come on until five-thirty in the afternoon, I at first made a brusque statement. I said, "He's not on now."

That, understandably, didn't sink in. Johnny pondered a moment. "Papa making clown come?" he asked.

His tone was such that I paid a little more attention. "I can't make him come right now, Johnny," I said as soothingly as possible.

"Papa get Howdy Doody?" he insisted, brushing aside my absurd contention that I couldn't do something.

I realized I would have to go into this with a more thorough explanation, however fanciful. The best I could scare up in my mind at the moment was to say, slowly and painstakingly, that Howdy Doody was asleep, that the clown was asleep, that a character he refers to as the funny man was asleep. It was logical enough, I thought. Unacceptable, however, to Johnny.

"Papa waking clown up?" he asked. I went into a longish, and no doubt incomprehensible, explanation of how rude it would be to wake all those people up at that hour. Fortunately, by the time I finished this song and dance, something diverted Johnny's attention, and he went away from the chair from which we both watch the television.

Then, for a few minutes, I found myself not really watching Garroway, but realizing that, at this time at least, my son Johnny thinks there is nothing the old man cannot do. Man, oh, man! What a responsibility! In the whole world, nobody else has any exaggerated idea of my powers, but he has.

Since the "Howdy Doody" episode (which has been repeated several times at odd hours), I have noted other instances of Johnny's belief. Like one day we were walking over to Central Park. As we came to a crossing, the traffic light was red against us. In an effort to instill in him knowledge and respect for traffic lights, I halted elaborately with him at the curb. Across the street, in the direction we were headed, was a beautiful big dog, playing with a boy. Johnny's crazy about dogs, I forgot to say. He saw this one.

"Oh, go play with big dog," he said, yanking at my hand, which was holding his.

I leaned over and said, "See the light?" I pointed at it, as I always do on such occasions. "We have to wait until the light changes."

He yanked my hand again. "Papa change light and play with big dog?" he asked, and looked up at me.

I gave up. He seemed so certain I could do it, I could change the light if only I wanted to. No use trying to explain to him the million things his father would like to do but cannot. Nice to have him think I can do them all, though. And embarrassing, too, in an inward way.

THE NEW TEACHER, AGED TWO YEARS, FOUR MONTHS

Johnny is at this time aged two years and four months. Recently, as I become, by small degrees, more wise (yet still dumb) in the role of father, I have come to realize that he is teaching me quite a lot. That isn't the way I had it doped out, all those years before I was a father. I used to take it for granted the old man had to teach the child. It's quite a lot the other way around, I'm beginning to think now.

Johnny goes about the task of teaching me things quite easily. Matter of fact, so easily that he isn't even conscious he's doing it.

One rainy day Johnny had his blocks spread around the floor and was busy with them. I was lying on the couch after reading the papers, and for want of something better to do, I got up and went to the piano and began drumming out "Basin Street Blues," or some tune like that.

Behind my back, Johnny dropped the blocks from his hand. I didn't see him do that. But I heard the blocks land, and they had an angry sound. Suddenly Johnny was standing beside the piano bench, a solemn look on his face and a finger waving at me in admonition, as I sometimes have to wave a finger at him. He talks pretty well, although oftentimes with gibberish mixed up with comprehensible sentences. This time he uttered not only a sentence, but a full paragraph. Far as I know, it was his first spoken complete paragraph. With fingers waving, Johnny said, "Don't play the piano while I am trying to build a house. You know better than that!"

"Aghast" is the word for what I was at that moment. I was dumfounded, nonplused, flabbergasted, and, as I say, aghast, for two reasons. One was because he had suddenly spoken so flawless a paragraph. The other reason had in it a lesson for me, and proved once more that my new teacher is a man two years and four months old. I said, "Okay, Johnny," stopped playing the piano, and went back to the couch, and he resumed his house-building with the blocks.

I'll be doggoned! I thought to myself. If that isn't what I've been doing all my life, off and on. I've been playing the piano while other people were trying to build a house! Perhaps not precisely that. But comparable to it. I've been going right ahead, now and then, with something I wanted to do, and never thinking how it might interfere with what somebody else might be trying to do at that moment. Doggone! I've got to be more considerate of what other people want to do.

I don't know how long this lesson will last, as I am a man who makes a resolution today and forgets it tomorrow. Nevertheless, I'll try to remember: "Don't play the piano while I'm trying to build a house."

Johnny is teaching me to notice more things, and to look at them more intently than I had been doing before he became my teacher.

Like every other child of his age, I presume, the two questions he asks a couple hundred times each day are simple, extremely direct questions. The first is "What's that?" and the second is "What's the man doing?"

Since those questions began to come at me from Johnny endlessly I have learned that I was taking too many things for granted, not noticing them, just going along the street only half aware of all the interesting small happenings around me; or passing, without thought, some object or building worthy of a moment's study.

Johnny is correcting that mental laziness in me. He sees a man on a stepladder painting a sign on a delicatessen-store window, and he stops walking along with his hand in mine, and he asks, "What's the man doing?"

In order to answer I look at the man on the ladder. "He's painting a sign on the store window," I reply.

So we both stand there and watch a few minutes. Without Johnny I doubtlessly would have passed by stodgily. Now I see that the man is painting in gold. I see him hold the book of gold leaf in one hand. I see him flick the dainty brush through his hair, then apply it to a leaf of gold in the book, and the gold leaf adheres to the brush until he applies it to the window. I deduce that the electricity generated by flicking the brush through his hair creates a sort of magnetism that permits the brush to pick up, unrumpled, the delicate gold leaf from the book. A deft, probably ancient, and thoroughly interesting procedure.

Johnny and I move along on our small neighborhood journey, and once again I know Johnny is teaching me things; it's not the other way around. He sure is teaching me to notice more things than I used to. It isn't only the What's-the-man-doing? question. The other one, the What's-that? question, comes in connection with inanimate objects. Perhaps Johnny and I will be passing a flower stand. Out comes "What's that?" So we pause a minute. I explain it is a florist's shop, and that those are flowers, which I name to the best of my scanty knowledge. I figure that's a few moments of pleasure for both of us, and if Johnny had not been with me I'd have sauntered by the place unseeing, and so Johnny is to be thanked once more.

There could not be a more enjoyable instructor than my new teacher, and I recommend his like to one and all.

SMALL CONFUSIONS OF A SMALL MAN

It would be very unfair if anybody complained about my son's being somewhat mixed up about certain things that go on around him, when it is taken into account that he has had only twenty-nine months to dope matters out. That's how old Johnny is, twenty-nine months. I don't know exactly how to straighten him out on the things that have him confused. Even at my own age I'm sometimes not very clear in understanding what's going on around me, so why should I criticize Johnny?

For example, there was last Christmas, which was the first one he really took any part in. Somehow, Johnny got the impression that all those toys, all those packages, tin trains and toy wagons and a toy farm that he found under the Christmas tree were intended *for* Santa Claus.

During the month before Christmas, in his frequent thumbing

through magazines, he had become familiar with the picture of Santa Claus, and, at least dimly, had him figured out as having something to do with a thing called "Christmas."

Then—or so I surmise—he must have heard a chance remark not intended for his ears. He must have heard somebody say something was "bought for Santa Claus." Because when Christmas morning came, and Johnny went into the living room and saw all those things beneath the tree, and heard so much mention of Santa Claus, that remark must have echoed in his head. The result was that he believed all those toys were intended for Santa Claus.

Johnny talks pretty well now. All morning he continued to ask why Santa Claus didn't hurry up and come to our house. His mother and I finally understood what he wanted to convey to us. What he wanted to tell us was that he wished Santa Claus would hurry up so that he, Johnny, could give him the nice train and the toy farm and all the other lovely things. "Bought 'em in a store for Santa Claus," Johnny repeated, time and time again. "Where is Santa Claus?"

Thinking it over, his mother and I came to the conclusion that it was not such a bad idea at that, giving presents to Santa Claus. After all these years, even centuries, somebody ought to give the Old Boy a gift or two. Perhaps Johnny isn't as confused on this particular matter as at first we thought he was.

There is another phase of Johnny's miniature bewilderment which may not be confusion at all, any more than was the Santa Claus affair. He seems to believe that the radio is strictly for dancing. I think I can safely declare that this boy we have hanging around the house is the only person in the United States who dances to news broadcasts.

The moment his mother or I turn on the radio, Johnny goes into his dance, no matter what is being broadcast. To be sure, his dance is not as deft or as difficult as the numbers that Fred Astaire, Gene Kelly, and the likes of them do. But it is definitely a dance. And Johnny can do it to the accompaniment of a man saying on the radio: "The present temperature is seventy-four, and the forecast for this afternoon is fair and warmer." Or, possibly, the announcer is giving out with more solemn news about international affairs. No difference to Johnny. He still does his "Off-to-Buffalo" dance routine to the broadcast. His rule appears to be: when the radio goes on, dance! Surely, it's a pleasant concept, however uncommon.

As to television, Johnny differs from most of us grown-ups in his attitude toward commercials. Sad as it may be to sponsors, grown-ups tend to be pretty lukewarm toward commercials, if not downright opposed to them. Not so with Johnny. He quite obviously likes commercials better than anything else.

Johnny is delighted when somebody on television holds up a package of cake mix, a bottle of shampoo or whatnot, and explains at great length the virtues and glories of the product. He stands only about two feet away from the screen, and gives it his rapt attention. When the commercial's over and the action starts he invariably moves away and devotes himself to his blocks or to some other pastime. I cannot explain this fascination that commercials have for him; I can merely observe it. His mother and I trust that it is a form of confusion he will overcome as time goes on. If he doesn't—well, what kind of child are we rearing, anyway, a lover of commercials?

There is a third bit of confusion in the mind of our son, which is somewhat embarrassing to me. It's even embarrassing to tell about it.

One Saturday, some time ago, I was preparing to leave the house, and Johnny asked me where I was going. Being a truthful man a large part of the time, I told him the truth and said, "I'm going to the club and play pool." I hasten to say that I had every right to do so; it was a nonworking day, and every red-blooded American husband has a right to go to the club and shoot a little pool once in a while.

Johnny, however, seized upon this one time as a permanent explanation for my every absence. So, if during the day anyone asks him where his daddy is, the reply always is, "Daddy's gone to the club and play pool." And if the questioner, usually a visiting neighbor, pursues the matter further and asks him where his mother is, Johnny always answers, "Mommy's gone to work in the office."

I submit that this is a libel on me. It certainly doesn't sound good to hear that Daddy's at the club playing pool every day, while Mommy's slaving away in the office. I hope the little guy gets this straightened out very soon. It's giving me a bad name around the neighborhood, I fear. But, after all, twenty-nine months is an awfully short time for anybody to understand everything that is going on around him in a fairly complex world.

THE FOUR-THIRTY PARADE

One of the many things that make me glad I have a three-year-old son is that it entitles me to be in the four-thirty parade. Only very special people can get into that. Only people who have small children.

This parade takes place every afternoon, winter and summer, in New York. It takes place as the sun starts to go down and it is time for Johnny to take a bath and have supper. We all know that. When that old sun starts sinking, then the day is over and it is time to take the children home. So we all start out of the park, and wait for the traffic light to change, and the four-thirty parade begins. That's the walk back home: mammas, and babies in gocarts, and walking-size babies, and their nurses, or once in a while their daddies, like me. In the papers, whenever it's the season for them, there is talk about the St. Patrick's Day parade and about other big parades like that; but for me, the four-thirty parade is the thing.

One day, before the sun started going down, this is what happened to Johnny and me. He won't remember it, but I will. He was playing in the sand box with a child named Carlton. I was sitting nearby, so I could watch and hear them.

"Where's your mommy?" Carlton asked.

"My mommy is home," Johnny said.

The two of them were in a big enterprise. It consisted of filling a dump truck and emptying it.

Carlton remarked, "Who you bring over, then? Who come over here with you?"

"My daddy. Look, look!" Johnny said. "You want to see my daddy?"

The two of them got up, sand all over them, and Johnny took Carlton's hand and led him out of the sand box a couple of steps, and they both looked straight at me.

Johnny pointed a bent first finger at me. When he points, he keeps the first finger bent a little. "Look, that's my daddy," Johnny said.

The two of them looked at me. Carlton made no comment. Johnny took his hand again, and together they went back to the sand box.

The sun was getting lower, and it was time to start home. I felt very good, because Johnny had thought it worth while to bring his friend over and point me out to him. This does not happen to me any too often.

About the parade: it goes east from the park, on Seventy-second Street. I believe that in New York we have the best doormen in the world. They know the names of the various children passing by each afternoon. They say, "How are you today, Johnny?" to my little boy. And they say, "Hello, Carlton, how are you today?" In little squeaky voices, Johnny and Carlton answer.

There are all kinds of us as we leave the playground, because in our neighborhood there is New York's own warm mixture of all kinds of people. There's Josephine, and there are her friends: Annabelle, who takes care of Tony, and Arlene, who tends to the two little boys, Louis and Scott; and there are lovely young mothers, lithe as dancers, which maybe some of them used to be; and there are some German nurses, *Fräuleins*, and some Mamselles, who speak French to their small boys and girls; and, occasionally, a quietly strutting father like myself.

As the parade moves east, there are fewer and fewer in it, as children and their mothers, nurses, or fathers turn into their apartment houses. We take up nearly the whole sidewalk going along, and everybody marches along together, talking of tumbles the children have taken, and of how much fun the children had in the winter when there sometimes was snow for them to play in; and the whole parade is a lovely camaraderie, as nice a thing as there is in this city.

I can't help thinking, as I go along, of how many times in the years before our Johnny was born I had walked along this same street, alone. The doormen and the passersby looked different to me then, as now, I feel most deeply, I look different to them. Though they are strangers, for the most part, they seem more friendly, more understanding, when I'm walking with Johnny holding my hand. They don't speak, but there's a look that plainly and wordlessly says, "I've got one at home, too. Aren't they great little things to have?" Or, if the glancing stranger is old, he or she seems to say, with ever so slight and fleeting a look of sadness in the eyes, "I used to have a little one like that, too."

Anyway, there are only two or three pairs of us by the time the straggly end of the four-thirty parade gets to Second Avenue and Seventy-second Street, where our home is. Maxie, the newsstand man on the corner, hollers, "Hi, Johnny!" in between waiting on customers, and Johnny perhaps replies by shooting Maxie with an imaginary pistol. "Have a good supper, Johnny!" Maxie shouts after us as we go along to our door.

Well, Johnny does have a good bath and a good supper, too, and he goes to bed. Afterward, Faith and I watch the television for a while, but half the time I'm not paying any attention; I'm just thinking how pleasant it is that there'll be another four-thirty parade tomorrow.

"AND IN SOME CORNER FIND THE TOYS OF THE OLD EGYPTIAN BOYS"

Johnny came up to me in the playground and he had two trucks, toy trucks, unfamiliar to me.

"Where did you get those, Mac?" I asked him.

"From the old Egyptian boys," he answered.

I was somewhat puzzled at this.

It was days afterward that I knew what he had meant. Nights afterward, I mean. He began hollering from his room, and so I went in to pacify him, although I had been determined that no matter how loud he hollered I would pay no attention. I finally gave in, and went to his room.

"What seems to be the trouble, Mac?" I asked him.

"Let's watch the old television," he said. "Shall we?"

Again I was rocked back on my heels because, to me, the television is something of a novelty, and it was unusual to my ears to hear it referred to as "the old television."

Giving in for a bit, I took him out of his bed and into the living room and sat him with me in the big chair, and together we watched the old television.

He got warm sitting next to me and fell asleep, but when I started to take him back into his bed he woke up again. He asked me to read him a story when we finally got to his bed. I picked up the first book I found handy and it was *A Child's Garden of Verses,* by Robert Louis Stevenson. I wished to goodness he would go to sleep and let me get back to the ball game, so I flicked open any old page and there it was:

And in some corner find the toys
Of the old Egyptian boys.

I had never read this to him, but his mother had. Matter of fact, I had seldom read anything to him, but I had either made up songs or sung things that perhaps I shouldn't have sung, such as chanteys. To put my best foot forward here, this is the song I made up and which he likes only moderately well. It goes:

Johnny woke up in the morning,
And climbed right out of bed;
He went into the living room
And this is what he said:
Oh, beedo, baddo
Beedo baddo, beedo baddo bee
Beedo baddo, beedo baddo
Beedo baddo bee.

Johnny sat down at the table
And ate up all his eggs
And then he got down from the table
And danced on both his legs.
Oh, beedo baddo, beedo baddo
Beedo baddo bee.

Well, that's the kind of junk I tried to make up for him, but thanks be to God he remembers Robert Louis Stevenson and says, ". . . from the old Egyptian boys."

The mystifying thing is that he remembers the good stuff, discards the hooey. Trying to lull him into quietness I used to sing an occasional chantey to him, getting the words only approximately, but getting the idea correctly. That bounced back on me because one day, only a few weeks ago, I was trying to keep him quiet in the lounge car from Kingston, Rhode Island, to New York, since I have enough W. C. Fields in me to hate lounge-car pest-children. In my efforts to keep him quiet I asked him to sing me a song. Instead of singing it to me, he stood in the middle of the joint and to my embarrassment sang:

What'll we do with the drunken sailor
What'll we do with the drunken sailor
What'll we do with the drunken sailor
Early in the morning?

My embarrassment was gradually blended with a shameless pride, until he continued in this fashion:

Put him in the cuppers till he gets sober
Put him in the cuppers till he gets sober . . .

"No, Johnny," I said. "The word is 'scuppers,' not 'cuppers.' You're talking like a little baby. Anybody passing by would think you were some kid born only August 27, 1950."

Nobody was as offended or annoyed as I would have been under the same circumstances and it had not been my son Johnny.

I don't know about other children except what I read in Spock and Ilg and Gesell and so on, but I do know Johnny likes rhythm and the beat of words. But it has to be good. It has to be better than "beedo baddo" and all that. It has to be something like "In some corner find the toys of the old Egyptian boys," and "Put him in the scuppers till he gets sober." This small man does not like junk. This is not for me to be saying Robert Louis Stevenson was the best poet in the world, but he certainly was better than "Johnny woke up in the morning."

And of course neither his mother nor I knows what is going on inside his head while either she or I reads to him. Correction: while she reads to him or while I make up stuff.

This we both do know: that he listens with rapt attention while we read the things that her mother read to her, and her mother's mother read to her mother. (My own mother did not have time to read to me, since we lived in a candy store and she had to tend to the customers. I must have just sat around.)

His mother reads to him, besides Stevenson, all those Red Riding Hoods and so on. It goes over fairly big.

"He likes Uncle Remus as well as anything, old or new," Faith told me. "Last night, he looked at a picture in the Walt Disney edition, which I was reading to him. It showed the animals all around a campfire. Johnny broke in on me and he said, 'I wish I could be in that book. I wish I could sit in there with the animals.' "

His mother reads *Mary Poppins* and *Babar the King* to him still. She says he's outgrown *The Three Bears,* which was a smash hit with him for many months.

But once I was eavesdropping and I heard the best story of all. I stood outside his room, sneaky, and Josephine was talking to him while he reluctantly ate his lunch. I know reluctantly because I also sneaked a look.

"Once upon a time," Josephine said, "there was a little boy. And he walked out of the big house and he left mammy and daddy behind, but he was very, very careful. He never walked in the middle of the road where the cars could hurt him." (I peeked at this point, and Josephine gave him another spoonful of potatoes.)

". . . and so," Josephine said, "this little boy looked down and there was a little green frog. 'Hello, frog,' the little boy said. The frog didn't say nothing because little frogs don't talk. 'I won't hurt you, frog,' the little boy said. So the frog came nearer."

Josephine gave Johnny some more potatoes, and then she said:

". . . and so the little boy picked the frog up, nice and easy, and walked all the way home and showed the little frog to his mammy and his daddy and they gave the frog something to eat and he got to be a great big frog and the little boy got big, too, and so the big frog and the big boy were friends for ever and ever and ever."

"Tell me the story about the little boy and the frog again," I heard my son say.

THE FLAG AND JOHNNY

The American flag got mixed up with Johnny's tonsils, in a manner of speaking, because before he went to the hospital we tried to prepare him for this first time in such a place. First time excepting, of course, when he was born, four years and three months ago.

For a long time Johnny made a rattly sound while he slept. His breathing then was noisy and we frequently mentioned that fact to the baby doctor we have for him.

For a long time, too, the doctor repeatedly told us that he was not of the school that believed in taking tonsils out as a matter of routine.

"I'm reluctant about that," he said several times, "unless it becomes definitely necessary."

When Johnny had snuffly colds, one after the other, the doctor finally told us one afternoon in his office, where we had taken Johnny for a check-up, that the tonsils, and also adenoids, would have to be taken out after all.

We have the notion, right or wrong, that there should be few, if any, secrets between Johnny and his parents. So Johnny was standing there in the office when the doctor told us that. We hadn't made him stay in the waiting room.

"We'll wait for a spell of cold weather," the doctor said, "and meantime we'll try to get this cold he has now under control."

Johnny spoke up with one of those surprising bits of knowledge that neither Faith nor I knows where he gets them at all.

"Under control means getting better," said Johnny, by way of explanation to us.

The doctor, Faith, and I all looked at each other, all pleased and at the same time perplexed at this remark.

"That's right, Johnny," the doctor said.

When we got home from the doctor's office we told Josephine what the doctor had said. Johnny would go to the hospital in a few weeks, we told Josephine, providing his snuffles cleared up and providing we had a cold spell.

"I know," Josephine said. "They rather take them out in cold weather better than in hot weather."

Johnny is the seventh child Josephine has helped parents to bring up. Her own mother helped Josephine bring up her own two children, because Josephine has always had to work, and, naturally, could not be home with her own son and daughter when they were little. Her son is now a great big six-footer in the United States Navy.

I forgot to say that while Faith was dressing Johnny in his snow suit in the outer room of the doctor's office that day, the doctor talked to me a little bit, with nobody else around.

"Let Johnny know well ahead of time that he's going to the hospital," the doctor said. "Then he won't get frightened. I don't mean make a big production number out of it, but try to take the surprise element out of it by telling him some casual way, as if it were a trip to the zoo or something."

As matters went, the doctor's advice on that point was not wholly necessary. Josephine, upon whom we depend so much, knew all about that already. She smiled when we told her what the doctor had said.

"I know," Josephine said, in her quiet way.

So, soon after that, one night when I was eavesdropping outside

Johnny's room and Josephine was in there keeping him company while he ate his supper of "toast-all-eggy" (a dish he named himself) I heard Josephine say to him,

"You got to eat everything all up and get strong for the big parade to the hospital."

The word "parade" did it. He loves parades, which are frequent enough in our neighborhood. Johnny and Josephine, or sometimes Johnny and I, often stop and watch a parade on Fifth Avenue on our way to the playground in the park.

"He was real cute today," Josephine said to me one evening a short time later, after Johnny was in bed.

"What did he do?" I asked.

"Well there was an ambulance parked here where we were waiting for a red light," Josephine said. "Private ambulance. Green one. Johnny said that's the ambulance he wants to go to the hospital in."

"He did?" I said. "That's right! Now I remember he had a plastic toy ambulance one time and I explained to him an ambulance is what people go to the hospital in. The guy remembers everything!"

"Yes," Josephine continued. "The cute was he told me all about it. He told me Mommy and Daddy and me'd sit up in the ambulance and he would lie down. Then he said he'd carry the American flag."

It took me a couple of minutes to figure that one out, and when I did figure it out I said nothing but "That's funny." I didn't want Josephine to know I had been eavesdropping when she said about "the big parade to the hospital." To Johnny "parade" means flags, and bands, and dressed-up men, and policemen on glorious horses. But mostly flags. Flags flying gaily on a jolly occasion.

In due time, the cold spell came, the cold that Johnny had went away, and it was the day for him to go to the hospital, only four blocks from where we live.

Josephine dressed him warmly. Faith had bought him a special toy for this occasion, and also a funny man in plastic to pin on the jacket of his snow suit. When he pulled a short chain on it the funny man lighted up. Josephine pinned that on his jacket, and it was a big hit with him. Not so much that he forgot his plans, though. As Faith and I left the apartment with him he said, "The American flag! I have to carry the American flag!"

He has one. We bought it for him one day at the zoo in Central

Park. We got him the American flag and he carried it as we got into the taxicab to go to the hospital. He did two things at once on the way there. He kept lighting the funny man on his jacket and he kept waving the American flag.

Somehow, I think, I liked him more that brief journey than I ever had before, and I always liked him a lot. A small boy, on the way to the hospital, waving the American flag.

It was me who turned cowardly yellow when the cab pulled up at the curb in front of the hospital.

"I think I'll leave it up to you, Faith," I said. "You take him in there and I'll run along somewhere. Call me up, huh?"

"O.K.," Faith said. "Maybe that's better."

"So long, Johnny," I said.

"So long, Daddy," he said. He sometimes echoes whatever I say, almost. I watched him march into the hospital, a great big place against whose doors Johnny looked very, very small. He held his mother's hand in his own left hand, and in the right hand he waved the American flag.

I hope, in vain, of course, that nobody ever uses the phrase "It's only a routine thing" to me again. That's about all I heard the next few hours, while Johnny was having his tonsils and adenoids taken out.

In those hours I went to a couple of places I hang out now and then, a club and a cigar store which is near our house. Big old me brought up the subject with a mighty casualness.

"Just took the little boy to the hospital," I said.

"What happen?" they asked in each place.

"Got to get the tonsils out," I said.

"Oh, that's only a routine thing, my kid had 'em out," somebody said in the club, and somebody else said in the cigar store.

"Yeah, routine," I said, elaborately. "He'll be O.K. tomorrow."

He was, too. His mother brought him home, where Josephine and I were waiting. Josephine kept busy doing small things, making the beds, having a cup of coffee, tidying up, saying nothing. I found myself at the window, watching up a New York street, for a cab that might look as if it had them in it, Johnny and Faith. That's silly, one cab looks like another, but by all that's holy, I did pick out the one. It pulled up to the curb in front of our house and I saw Faith step out, with Johnny bundled up in her arms. He was O.K. and his left arm was out of the bundling. His left hand held the American flag, drooping a little, but it was there. He was fine in about a week. Routine thing, of course.

THE FOURTH STRIKE

I made up my mind, long before Johnny was born, that he would not be my fourth strike. That is, I would not try to make him be all the things I failed to be. He would not be a miniature of me. That was before he was born.

I went to a movie the other night, and I found myself beginning to do things I once said I would not do. It was *An American in Paris.* Gene Kelly danced, and made love to a lovely girl called Leslie Caron, and Oscar Levant played piano. While all this was going on I thought of my Johnny. I wanted him to be able to dance like Gene Kelly; I wanted him to play piano like Oscar Levant. In other words, I was doing exactly what I said I would never do. It must be understood that I said it before Johnny was born and things have changed since then.

They give you only three strikes. Then you are through. You walk back to the bench. But God, in His goodness, has given me a fourth strike. Johnny. Everywhere I go, it's Johnny all over again. But better. All this came sauntering through my mind while I watched *An American in Paris*. Do other fathers think the same thing, sitting in the darkness at a movie?

We have a piano in our house, a small piano. The day after I saw the movie I hoisted Johnny on my lap and sat him in front of the piano. He banged on it. Probably the people downstairs were sore at the racket. How in the world were they to know that I was trying to let the small man, Johnny, give me my fourth strike? How were they to know that I was trying to have my son learn to play piano like Oscar Levant?

After my effort at the piano, I tried to show Johnny how to dance. First I played, on the piano, *Sweet Sue*, in time-step. Then I did my best at dancing, which I cannot do very well, but hope he will be able to do.

In other words, I was having my fourth strike. I never became all the things I one time hoped to be, but could it be that Johnny will? He'll have dreams of his own. Perhaps he'll achieve them. Who knows?